TheOpen University

Science: Level 2

S278
EARTH'S PHYSICAL RESOURCES
ORIGIN, USE AND
ENVIRONMENTAL IMPACT

METALS
ORE DEPOSITS AND
THEIR EXPLOITATION

PETER WEBB

The S278 Course Team

Chair

Peter Webb

Course Managers

Jessica Bartlett
Annemarie Hedges

Authors

Tom Argles
Steve Drury
Peter Sheldon
Sandy Smith
Peter Webb

Course Assessor

Professor David Manning
(*University of Newcastle*)

Block Assessor

Dr Alwyn Annels

Production Team

Jessica Bartlett (*Indexer*)
Gerry Bearman (*Editor*)
Steve Best (*Graphic artist*)
Kate Bradshaw (*Software designer*)
Roger Courthold (*Graphic artist*)
Rebecca Graham (*Editor*)
Sarah Hack (*Graphic artist*)
Liz Lomas (*Course team assistant*)
Judith Pickering (*Project manager*)
Jane Sheppard (*Graphic designer*)
Andy Sutton (*Software designer*)
Pamela Wardell (*Editor*)
Damion Young (*Software designer*)

Acknowledgements

The S278 Course Team gratefully acknowledges the contributions of members of the S268 *Physical Resources and Environment* Course Team (1995) and of its predecessor, S238 *The Earth's Physical Resources* (1984).

This publication forms part of an Open University course S278 *Earth's Physical Resources: Origin, Use and Environmental Impact*. The complete list of texts which make up this course can be found on the back cover. Details of this and other Open University courses can be obtained from the Student Registration and Enquiry Service, The Open University, PO Box 197, Milton Keynes, MK7 6BJ, United Kingdom: tel. +44 (0)845 300 60 90, email general-enquiries@open.ac.uk

Alternatively, you may visit the Open University website at http://www.open.ac.uk where you can learn more about the wide range of courses and packs offered at all levels by The Open University.

To purchase a selection of Open University course materials visit http://www.ouw.co.uk, or contact Open University Worldwide, Michael Young Building, Walton Hall, Milton Keynes MK7 6AA, United Kingdom for a brochure. tel. +44 (0)1908 858793; fax +44 (0)1908 858787; email ouw-customer-services@open.ac.uk

The Open University
Walton Hall, Milton Keynes
MK7 6AA

First published 2006. Second edition 2007.

Edited, designed and typeset by The Open University.

Printed and bound in the United Kingdom at the University Press, Cambridge.

ISBN 978 0 7492 1920 8

2.1

CONTENTS

INTRODUCTION TO METALS PRODUCTION AND ORE DEPOSITS

1

Without metals, the world in which we live and work would not exist in the form that we know it. Nonetheless, it may not be immediately obvious how important metals are and how much we depend on them. Objects made of metals, and examples of their *direct use*, may not be as common as objects made of minerals, wood, cloth and plastics. However, production of all such materials demands the *indirect use* of metals in the extraction and harvesting of the raw materials and in their subsequent processing and shipment. Metals are needed for machinery, in construction, for power supply, and in transport (Figure 1.1). In addition, many activities vital to humans, such as food production and healthcare, depend on metals. On reflection, can you imagine the world today without metals?

Metals are probably more important today than ever before, although their value to humans has been appreciated for almost 10 000 years. The first usage involved

(a)

(b)

(c)

(d)

Figure 1.1 The importance of metals: their indirect uses. (a) Mining for metals and fuel requires massive earth-moving equipment. (b) Communications links for transport require, for example, bridges and track. (c) Manufacturing of all kinds requires plant and machinery. (d) Supply of energy requires pipelines, transmission lines and complex plant.

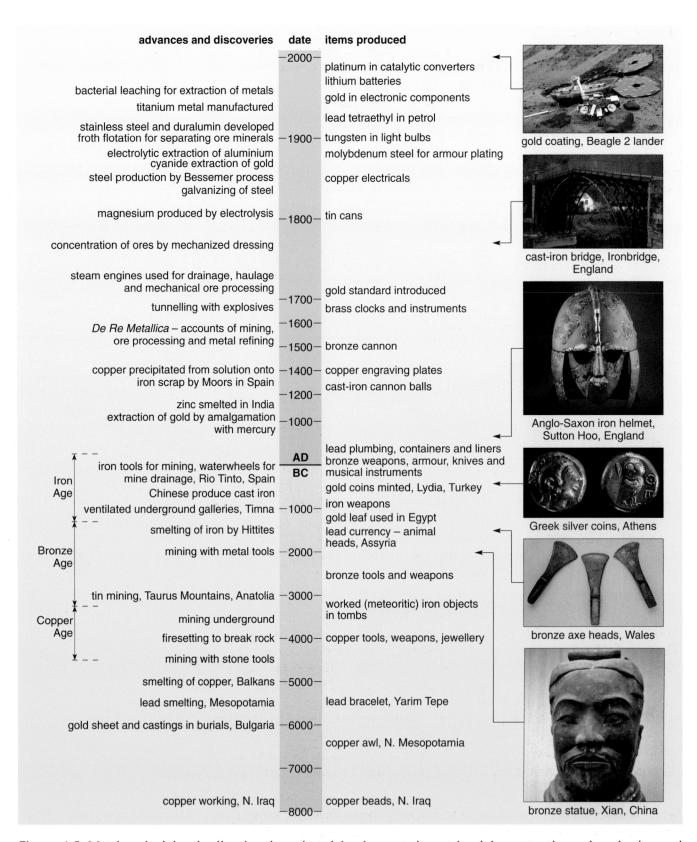

advances and discoveries	date	items produced
	—2000—	platinum in catalytic converters
		lithium batteries
bacterial leaching for extraction of metals		gold in electronic components
titanium metal manufactured		lead tetraethyl in petrol
stainless steel and duralumin developed		
froth flotation for separating ore minerals	—1900—	tungsten in light bulbs
electrolytic extraction of aluminium		molybdenum steel for armour plating
cyanide extraction of gold		
steel production by Bessemer process		copper electricals
galvanizing of steel		
magnesium produced by electrolysis	—1800—	tin cans
concentration of ores by mechanized dressing		
steam engines used for drainage, haulage and mechanical ore processing	—1700—	gold standard introduced
tunnelling with explosives		brass clocks and instruments
De Re Metallica – accounts of mining, ore processing and metal refining	—1600—	
	—1500—	bronze cannon
copper precipitated from solution onto iron scrap by Moors in Spain	—1400—	copper engraving plates
	—1200—	cast-iron cannon balls
zinc smelted in India		
extraction of gold by amalgamation with mercury	—1000—	
	AD	lead plumbing, containers and liners
	BC	bronze weapons, armour, knives and musical instruments
iron tools for mining, waterwheels for mine drainage, Rio Tinto, Spain		gold coins minted, Lydia, Turkey
Chinese produce cast iron		iron weapons
ventilated underground galleries, Timna	—1000—	gold leaf used in Egypt
smelting of iron by Hittites		lead currency – animal heads, Assyria
mining with metal tools	—2000—	
		bronze tools and weapons
tin mining, Taurus Mountains, Anatolia	—3000—	worked (meteoritic) iron objects in tombs
mining underground		
firesetting to break rock	—4000—	copper tools, weapons, jewellery
mining with stone tools		
smelting of copper, Balkans	—5000—	
lead smelting, Mesopotamia		lead bracelet, Yarim Tepe
gold sheet and castings in burials, Bulgaria	—6000—	
		copper awl, N. Mesopotamia
	—7000—	
copper working, N. Iraq		copper beads, N. Iraq
	—8000—	

Iron Age, Bronze Age, Copper Age

gold coating, Beagle 2 lander
cast-iron bridge, Ironbridge, England
Anglo-Saxon iron helmet, Sutton Hoo, England
Greek silver coins, Athens
bronze axe heads, Wales
bronze statue, Xian, China

Figure 1.2 Metals and mining timeline, locating selected developments in metals mining, extraction and production, and in metals use in the past 10 000 years.

naturally occurring metals, such as nuggets of native copper and gold that could be hammered into useful shapes. Since then, there has been a slow discovery — probably by accident at first — of techniques involving fire and charcoal that could extract metals from minerals rich in lead, copper, zinc and tin. A lead bracelet from Mesopotamia dates to nearly 8000 years ago, well before copper smelting and mining of the copper minerals, malachite and azurite, became established in the Balkans about 7000 years ago. Copper working later became more extensive in central Europe, and led to the discovery of bronze about 5200 years ago when tin and copper minerals were roasted with charcoal. Around 1700 years elapsed before iron was produced by chemical reduction and yet another 3400 years before aluminium was produced by electrolysis (Figure 1.2).

Sn Cu

Early demand for metals was mainly for use as tools and ornaments, but with the development of technologies to mine and produce stronger metals, the use of metals in weapons became important. By the time the Romans came to Britain about 2000 years ago, metals were being used in a variety of ways:

- iron and bronze for weapons, tools and farming implements;
- copper for jugs and ornaments;
- lead for pipes and coffins;
- tin, gold and silver for ornaments;
- gold, silver, brass and bronze for coinage.

Brass Cu Zn

In the past 200 years or so, since the Industrial Revolution gained pace, technological developments have snowballed, leading to today's widespread and diverse uses of metals and to the dominance of iron, used mainly as steel.

This book examines metals as physical resources. It considers what makes natural materials suitable to be sources of metals; how and where these deposits form; why some metals are more readily available than others; how the metal resources industry operates; how metal ores are found and extracted from the Earth; how mining affects the environment; and how changing technologies, consumer demands, environmental and economic factors influence the industry. But first — why is it worth extracting metals from the Earth?

1.1 The use and production of metals

About three-quarters of the 94 naturally occurring chemical elements are metals. There are far fewer non-metals, which occur mainly at the top and towards the far right of the Periodic Table of elements (see the Periodic Table at the back of the book). They include the noble gases and the halogens. A few elements, including boron, silicon and arsenic, are classified as metalloids, which have properties intermediate between metals and non-metals. In general, the metallic character of elements *increases* down the columns of the Periodic Table and *decreases* across the rows. At the left-hand side of the Periodic Table are the alkali metals, such as sodium and potassium, which are rarely used uncombined because they are so reactive.

What are metals? People use different criteria to recognize them, but many of us think of **metals** as opaque, shiny, often silvery or grey-coloured materials that can be drawn out into a wire and shaped by hammering, bending, or by melting and casting. A physicist may consider metals as being good conductors of both electricity and heat, whereas a chemist might think of them as elements that form positive ions (i.e. they tend to lose electrons). An engineer might be more interested in the strength of the metal, while a metallurgist may be concerned with their atomic structure and response to heating and shaping.

Let's take lead as an example, and consider its properties. Where did you last see lead used? Why was it being used? Perhaps it was as sealing strips (flashing) along the edges of roofs because of its capacity to be easily cut and shaped; for its high density and moderate strength, giving it stability; and for its resistance to corrosion by the atmosphere and rainwater. Lead is also used in car batteries because of its capacity to conduct electricity and yet resist corrosion by battery acid.

● Among these mainly physical properties of lead there is one *chemical* property. What do you think it is?

○ Chemical properties involve **reactivity** — the ability of substances to interact chemically. Lead is fairly unreactive in air, water, and even in solutions of corrosive acids. Its resistance to corrosion is a very useful chemical property.

Characteristics associated with chemical reactivity and electrical conductivity have led to a range of metals being employed in battery construction (Box 1.1).

Box 1.1   Metals in batteries

Portable sources of electrical energy (batteries) are becoming increasingly important as more electrical devices themselves become miniaturized and portable. Early batteries were bulky lead–acid accumulators, derivatives of which still dominate their use in motorized transport. Nowadays, batteries have an infinite number of uses — their energy can produce light, sound, heat, motive power, and power for electronic devices such as laptop computers. Japan alone produces about 6 billion batteries each year.

Batteries develop electrical energy from chemical reactions that involve an electrolyte and two electrodes. When the electrodes are connected externally, a reaction starts in the cell and supplies electrons, which pass from the anode (–) to the cathode (+). There are many battery types, each with different output characteristics, depending upon their construction, their electrode–electrolyte chemistry and their size. Some batteries can be used only once, others are rechargeable. A huge variety of combinations of metals and their compounds are used in batteries, as shown in Table 1.1.

Table 1.1   Examples of battery type, uses and characteristics.

Battery type	Application	Rechargeable
lead–acid	cars, stairlifts	yes
zinc–carbon	torches, clocks	no
alkaline (zinc–manganese oxide)	audio equipment, toys	no
silver oxide	cameras, calculators	no
zinc–air	hearing aids	yes
nickel–cadmium	power tools	yes ('memory' effect*)
nickel metal hydride	mobile phones, cameras, laptop computers	yes (no 'memory' effect*)
lithium	cameras	no
lithium ion	mobile phones, camcorders, laptop computers	yes

*The so-called 'memory' effect in rechargeable nickel–cadmium batteries has been held responsible for the drop-off in performance. Nickel–cadmium batteries, however, are susceptible to loss of performance owing to overcharging. Nickel metal hydride batteries, which have no 'memory' effect, were developed to replace them in many applications, e.g. cameras and cordless phones.

To get a better idea of the range of properties that metals can have, examine Table 1.2. Values are given for density in tonnes per cubic metre (t m^{-3}) and for melting temperatures in degrees Celsius (°C). Clearly, although lead is very dense (11.3 t m^{-3}) it is not the densest of metals. Its relatively low melting temperature means that it can be melted easily and cast into shape. Metals have a wide range of densities ranging from lithium, the least dense (0.53 t m^{-3}), to osmium (not listed in Table 1.2), the densest (22.6 t m^{-3}). Apart from mercury, all metals are solid at room temperature.

In Table 1.2, strength and conductivity (both electrical and thermal) are given in relative terms. Clearly, some metals are much better conductors than others: copper is a very good conductor of heat and electricity whereas lead is a poor conductor of both (for a metal). In fact, copper conducts them both more than 10 times as efficiently as lead.

Ease of atmospheric corrosion is the only chemical property listed in Table 1.2, and is of great practical significance, but it does not always reflect accurately the chemical reactiveness of a metal. Some metals are reactive enough for their surface layer to combine with atmospheric oxygen and form an oxide layer that protects the metal beneath from further attack. This applies especially to

Table 1.2 Properties of selected metals involved in world trade.

Metal	Symbol	Density[†] /t m^{-3}	Melting temperature /°C	Tensile strength[‡]	Electrical conductivity[‡]	Thermal conductivity[‡]	Ease of atmospheric corrosion	Price[§] /US$ t^{-1}
aluminium	Al	2.70	660	**	***	***	oxide coating	1 430
chromium	Cr	7.19	1 860	****	**	**	very slow	3 500
copper	Cu	8.96	1 084	***	****	****	slow	1 780
gold	Au	19.3	1 064	**	***	****	does not corrode	1.17×10^7
iron	Fe	7.89	1 535	***	**	**	corrodes easily	[1]174
lead	Pb	11.3	334	*	*	*	very slow	515
lithium	Li	0.53	181	*	**	**	oxide coating	—
magnesium	Mg	1.70	650	**	***	**	corrodes	1 900
mercury	Hg	13.5	−39	—	*	*	does not corrode	5 370
nickel	Ni	8.90	1 453	****	**	**	very slow	9 630
silver	Ag	10.5	962	***	****	****	tarnishes	157 000
tin	Sn	7.31	232	*	**	**	does not corrode	4 890
titanium	Ti	4.55	1 660	****	*	*	does not corrode	[2]8 800
tungsten	W	19.3	3 410	****	**	***	does not corrode	7 860
zinc	Zn	7.13	420	*	**	**	very slow	827

[†]1 t m^{-3} = 1 Mg m^{-3} = 10^3 kg m^{-3} = 1 g cm^{-3}.

[‡]Star rating: **** = high; * = low.

[§]Prices are averages for 2003. Values mainly derived from data made available by *Metal Bulletin*. Note that prices may fluctuate considerably from year to year, month to month, and even from day to day. The US dollar is the most widely used currency for metals pricing.

[1]Pig iron price, US import. Pig iron is the crude, molten iron obtained from a blast furnace and from which other forms of iron and steel are manufactured (Sheldon, 2005).

[2]Estimated price.

aluminium, on which a very thin invisible oxide layer resists further reaction. An extra 'property' given in Table 1.2 is price, which is often the main reason for choosing one metal in preference to another.

Question 1.1

Use the information in Table 1.2 to attempt the following questions.

(a) Why is tungsten used as the filament in light bulbs?

(b) Why is mercury used in glass thermometers?

(c) Why is titanium sometimes used in preference to aluminium for the construction of aircraft?

(d) Why are overhead electric power cables made largely from aluminium rather than copper?

The importance of metals in engineering applications, such as construction, transportation and manufacturing, depends on several properties, including tensile strength, hardness and workability. *Tensile strength* — given in relative terms in Table 1.2 — is the ability to resist being pulled apart, which enables a bar, rod or beam to support a heavy load, and is essential for the construction of buildings and bridges. *Hardness* is the ability to resist wear and pitting, which is essential for weapons and tools to enable them to cut through or penetrate other materials. *Workability* takes several forms, including *malleability* (the ability to be shaped through bending or hammering) and *ductility* (the ability to be drawn out to form a rod or wire). Both malleability and ductility involve mechanical deformation without breaking. All these properties tend to be well developed in metals; malleability enables gold leaf to be made in ultra-thin sheets and special shapes to be pressed from sheets of steel, such as car body panels. The metal objects in Figure 1.3 illustrate some typical properties of metals.

(a)

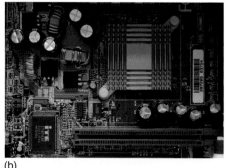
(b)

(c)

(d)

Figure 1.3 Objects made from common metals, illustrating the usefulness of some of their properties. (a) Aluminium is used to make very thin, lightweight, corrosion-resistant, watertight cans. (b) A variety of metals, including copper, silver and gold, are used in electronic components and circuitry for their electrical conductivity, resistance to corrosion and ability to be produced as very thin sheets and fine wires. (c) Gold jewellery is popular because it can be shaped to virtually any form and is unreactive, so it retains its bright, shiny appearance for a very long time; it is also valuable. (d) Aluminium cookware is durable, corrosion resistant and readily formed to the required shape.

1.1.1 Extending the uses of metals

Although pure metals exhibit a wide range of properties, with many potential uses, finding ways to alter and enhance their basic properties has long been a priority of the metallurgical industry. One early discovery was that certain types of copper ore made much harder copper metal. We now know that this was due to small amounts of arsenic in the copper that originated from impurities in the ore. This was followed by the discovery of bronze, a tougher metal, made from the ores of copper and tin. Such metals, which are mixtures of other metals, are known as **alloys**. They can be likened to *solid solutions* (see Section 1.2) in minerals, where a range of compositions is formed when one element replaces another. An example is duralumin, in which the main component, aluminium, confers lightness, but the addition of copper and magnesium increases its tensile strength many times. The addition of lithium (the lightest metal known) to aluminium alloys can make them significantly lighter in weight, giving them clear advantages in the construction of aircraft.

Table 1.3 gives the compositions of a number of common alloys and shows how their properties are enhanced when compared with the pure metal. The metal that is most commonly used in alloyed form, partly because of its widespread availability and low price, but also for the enhancement of its properties, is iron. Iron is the basis of a vast range of steel alloys that have been developed for their improved strength, hardness, high-temperature performance and corrosion resistance (Table 1.3). Some metals, such as chromium, nickel, manganese, molybdenum, vanadium and tungsten, are more important as minor, but critical, components of steels than they are as metals in their own right.

Table 1.3 Typical compositions and special properties of alloys.

Alloy	Typical composition	Special properties
brass	Cu 70%, Zn 30%	harder than pure copper
bronze	Cu 90%, Sn 10%	harder than pure copper
duralumin	Al 94%, Cu 4%, Mg 2%	stronger than pure aluminium
solder	Sn 50%, Pb 50%	low melting temperature (203 °C)
mild steel	Fe 98.3%, Mn 1.5%, C 0.2%	stronger and more ductile than pure iron, but rusts
high-carbon steel	Fe 98.5%, C 1%, Mn 0.5%	harder than mild steel, but rusts
cast iron	Fe 97%, C 3%	hard but brittle; rust resistant
stainless steel	Fe 70%, Cr 20%, Ni 10%	harder than mild steel and rust resistant, but costly
manganese steel	Fe 86%, Mn 13%, C 1%	very hard; resistant to abrasion
18-carat gold	Au 75%, Ag + Cu 25%	harder and cheaper than pure, 24-carat gold

Question 1.2

Use information given in Tables 1.2 and 1.3 to answer the following:
(a) 'Silver' coins in the UK (e.g. 50p piece) are made of a cupro-nickel alloy that is composed of 75% copper and 25% nickel. Why have such alloys replaced silver metal for use in coins?
(b) Why is stainless steel rather than mild steel used to make knives?
(c) Why is solder made of tin *and* lead rather than just one of these metals?
(d) What type of steel might be most suitable for crushing rock?

Another way to extend the uses of metals is by coating a thin layer of one metal onto the surface of another, enabling useful properties of both metals to be exploited. Thus, one of the main uses of zinc is in coating steel (galvanizing), which provides resistance to rusting without impairing the strength of the steel or increasing its price appreciably. Thin layers of chromium in chrome plating or of aluminium for aluminizing can often provide a finish that is attractive and corrosion resistant. Another reason for using a coating is to minimize cost, for example coating an expensive metal onto a low-value one, such as silver on nickel (electroplated cutlery) or gold on silver (silver gilt).

● Why are 'tin' cans not made entirely of pure tin?

○ Tin is very resistant to corrosion and is non-toxic, but it is a relatively dense and expensive metal. Steel is stronger, more rigid, lighter in weight and much cheaper than tin, but is subject to corrosion. 'Tin' cans are therefore made of tinplate, which is steel sheet coated with a very thin layer (only 2 µm thick) of tin, combining the advantages of both metals.

Materials known as *composites* use both metals and non-metals in combination. Familiar examples include car tyres, in which steel wire is embedded in rubber for strength and flexibility, and reinforced concrete, in which steel mesh or rods are used to increase the flexibility and the tensile strength of concrete slabs, pillars and beams.

Some metals are used in a chemically combined form. For example, the hardness of tungsten carbide (WC) makes it suitable for use in cutting tools, rock-crushing equipment, and for the writing tips of high-quality ballpoint pens. For many years, a large proportion of lead was used as tetraethyl lead ($Pb(C_2H_5)_4$), the 'anti-knock' additive in high-octane petrol. An important use of molybdenum is as molybdenum disulphide (MoS_2), a high-temperature lubricant.

1.1.2   The substitution of metals

The demand for a metal ultimately depends on the properties that make it useful. If another substance, whether a metal or not, can do the same job, there is an opportunity for **substitution**. Probably the most common reason for substitution is economic — the metal is replaced by a cheaper material. However, technical advances, such as substitution by materials that have improved specification, are also important. For example, the last few decades have seen the phasing out of cast-iron pipes for gas and water supplies and their substitution by PVC (polyvinyl chloride) pipes, which are considerably lighter and not susceptible to corrosion. Sometimes a substitute may cost more, but may be preferred for other good reasons. The replacement of copper wire by fibre optics in telecommunications is an example of substitution for practical reasons. To transmit the same amount of information by copper wire requires a cable ten times larger in cross-section than the fibre optic.

An increasingly important reason for substitution is to minimize adverse environmental effects, particularly relating to health. Regulations are often necessary to motivate change when the cost is high. Public opinion is also very important, particularly if it can be turned to commercial advantage. Concern about the toxicity of lead is the main reason for discontinuing its use in water pipes, paints and petrol. Bismuth could be a substitute for lead in many applications where toxicity is a problem, as it has similar physical properties yet is non-toxic. This has not happened, however, perhaps because bismuth is more costly (as much as US$9000 per tonne in 2005) and has more limited availability. Plastics have replaced lead in pipework and cable coverings.

Substitution may bring about a change in the demand for a resource. A fall in demand tends to drive prices down, such that profitability suffers and the supply industry declines. Alternatively, increased demand may drive up prices, leading to greater profitability and a thriving supply industry. Demand, supply and prices are interlinked and depend on a multiplicity of economic, political and technological factors (Sheldon, 2005). For example, a rapid surge in the price of the rare metal, tantalum, in recent years has resulted from the explosive demand created by its use in mobile phone components. Obtaining valuable tantalum ores (known as 'coltan') has fuelled conflict, especially in the Congo, involving rebel militia and bandits.

1.1.3   The availability and production of metals

Prices depend not only on demand, and ultimately on the usefulness of a particular product, but also on the ease with which that product can be supplied. In fact, the ultimate constraint on the supply of a resource is its availability — the ease by which it can be obtained from the Earth. For metals, this depends partly on their average abundance in the Earth's crust and, more importantly, on the extent to which geological processes concentrate them; how large and how common such concentrations are, and how easy it is to extract them.

Table 1.4 shows one measure of the availability of metals — their crustal abundance — alongside the quantities produced and price in 2003. It is clear that iron is produced in much larger quantities than any other metal and at by far the lowest price. This is because there is a high demand for iron and there are many

Table 1.4   The annual production, crustal abundance, price and notional value of selected metals. (Production data from USGS, 2005; prices data: see notes, Table 1.2)

Metal	Production/1000 t (2003)	Abundance in continental crust/%	Price/US$ t^{-1} (2003)	Notional value of world production/US$ $\times 10^9$
iron	647 000	7.1	174	
aluminium	27 700	8.4	1 430	39.6
copper	13 600	0.007 5	1 780	24.2
zinc	9 000	0.008	827	7.44
manganese	8 200	0.14	1 120	9.18
lead	2 950	0.000 8	515	1.52
nickel	1 400	0.011	9 630	13.5
magnesium	510	3.2	1 900	0.97
tin	210	0.000 25	4 890	1.03
titanium	65	0.54	8 800	0.57
tungsten	62	0.000 1	7 860	0.49
silver	18.8	0.000 008	157 000	2.95
gold	2.52	0.000 000 3	11 700 000	
mercury	1.5	0.000 008	5 370	0.008

Note: this table is to be completed as part of Question 1.3.

large, rich ore deposits from which iron can be extracted relatively easily. Thus, as iron is readily available, and economies of scale in its mining and extraction are possible, its price is low. In contrast, although it is more abundant than iron in the Earth's crust, aluminium commands a much higher price (Table 1.4) because it is more costly to extract from its ore. Price can be low even for metals with quite low average crustal abundances, providing their ores are readily available and easily extractable; lead is one example. However, if demand is high and availability is low, as for the precious metals gold and platinum, then prices are especially high. The relationships between the amounts of metals produced and their crustal abundances are more easily seen in Figure 1.4.

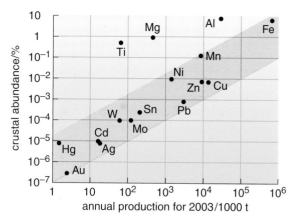

Figure 1.4 A graphical comparison between the annual amounts of metals produced from ores and their crustal abundance (data from Table 1.4). Most metals plot within the shaded band, which represents a range of constant abundance-to-production ratios. Note the logarithmic scales.

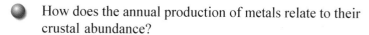 How does the annual production of metals relate to their crustal abundance?

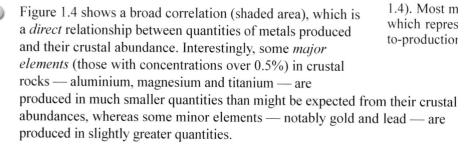 Figure 1.4 shows a broad correlation (shaded area), which is a *direct* relationship between quantities of metals produced and their crustal abundance. Interestingly, some *major elements* (those with concentrations over 0.5%) in crustal rocks — aluminium, magnesium and titanium — are produced in much smaller quantities than might be expected from their crustal abundances, whereas some minor elements — notably gold and lead — are produced in slightly greater quantities.

Table 1.4 also reveals a broadly inverse relationship between price and crustal abundance. It is hardly surprising that rarity tends to give rise to higher prices. However, the declining demand for lead and mercury, largely in recognition of their toxicity and substitution by safer alternatives, results in much lower prices than their low crustal abundances might suggest.

The overwhelming importance of iron, with about ten times more produced than all the other metals put together (Table 1.4), and shown graphically in Figure 1.5a, is due to the importance of steel. The relatively high level of manganese production when compared with the lesser major metals, such as zinc and lead, is explained by the fact that manganese is used extensively as a minor component of many steels. Table 1.4 also uses another measure to assess the relative importance of different metal resources — their *notional value* (i.e. production × price), reflecting the importance of their extraction and refining industries to the world economy. The reason for calling it a notional value is because large quantities of many metals, such as manganese and chromium, are used mainly as components of steels, and not as pure metal. Estimating the true value of metals used mainly in alloys is difficult because the component price is not the same as the pure metal price. Purification of metals can be a complex process and adds greatly to the costs. The relative notional values are illustrated in Figure 1.5b, where nickel (important in steel production) features quite strongly, yet its presence is hardly apparent in Figure 1.5a. A large proportion of a metal's value is added in smelting and refining, so the values estimated in Figure 1.5b do not represent income to the mining industry alone, but to the metals extraction industry as a whole. Note that these data represent only a snapshot in time, however, as both production and price respond to variations in demand from day to day and from year to year.

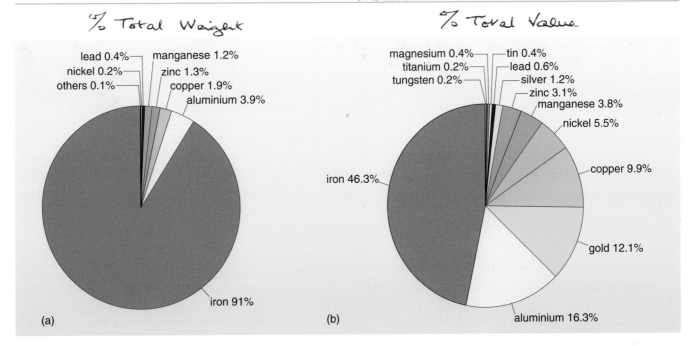

% Total Weight

% Total Value

Figure 1.5 Metals production in 2003: (a) as a percentage of the total weight of metals produced — including metal contained in alloys (corresponding data for chromium not available); (b) as a percentage of the total notional value of metals produced.

Question 1.3

(a) Calculate the notional values of iron and gold production to the world economy in 2003 using data from Table 1.4. Enter your results in Table 1.4.

(b) Compare the combined notional value of those metals mainly used in steels — including manganese, chromium and nickel — with the notional value of the metals aluminium, copper and zinc, which are more often used as metals in their own right.

1.1.4   Trends in metals production from mines

Figure 1.6 shows how mine production of metals on the world scene has changed during the past century. Fluctuating production levels reflect variations in the demand for and the availability of metals. Copper, zinc and lead were produced in roughly equal amounts in the early 1900s, but in more recent years, copper has overtaken zinc, and more than twice as much zinc is produced as lead, which has been declining since the late 1970s. Very little aluminium was produced in 1920, yet aluminium production now exceeds the combined production of copper, zinc and lead.

- Given the striking growth in aluminium production in the 17 years between 1955 and 1972, from about 3 Mt to about 12 Mt (Figure 1.6), what is the difference between the production you might have expected to see by 1989 (in the following 17 years) and the production that actually occurred?

- If growth had continued at the 1955–72 rate (i.e. doubling about every 8.5 years), production in 1989 would have reached 12 Mt × 2 × 2 = 48 Mt. In fact, production in 1989 was less than 20 Mt because growth did not continue to rise at the same rate after 1974 (Figure 1.6).

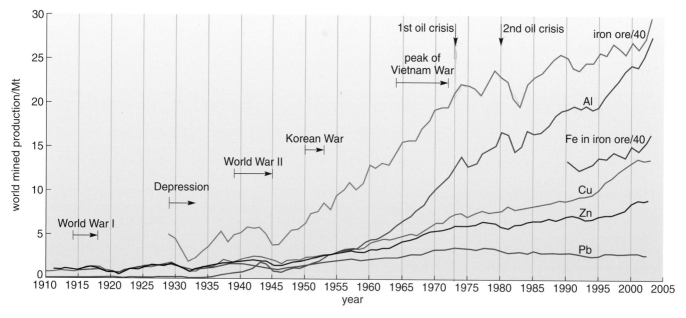

Why has there been a change in the proportion of aluminium produced today, compared with production in the early part of this century?

Aluminium is easily the least dense of the common metals and is very versatile in manufacturing and use. Its low density is especially important because less energy is required to transport it than many cheaper but denser metals, iron in particular. So, the use of aluminium in vehicles and aircraft keeps transport costs down and conserves fuel. However, the extraction of aluminium from its ores is an energy-intensive process, and the increase in production since the Second World War became possible only when electricity became available in sufficient quantity and at low cost.

Trends in primary metal production during the past century generally reflect the increased use of metals that are variously light in weight, versatile and non-toxic, such as aluminium and copper. The prices of aluminium and copper have remained competitive despite a high demand because of large-scale production and relatively cheap energy supplies.

1.1.5   Global trends in metals production

At times in the 18th and 19th centuries, the UK was a leading world producer of particular metals, such as tin, copper, lead and iron. However, by the mid-1990s, only one metal mine remained in the UK — the South Crofty tin mine in Cornwall — and that closed in 1998 although, recently, interest has been shown in reopening it. Unsurprisingly, world patterns of metals production do not remain static. Although geological circumstances determine where mineral deposits occur, as well as the form and grade of a deposit, there are many other factors that determine whether or not a deposit is economic to mine. Table 1.5 compares world patterns of metals production in 1930 and 2000. Answer Question 1.4 to help you to appreciate some of the major changes that have occurred.

Figure 1.6 World annual mined production of selected metals from 1910 to 2003. Note that iron ore production and its iron content (1990–2003) are shown as one-fortieth of their true values in order to fit on this graph.

Table 1.5 The main producers of iron, copper, zinc, lead, tin and gold in 1930 and 2000, in order of decreasing share of world mine production.

Year	Iron	Copper	Zinc	Lead	Tin	Gold
1930	USA	USA	USA	USA	Malaya	South Africa
	France	Chile	Germany	Mexico	Bolivia	USA
	UK	Congo	Mexico	Australia	East Indies	Canada
	Sweden	Canada	Australia	Canada	Thailand	Russia
	Russia	Japan	Poland	Spain	Nigeria	Mexico
	Luxemburg	Mexico	Canada	India	China	Rhodesia
2000	China	Chile	China	China	China	South Africa
	Brazil	USA	Australia	Australia	Indonesia	USA
	Australia	Indonesia	Canada	USA	Peru	Australia
	Russia	Australia	Peru	Peru	Brazil	China
	India	Canada	USA	Canada	Bolivia	Canada
	USA	China	Mexico	Mexico	Australia	Russia

Question 1.4

Use Table 1.5 to answer the following:

(a) Which country dominated world metals production in 1930 and how had its position changed by 2000?

(b) The major producers of iron changed between 1930 and 2000. What are they? Suggest reasons for these changes.

(c) Which countries have elevated their position in terms of world production for copper, zinc, lead and tin, individually, since 1930?

According to Table 1.5, the two countries that have become increasingly important as producers of metals are China and Australia, whereas the previously strong position of the USA has declined and many of the former producer countries of Western Europe have faded out of the frame. Today's producers are generally large countries in which deposits are often mined far from centres of industry. The reasons for these changes include political, social, technological and environmental factors, as well as geological ones. For instance, some large ore deposits have been found only after exploration in remote areas. With cheap bulk transportation, many ores now have a much lower place value than they once had, but the growing trend towards mining low-grade ores with a high place value encourages the extraction of metals on site. Much of China's success has been based on cheap labour and few environmental safeguards: consequently, industry's costs are low. Under these circumstances, metals can be produced cheaply, helping to promote the massive industrial expansion in China in recent decades, itself creating huge demands for raw materials. Indeed, China is now not only the top iron ore producer but is also the top producer of pig iron — producing more than two and a half times as much as Japan, the next largest producer.

Clearly, metals are important to the world as a whole and their production is a significant part of the world's economy, although much less than the contribution of fossil fuels.

1.2 Where do metals come from?

You may be surprised to know that almost any rock that you pick up contains just about every natural chemical element there is. Many elements, however, may be present only in vanishingly small, trace amounts, perhaps only one atom in a million, or one in a billion, or even one in a thousand billion. Extraction of elements that exist only at such low concentrations would be very costly indeed. To extract any element from a rock, it is essential to take advantage of geological processes that have concentrated chemical elements in certain rocks and minerals. However, to be a viable source of any metal, a rock must not only contain a relatively high concentration of the metal but the metal must also be in a form and in a quantity that is profitable to extract and process. Such a rock from which a metal can be extracted economically is an **ore**. However, *mineral deposits* only become ore deposits after they prove to be economic.

In what forms do metals occur naturally? Only a few metals (e.g. copper and gold) are found on Earth in their native, or uncombined, state. Most metals are combined with other elements in minerals. The rock-forming silicate minerals, such as quartz, feldspars, clays, micas and pyroxenes, are common, but their component metals (Sheldon, 2005: Table 3.1) do not include all those in demand and those present are generally difficult to extract. Oxides, sulphides and some carbonate minerals are less common, even rare, but exist for most metals; they contain much higher concentrations of metals, and are better suited to the extraction of metals by processes such as smelting. Minerals like these, which can be used as economic sources of metals, are known as **ore minerals** whether or not they occur in an ore deposit. Table 1.6 lists many of the more common ore minerals, grouped as sources of major metals (large quantities of the metal are produced), minor metals (small quantities of the metal are produced) and precious metals (valued for their special properties and their rarity).

Ores, even rich ores, contain waste material, worthless minerals and rock known as **gangue** (pronounced 'gang'). Expressed simply:

$$\text{ore} = \text{ore mineral(s)} + \text{gangue} \qquad (1.1)$$

rock   economic   waste fraction
         fraction

In many cases, the proportion of ore minerals and, ultimately, of the metal obtained from an ore, is very small in relation to the amount of ore mined, as illustrated for a typical copper deposit in Figure 1.7.

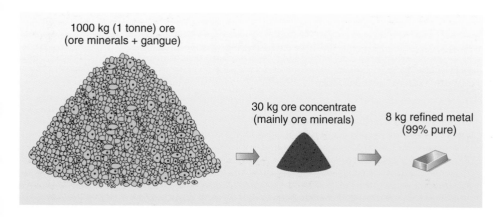

1000 kg (1 tonne) ore
(ore minerals + gangue)

30 kg ore concentrate
(mainly ore minerals)

8 kg refined metal
(99% pure)

Figure 1.7 Relative quantities of ore, derived ore mineral concentrate and extracted metal for a typical copper deposit. Each pile contains the same amount of copper.

Table 1.6 Typical ore minerals (those most commonly encountered are shown in italics).

	Ore mineral, formula	Type of mineral
Major metals		
aluminium, Al	*gibbsite*, $Al(OH)_3$	hydrated oxide
copper, Cu	*chalcopyrite*, $CuFeS_2$; bornite, Cu_5FeS_4; covellite, CuS; chalcocite, Cu_2S	sulphide
	malachite, $CuCO_3.Cu(OH)_2$; azurite, $2CuCO_3.Cu(OH)_2$	carbonate/hydroxide
	cuprite, Cu_2O	oxide
	native copper, Cu	metal
iron, Fe	*magnetite*, Fe_3O_4; *haematite*, Fe_2O_3	oxide
	goethite, $FeO(OH)$	hydrated oxide
	siderite, $FeCO_3$	carbonate
	(*pyrite*, FeS_2; *pyrrhotite*, FeS)*; arsenopyrite, $FeAsS$	sulphide
lead, Pb	*galena*, PbS	sulphide
zinc, Zn	*sphalerite*, ZnS	sulphide
Minor metals		
beryllium, Be	beryl, $Be_3Al_2(SiO_3)_6$	silicate
bismuth, Bi	bismuthinite, Bi_2S_3	sulphide
cadmium, Cd	substitution of Cd for Zn in sphalerite	sulphide
cerium, Ce	*monazite*, $(Ce,Th)PO_4$	phosphate
chromium, Cr	*chromite*, $(Fe,Mg)Cr_2O_4$	oxide
lithium, Li	spodumene, $LiAlSi_2O_6$	silicate
manganese, Mn	pyrolusite, MnO_2	oxide
mercury, Hg	cinnabar, HgS	sulphide
molybdenum, Mo	*molybdenite*, MoS_2	sulphide
nickel, Ni	*pentlandite*, $(Ni,Fe)_9S_8$	sulphide
niobium, Nb	columbite, $FeNb_2O_6$	oxide
tantalum, Ta	tantalite, $FeTa_2O_6$	oxide
thorium, Th	*monazite*, $(Ce,Th)PO_4$	phosphate
	thorite, $ThSiO_4$	silicate
tin, Sn	*cassiterite*, SnO_2	oxide
titanium, Ti	*ilmenite*, $FeTiO_3$; *rutile*, TiO_2	oxide
tungsten, W	wolframite, $FeWO_4$	oxide
uranium, U	*uraninite*, UO_2 (sometimes quoted as U_3O_8)	oxide
vanadium, V	substitution of V for Fe in magnetite	oxide
zirconium, Zr	*zircon*, $ZrSiO_4$	silicate
Precious metals		
gold, Au	native gold, Au, and gold–silver alloy, electrum	metal
platinum, Pt	native platinum, Pt	metal
silver, Ag	acanthite, Ag_2S; minor component in galena	sulphide
	native silver, Ag; naturally alloyed with gold (electrum)	metal

*Pyrite and pyrrhotite are included because they are closely associated with many ore minerals. Currently, they are not regarded as true ore minerals. You should know the names and recognize the formulae of the ore minerals shown in italics.

The presence of more than one metal in an ore deposit is common and production of additional metals as **by-products** is often important in ensuring a deposit's economic viability. For example, gold is often a by-product of copper mines and, although volumetrically insignificant, can be the most valuable product.

What are the two most common types of ore mineral listed in Table 1.6?

Oxides and sulphides.

There are two reasons for the dominance of these types of ore minerals:

- Metals are often more easily extracted from oxide and sulphide minerals.
- Oxides and sulphides usually contain higher concentrations of metals compared with many other types of mineral, such as silicates. For example, by mass there is 70% Fe in haematite (Fe_2O_3) but only 42% Fe in $FeSiO_3$ (Fe-pyroxene).

What may seem strange about Table 1.6 is that few metals commonly form both oxide and sulphide ore minerals. In natural circumstances, metals tend to form more commonly either oxide or sulphide minerals — rarely both. Part of the reason for this is a chemical one: the relative ease by which metal atoms combine with oxygen and sulphur atoms depends on how readily they lose electrons. This is, in effect, a chemical property called **electronegativity**, which is related to an element's atomic structure and therefore to its position in the Periodic Table. Most metals on the left-hand side of the Periodic Table are weakly electronegative, tending to give up electrons more easily, thus forming *ionic* bonds and, except for molybdenum, oxide minerals; whereas most metals towards the right-hand side are more electronegative, giving up electrons less easily, thus tending to form *covalent* bonds and, except for aluminium and tin, sulphide minerals (Figure 1.8). Iron, in the middle of the table, commonly forms bonds of either type and both oxide and sulphide minerals.

Figure 1.8 The Periodic Table, showing which of the more common metals tend to form sulphide minerals, oxide minerals or both.

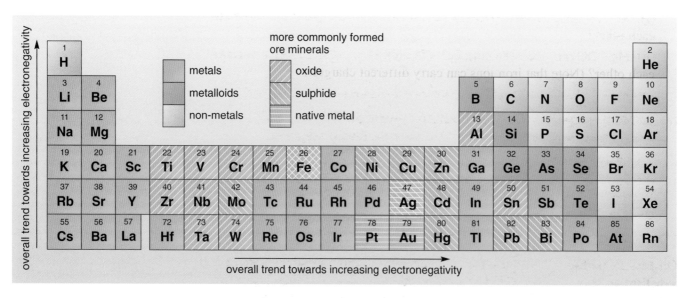

Many of the ore minerals in Table 1.6, such as galena (PbS) and sphalerite (ZnS), appear to be simple compounds. Their chemical formulae correspond to the proportions of atoms occupying their mineral structure in which the atoms fit together in a continuous, repeating arrangement to form a three-dimensional lattice. Certain atoms can substitute for other atoms in such a lattice, but for this to be possible, their *ionic charges* must be the same to maintain charge balance and their *sizes* (measured in terms of their ionic radii) must be similar so as not to disrupt the lattice. To understand substitution better, study Figure 1.9, which is a plot showing the size (in picometres) and the effective ionic charge of some common metal ions, then answer Question 1.5.

10^{12} picometres (pm) = 1 m
1 pm = 10^{-12} m

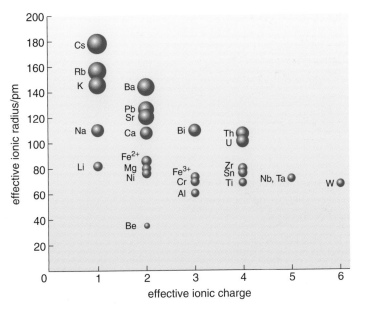

Figure 1.9 Plot of effective ionic charge against effective ionic radius for selected metals. Elements with a similar ionic radius and the same ionic charge are capable of substituting for each other in minerals.

Question 1.5

(a) Locate on Figure 1.9 the representations of the following ions and answer these questions:

(i) Na^+ (110 pm), K^+ (146 pm), Ca^{2+} (108 pm). How are these ions related to each other?

(ii) Mg^{2+} (80 pm), Fe^{2+} (86 pm), Fe^{3+} (73 pm). How are these ions related to each other? (Note that iron ions can carry different charges.)

(iii) Ba^{2+} (144 pm), Rb^+ (157 pm). How do these ions relate to Na^+ and K^+?

(b) Iron and lead form sulphide ore minerals — pyrrhotite (FeS) and galena (PbS), respectively. Into which would nickel more readily substitute?

(c) Taking account of their ionic charges and ionic radii, which of the following ions: Ba^{2+} (144 pm), Fe^{3+} (73 pm), Rb^+ (157 pm), Fe^{2+} (86 pm), Ti^{4+} (69 pm), Bi^{3+} (110 pm) and Nb^{5+} (72 pm) could substitute for tin, Sn^{4+} (77 pm), and therefore might be present as impurities in the ore mineral, cassiterite (SnO_2)?

Olivines are perhaps the simplest group of minerals to exhibit substitution. **Ionic substitution** between Mg^{2+} (80 pm) and Fe^{2+} (86 pm) — ions of like charge and similar size (see Figure 1.9) — accounts for a complete range of **solid solution** between the end members, forsterite (Mg_2SiO_4) and fayalite (Fe_2SiO_4), of the mineral olivine. Substitution involving the alkali feldspar end members, albite ($NaAlSi_3O_8$) and orthoclase ($KAlSi_3O_8$), is less ideal: an incomplete range of solid solution exists between these end members. Only limited amounts of exchange occur between Na^+ (110 pm) and K^+ (146 pm) because these ions have the same charge but somewhat different sizes (Figure 1.9).

If you examine Figure 1.9 in more detail, it is easy to see groups of ions with similar ionic radii and the same charge, among which ionic substitution would be possible.

● The ore mineral, chromite, $(Fe,Mg)Cr_2O_4$, often contains not only iron, magnesium and chromium but also aluminium. With reference to Figure 1.9, decide which of its dominant ions, Fe^{2+} or Cr^{3+}, would be substituted by Al^{3+}.

○ Al^{3+} will substitute for Cr^{3+} because it has the same charge and a similar ionic radius.

Similar substitutions arise among the major constituents of other ore minerals, such as the solid solutions involving Fe^{2+} and Ni^{2+} in pentlandite, $(Ni,Fe)_9S_8$; Zn^{2+} and Fe^{2+} in sphalerite, $(Zn,Fe)S$; and Cu^{2+} and Fe^{2+} in chalcopyrite, $CuFeS_2$. However, it is one thing for substitution to be theoretically possible, but another for it to occur; that depends also on the availability of a potentially substituting element, and then on its preference to occupy alternative sites in another mineral.

● Iron and magnesium commonly substitute for each other in silicate minerals, but magnesium does not substitute for iron in the iron sulphide minerals, pyrrhotite (FeS) and pyrite (FeS_2). How can we explain this?

○ Owing to its weak electronegativity, magnesium tends to form oxide (and silicate) minerals in nature and not sulphides (Figure 1.8). Iron can form either oxide or sulphide minerals, depending on the availability of oxygen and sulphur and the conditions of formation.

Major elements are often substituted in small amounts by trace elements, for which ionic size equivalence is critical, but small differences in charge can often be tolerated. Ba^{2+} (144 pm) has a similar ionic radius to K^+ (146 pm) and, although it has a different charge, it may, like Rb^+ (157 pm), substitute for potassium in alkali feldspars. Of the metals listed in Table 1.6, the occurrence of cadmium in sphalerite and vanadium in magnetite are examples where trace element substitution can provide important sources of metals. Although mineral formulae are normally written simply (as in Table 1.6), they are often more complex and contain additional minor constituents. For example, sphalerite may contain up to 10% FeS and 1% CdS. In this case, the formula of sphalerite would be $(Zn_{0.89},Fe_{0.10},Cd_{0.01})S$ rather than ZnS. When writing mineral formulae, these small components are often ignored.

During ore processing, especially smelting, elements that substitute can be a problem to separate. As impurities, they reduce the value of an ore, but as by-products they may enhance its value. Cadmium, for example, has no ore mineral of its own, but can be obtained as a by-product from some forms of sphalerite.

However, cadmium is highly toxic and can create severe health problems if it contaminates crops and enters the food chain. Safeguarding the environment adds to the cost both of zinc smelting and cadmium production. The presence of silver can enhance the value of some occurrences of galena. Even silver concentrations of only 1% have been the main reason for mining galena because silver has a much greater value than lead (Table 1.4).

1.3   What makes an ore deposit?

The first step in evaluating a potential ore deposit is to confirm the presence of ore minerals, such as those in Table 1.6, which contain extractable metals. Next, the *concentration of metal present*, its **grade**, and the spatial extent to which that grade is developed must be evaluated to define the size and metal content of the deposit. Grades are usually expressed in weight per cent (wt %; often written as % for brevity) metal, but for rare or precious metals, grade may be quoted in grams per tonne (g t^{-1}, numerically equivalent to parts per million, ppm).

⬤   If 20 kg of copper were contained in 1 tonne of rock, what would be its grade?

$$0.8\% = \frac{x}{400} \atop 100$$

◯ $$\text{Grade} = \frac{\text{mass of metal in rock}}{\text{mass of rock}} \times 100\% \qquad\qquad (1.2)$$

In this example, the grade $= \dfrac{20 \text{ kg} \times 100\%}{1000 \text{ kg}} = 2\%$ copper

A full economic evaluation is necessary to determine the **breakeven cut-off grade**, which is the concentration of metal that represents the *breakeven point of mining*, the limit of economic exploitation. This (breakeven) cut-off grade depends on world conditions, such as market price, as well as local factors, such as the presence of valuable by-products or the costs of environmental protection. It also depends on the scale and form of the mining operation.

Breakeven cut-off grade will subsequently be referred to simply as cut-off grade

Reserves are defined as *quantities of a resource that can be extracted profitably and legally under existing conditions, taking into account all mining factors*. Thus reserves of metal take account of losses during processing and extraction of the metal. It is also necessary to demonstrate that the mining and processing methods are technically and economically viable. The mining industry is becoming ever more rigorous in defining reserves and uses specific criteria as recommended by established international organizations.

Although reserves are subdivided into 'probable' and 'proved', there remains a significantly greater certainty that all categories of *reserves* are exploitable whereas quantities of *resources* relate to materials for which there are reasonable prospects of eventual economic extraction (see also Sheldon, 2005). The quantity of reserves may correspond to the amount of rock (i.e. ore) that exceeds the cut-off grade, or to the amount of the resource (metal) contained, with allowance made for losses. Cut-off grade, and therefore the reserves of ore in a deposit, will vary with economic circumstances.

Activity 1.1 examines the size–grade relationships for contrasting types of mineral deposit. At one extreme there are **dispersed deposits**, in which ore minerals are distributed mainly at *low grades* throughout *large volumes* of rock. At the other extreme, there are **confined deposits**, in which ore minerals are concentrated at *high grades* in relatively *small volumes* of rock. The way that quantities of reserves vary with cut-off grade differs in each case.

Activity 1.1   Size–grade relationships for dispersed and confined deposits

A dispersed deposit

Figure 1.10a shows an idealized example of a dispersed mineral deposit, where the grade of copper (contoured) decreases gradually away from the centre of the deposit. Table 1.7a shows how the average grade and size of the orebody would vary if each of these contours were the cut-off grade.

Figure 1.10   Block diagrams showing the distribution of copper grades in idealized examples of (a) dispersed, and (b) confined deposits. Note the differences in scales.

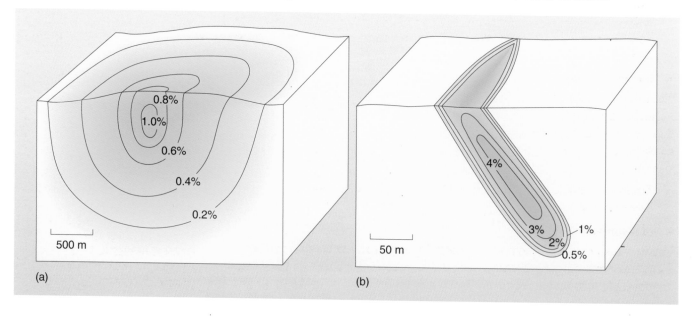

(a)   (b)

Table 1.7   The variation of average grade, size of orebody and reserves of copper with changing cut-off grade for examples of (a) dispersed and (b) confined deposits shown in Figure 1.10.

(a) Dispersed deposit				(b) Confined deposit			
Cut-off grade /%Cu	Average grade of orebody /%Cu	Size of orebody /Mt	Reserves of copper/Mt	Cut-off grade /%Cu	Average grade of orebody /%Cu	Size of orebody /Mt	Reserves of copper/Mt
1.0	2.5	20	0.5	4.0	5.0	0.04	0.002
0.8	2.0	50	1.0	3.0	3.3	0.3	0.0099
0.6	0.8	250	20	2.0	2.5	0.8	0.02
0.4	0.5	800	4.0	1.0	2.2	1.0	0.022
0.2	0.4	2000	8.0	0.5	2.1	1.1	0.023

For simplicity, these calculations assume complete (100%) recovery of metal, i.e. no losses during processing and extraction.
Note: this table is to be completed as part of Activity 1.1.

● At a cut-off grade of 0.8% Cu, what is the shape of the orebody in Figure 1.10a? How much copper would it contain?

○ The orebody would be roughly spherical (or elliptical — within the 0.8% contour). The 50 Mt orebody at an average grade of 2% (Table 1.7a) would contain 50 Mt × 0.02 = 1.0 Mt of copper.

(a) For cut-off grades of 0.6% and 0.4% Cu, calculate the reserves of copper in the orebody and write your answers in Table 1.7a.

(b) With increasing *size* of this orebody, how do the average grade and the corresponding reserves of copper vary?

(c) If economic conditions changed and the cut-off grade for this orebody were reduced to 0.4% Cu, how would the size of the orebody change compared with a cut-off grade of 0.8% Cu, both in terms of the amount of ore and the reserves of copper it contains? How would the amounts of waste produced differ?

A confined deposit

The distribution of copper grades for a typical confined deposit is illustrated in Figure 1.10b. Data are given in Table 1.7b in the same form as for dispersed deposits. Notice, however, that the scale is quite different: although the cut-off grades and average grades are much greater, the size of the deposit is much smaller.

(d) For cut-off grades of 3%, 2% and 1%, calculate the reserves of copper and write your answers in Table 1.7b.

Grade–tonnage charts

The variation of metal reserves with cut-off grade in an ore deposit can be illustrated graphically by plotting grade–tonnage charts (Figure 1.11) from the data in Table 1.7a and b, respectively.

Figure 1.11 Grade–tonnage graphs, showing variation of copper reserves with cut-off grade, for the (a) dispersed and (b) confined deposits featured in Figure 1.10. These graphs to be completed as part of Activity 1.1.

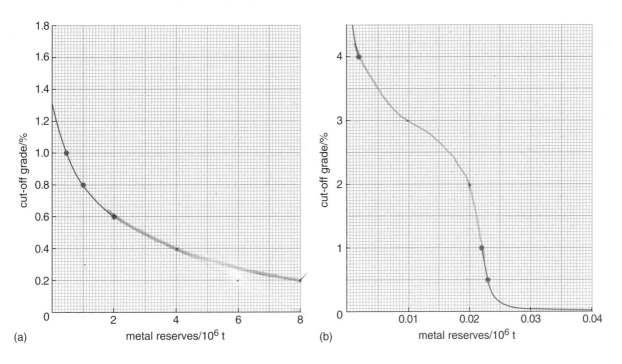

(a)

(b)

(e) For the dispersed deposit, complete the plot of cut-off grade against copper reserves on Figure 1.11a.

⬤ How do the reserves of copper vary with decreasing cut-off grade?

◔ For successively lower cut-off grades, copper reserves increase dramatically.

(f) Complete the grade–tonnage chart (Figure 1.11b) for the confined deposit.

The completed curve in Figure 1.11b is more complex than that in Figure 1.11a, but it does indicate that mining beyond a grade of 2% (where the curve steepens) would increase copper reserves very little because the grade falls so rapidly at the margins of the deposit.

Activity 1.1 illustrates several distinctions between dispersed and confined deposits, and especially how reserves of metal vary with levels of cut-off grade. The extent of a confined orebody is controlled mainly by *geological* factors, whereas the extent of a dispersed orebody depends on cut-off grade, and therefore can vary with *economic* circumstances. In general, a large-scale dispersed deposit can be mined at a lower cut-off grade than a smaller, confined deposit. Progressive development of mechanized, large-scale mining methods has reduced the cut-off grades of many metals over the years, enabling many low-grade, large-volume deposits to be mined profitably today.

The *breakeven* cut-off grade marks the limit of profitable extraction at a particular mining location. When such cut-off grades for a particular metal are averaged for mines worldwide, a guide value, called the **average minimum exploitable grade**, is obtained. Table 1.8 lists the average minimum exploitable grades (as appropriate to surface mining) for a number of important metals alongside their average abundances in continental crust. To be worth mining, therefore, metals must be concentrated by geological processes to levels well above their average abundance in the crust. The extent of enrichment can be expressed as a concentration factor.

Question 1.6

For the metals zinc, nickel, copper, tin and gold, use data in Table 1.8 to calculate the concentration factors required to form ore deposits from average continental crust. Fill in the gaps in Table 1.8.

⬤ Is there any correlation between average minimum exploitable grade and average crustal abundances for metals?

◔ Table 1.8 appears to show a trend towards smaller values of both from top to bottom, but concentration factors vary widely, from 3.6 up to 25 000. The relationship is shown more clearly in Figure 1.12a.

Average minimum exploitable grades reflect a number of factors — not only the crustal abundance of the metal, but also the extent to which metals tend to be

Concentration factor = (Av. min. exploitable grade/%) / (Abundance in cont. crust/%)

Table 1.8 The average minimum exploitable grades (for surface mining), abundance in continental crust, concentration factors and prices of mined metals. (Prices data: see notes, Table 1.2)

Metal	Average minimum exploitable grade/%	Abundance in continental crust/%	Concentration factor	Price 2003 /US$ t^{-1}
iron	55	7.1	7.7	174
aluminium	30	8.4	3.6	1 430
lead	5	0.000 8	6 250	515
zinc	3	0.008	375	827
nickel	1	0.011	91	9 630
copper	0.5	0.007 5	66.7	1 780
tin	0.5	0.000 25	2000	4 890
mercury	0.2	0.000 008	25 000	5 370
silver	0.01	0.000 008	1 250	157 000
gold	0.000 4	0.000 000 3	1333	11 700 000

Note: this table is to be completed as part of Question 1.6.

concentrated by geological processes to form ore deposits. The examination of these concentration processes forms a major part of this book. However, global average minimum exploitable grades, like cut-off grades, also depend on economic factors.

● Is there any correlation between metal price and average minimum exploitable grade?

● Yes. Figure 1.12b shows quite a good correlation — but in this case an *inverse* one, in which the average minimum exploitable grade decreases as price increases.

Figure 1.12 A graphical comparison between the average minimum exploitable grades for metals and (a) their crustal abundances, extending across a wide range of concentration factors, and (b) their prices, which fall in a linear shaded band. Note that both graphs have log–log scales. (Data from Table 1.8.)

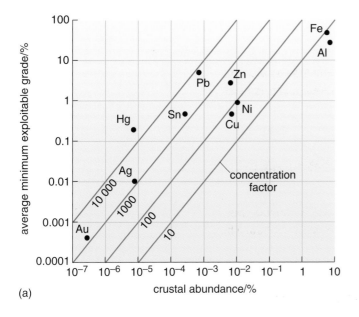

(a)

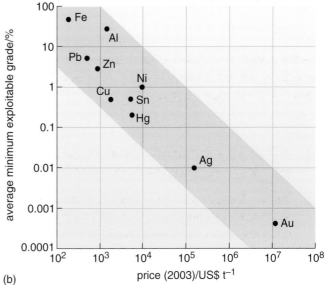

(b)

Metal price is the main economic factor that constrains exploitation. A higher price will permit exploitation of lower-grade material because it will be possible to finance the additional costs of mining and processing needed to extract the metal. For example, gold can be worked profitably at very low grades, but mercury cannot, and for a relatively abundant, low-cost metal, such as iron, only high-grade ores are economic.

1.4   Sustainability of metals supplies

Metals occurring naturally, mostly contained in minerals and rocks or in solution (especially in seawater), take part in many of the geological processes that shape our global environment. However, the timescale of geological processes and natural recycling of metals via the rock cycle (Sheldon, 2005) is extremely long (tens of thousands to hundreds of millions of years) in relation to the rates at which metals are being mined by humans and the predicted reserves lifetimes of metals (see Table 1.9). A reserves lifetime is obtained by dividing the current reserves by the annual production (Sheldon, 2005), giving an estimate of how long the reserves will last. It is only a very rough guide, however, as reserves and annual production vary from year to year and reserves inventories are unlikely to be complete. Also, as far as mining companies are concerned, reserves lifetimes need not be more than a few decades, in the expectation that exploration will find more deposits before they are needed. Inevitably, production depletes resources and extraction of very few metals is sustainable — the exceptions being magnesium and lithium, which are obtained from seawater and brines respectively, and are replenished continually by natural processes.

Reserves lifetime is analogous to the R/P ratio for petroleum (Drury, 2006)

In general, because metal ores are extracted faster than they can be naturally replenished, metals must be regarded as non-renewable resources.

Table 1.9   Reserves lifetimes of selected metals.

Metal	Reserves (2004)/Mt contained metal[†]	Annual production (2003)/10^3 t y^{-1}	Reserves lifetime/y
iron	80 000	647 000	124
aluminium (bauxite)	23 000	146 000	158
copper	470	13 600	27.9
manganese	380	8 200	57.3
zinc	220	9 000	24.4
lead	67	2 950	22.7
nickel	62	1 400	44.3
molybdenum	8.6	125	68.8
tin	6.1	210	29.0
tungsten	2.9	62	46.8
cadmium	0.6	16.9	35.5
silver	0.27	18.8	14.4
mercury	0.12	1.5	80.0
gold	0.042	2.52	16.7

[†]Except for aluminium where bauxite is quoted.

● The exploitation of ore deposits is not sustainable indefinitely. In what ways can the lifetimes (i.e. reserves/annual production) of metals be extended?

○ Metals lifetimes can be extended by:
  ● finding new reserves;
  ● exploiting lower-grade deposits and processing ore more efficiently;
  ● reducing usage and hence demand — either through substitution of metals by other materials or by recycling metals.

Exploration techniques are becoming more sophisticated, especially in finding hidden deposits (Chapter 5). However, eventually all the Earth's surface and the accessible subsurface will have been explored, leaving no more deposits to be found — but for most metals that time is a long way off.

Extraction methods are becoming more efficient, reducing cut-off grades and enlarging reserves, but in practice there is a limit to the minimum grade at which metal recovery is economic. This is because energy demands escalate with the processing of lower ore grades. A marked increase in energy costs would raise cut-off grades and thus reduce reserves.

Recycling of metals is becoming more widespread and efficient, but complete recycling is impossible because of some irrecoverable wastage during manufacturing, use, and in recycling itself. The scale of global recycling of metals is shown in Table 1.10, which compares mining, or *primary*, production, with quantities of recovered scrap, or *secondary* production, for a range of metals.

Table 1.10 Comparison of world primary (mined) production and secondary production (scrap recovery) for a selection of important metals in 2003.

Metal	Primary production/1000 t	Secondary production/1000 t	Proportion recycled/ % of total production
iron	647 000	406 000	38.6
aluminium	27 700	7 920	22.2
copper	13 600	1 100	7.5
zinc	9 000	1 570	14.9
lead	2 950	2 950	50.0
tin	210	23	9.9
silver	18.8	5.7	23.3
gold	2.52	0.94	27.2

Quantities of scrap metal recycled globally (Table 1.10) are surprisingly high. This probably reflects recycling opportunities at various stages of manufacture, rather than the amounts recycled after use. The advantage of recycling manufacturing waste is that it often needs only simple separation before being returned to the refinery. Recycling of used materials is more difficult, partly because metals leave manufacturing in many different forms, for example as alloys, coatings on other metals or plastics, or even as chemical compounds. They often become dispersed at low concentrations, and it is uneconomic to separate and recycle them. This may explain why recycling rates for tin and zinc — used mainly as coatings on steel — are low compared to some other metals (Table 1.10). Many metal products may be used and reused over long periods of time, and may not be recyclable — sheet steel, for example, may corrode to form rust, which flakes off or wears away. Uncombined metals used in short-lived products are particularly suitable for recycling. This helps explain why so much lead is recycled, especially that used in car batteries. The packaging used for foodstuffs, such as aluminium foil and cans, is also ideal for recycling.

Recycling of metals not only conserves metal reserves but also saves energy. Recycling aluminium makes a saving of 95% of the energy required to produce aluminium from primary sources. Similar energy savings amount to 85% for copper, 74% for iron and 65% for lead.

1.5 Geological concentration processes

The presence of ore deposits depends on the concentration of metals by geological processes. These are sometimes called **fractionation** processes — that is, natural processes that separate materials (often minerals) into compositionally distinct fractions. Many common rocks form by fractionation processes involving selective separation and accumulation of minerals. These include quartz sands, clays, evaporites, limestones and coal, where concentration is due to sedimentary and weathering processes. Similar processes are responsible for the formation of some ore deposits at the Earth's surface (Chapter 3). Concentration of metals can also involve igneous fractionation processes (Chapter 2) or fractionation involving hot, watery solutions (Chapter 4).

Although fractionation of elements is not unusual in geological processes, to achieve sufficient levels of concentration to form an ore deposit usually requires extreme conditions or a combination of the factors. A useful way of appreciating how an ore deposit forms is by systematic evaluation of the factors involved: the Source of the metals, the Pathways through which an Agent transports them to a site of Deposition and the Energy required to drive the system. The mnemonic 'SPADE' is a useful aide-memoire for exploring processes of element enrichment and ore deposit formation. These factors are set into a schematic context in Figure 1.13.

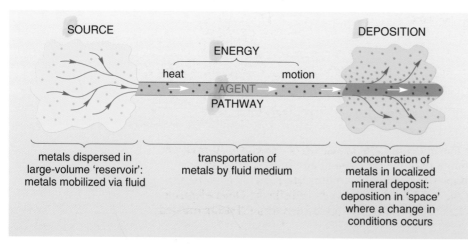

Figure 1.13   A schematic relationship between source, pathway, agent, deposition and energy involved in element enrichment. Although these spatial relationships may not be appropriate for all types of ore deposit formation, the principle has general applicability.

1.5.1 SPADE: sources, pathways, transporting agents, deposition and energy

Sources of metals

The sources that supply metals for ore deposits include the major reservoirs of the upper Earth: the mantle, the continental and oceanic crust, and the oceans. Their compositions are shown schematically in Figure 1.14. Opportunities for metal enrichment depend both on the source reservoir composition and the nature of the enrichment processes. Rocks of the Earth's crust and upper mantle, and more especially any large bodies of rock of extreme composition that are rich in particular elements or minerals, are potential sources from which metals can be derived. Enrichment processes include the breakdown of rocks by weathering at the Earth's surface to form sediments, partial melting of rocks to form magmas, and leaching of rocks by hot watery fluids and precipitation of mineral deposits.

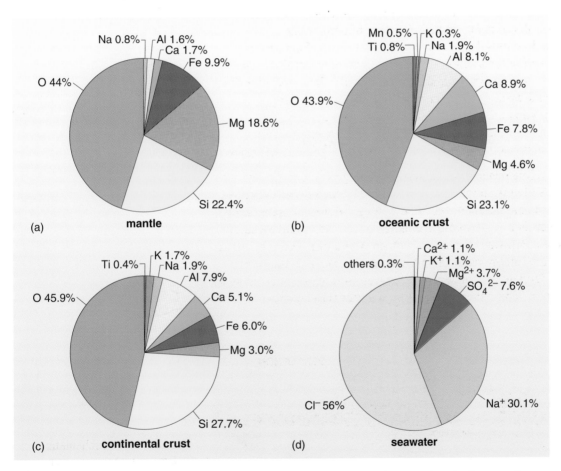

Figure 1.14 Proportions of major elements in the Earth's main active geochemical reservoirs: (a) the mantle; (b) the crust of oceanic regions; (c) the crust of continental regions; (d) seawater (as a proportion of its dissolved constituents — totalling 3.5%). Excluding the Earth's core, the main constituents of the solid Earth are oxygen and silicon. Other elements comprise roughly one-third in total (elements at concentrations of less than 0.1% are omitted in (a) to (c)).

Table 1.11 illustrates the differing and contrasting chemical compositions of three important rock types:

- peridotite, the main rock type of the Earth's mantle;
- basalt, the main rock type of the oceanic crust and the main product of mantle melting;
- granite, the main igneous rock of the continental crust, derived by the melting of the continental crust.

Not only are the major element constituents of these rocks present in quite different proportions, reflecting differences in their mineralogy, but so too are their trace metal constituents, which often have more relevance in terms of mineralization and ore deposits.

Table 1.11   Typical compositions of some important rock types.

	Peridotite	Basalt	Granite
Main minerals	olivine, pyroxene, minor plagioclase feldspar	pyroxene, plagioclase feldspar	potassium feldspar, plagioclase feldspar, quartz
Major element oxides/wt %			
SiO_2	43.54	50.83	73.86
TiO_2	0.81	2.03	0.20
Al_2O_3	3.99	14.07	13.75
Fe_2O_3	2.51	9.06	0.78
FeO	9.84	2.88	1.13
MnO	0.21	0.18	0.05
MgO	34.02	6.34	0.26
CaO	3.46	10.42	0.72
Na_2O	0.56	2.23	3.51
K_2O	0.25	0.82	5.13
P_2O_5	0.05	0.23	0.14
H_2O	0.76	0.91	0.47
Total	100.00	100.00	100.00
Trace metals/ppm			
Cr	2000	200	10
Li	0.5	10	40
Ni	2000	130	5
Ti	5	10 000	1000
U	0.005	1	3.5
V	60	400	30

Major element abundances are quoted as oxides because oxygen is in combination with major elements in silicate and oxide minerals.

 Considering the data given in Table 1.11, which two trace metals are the more likely to be sourced from each of peridotite, basalt and granite rocks, respectively?

Potential sources are most likely to be the rocks with the higher trace metal contents. Peridotite contains higher levels of chromium and nickel than basalt or granite; basalt contains higher levels of titanium and vanadium; and granite contains higher levels of lithium and uranium.

Extensive bodies of other kinds of rocks, such as limestone or shale, with quite different compositions and elemental enrichments, could also be sources for particular metals.

Many metals mined as ores are normally present only as trace elements in rocks (see their crustal abundances in Table 1.4). So how might the major element compositions of the Earth's near-surface geochemical reservoirs (in Figure 1.14) control the distribution of those trace metals? Trace elements usually substitute to a small extent for major elements in rock-forming minerals rather than form minerals of their own (Section 1.2). Thus, chromium and nickel, which often substitute for iron and magnesium (Figure 1.9) in the *ferromagnesian* (i.e. iron- and magnesium-rich) minerals, olivine and pyroxene, are preferentially concentrated in mantle rocks. Barium and lead, on the other hand, tend to substitute for alkali metals (Figure 1.9) in feldspars, which are much more abundant in crustal rocks (Figure 1.14).

Seawater is also a reservoir for metals, especially sodium, magnesium, calcium and potassium, which are soluble in the predominantly chloride- and sulphate-bearing solution and are largely responsible for the salinity of seawater (Figure 1.14d). Compounds of these metals, such as common salt (NaCl) and anhydrite ($CaSO_4$), may crystallize out of seawater to form evaporites. These are deposits from which industrial minerals can be obtained (Argles, 2005). Seawater can also be trapped in marine sediments during their deposition and burial and is then known as **formation water**. This can be released on compaction as saline fluids called **brines**. The salinity of seawater is maintained globally by the supply of ions released from rocks by weathering and balanced by biological and chemical precipitation from the oceans.

Pathways for fluids

To transport material from its source to a site of deposition, it is necessary to have *pathways* through which a fluid medium can migrate (Figure 1.13). Without pathways, transportation cannot function to supply the metals needed to form an ore deposit — just as porous rock is of little use as an aquifer for water supply unless it is also permeable (Smith, 2005). A pathway could be:

- a geological fault or fissure that allows the flow of magma or watery fluids in the Earth's crust;
- a river channel that confines the flow of surface water;
- connected pores in an aquifer through which watery fluids can flow.

Agents of transportation

Essentially, agents are the fluids (liquids and gases) that take metals from their source and transport them to a site of deposition (Figure 1.13). Agents may operate in a physical sense, by transporting solid material such as mineral grains, or chemically, by transporting soluble materials as ions in solution. Agents may also chemically interact with rocks to extract or leach out metals and to deposit minerals. Mobility and the ability to carry metals (physically or chemically) are critical properties of any agent.

Source (dispersed in large vol)
Pathway
Agent (fluid medium)
Deposition (space conditions)
Energy (heat motion)

⬤ Which natural media might be potential agents?

◔ Magma, water, fluid hydrocarbons and air.

Magmas form when rocks of the Earth's crust or mantle melt. As liquids, they have lower densities than their surroundings, making them buoyant. This, together with their fluidity, enables them to rise into the crust, sometimes erupting to form volcanoes. Magmas vary greatly in composition depending on their place of origin. A variety of physical and chemical processes can operate to enrich trace metals during their migration and ultimate crystallization. Igneous processes are considered further in Chapter 2.

Water may operate as a *physical* agent, involving the movement of mineral grains (containing metals) in surface sedimentary environments such as rivers and beaches. Many metal ions are soluble in water, particularly in the presence of certain anions such as Cl^- and SO_4^{2-}. Water, therefore, also has a role as a *chemical* agent as it is capable of both dissolving minerals and leaching trace constituents from rocks. Even though water may contain only relatively small concentrations of metals in solution, it can move over large distances and for long periods of time, both at the Earth's surface and within the crust. The most familiar form of saline water is seawater, which contains 3.5% of dissolved salts including quite high levels of some major metals (Figure 1.14d), but relatively low levels of trace metals. Surface processes involving water as an agent are examined in Chapter 3.

Beneath the Earth's surface, water moves under the influence of gravity and, when heated, it also moves by convection. Pressure due to an overlying mass of rock results in compaction of sediments, particularly those rich in clay minerals, and reduction of pore space, which leads to the expulsion of pore water. These processes may bring about the mobility of water as an agent (Figure 1.13). Flow of groundwater is very slow, but it can transport metals in solution. Most groundwater starts out as rainwater, which is almost pure and is called **meteoric water**. However, once in the ground it passes through rocks and dissolves small amounts of minerals to emerge with a complement of dissolved metal ions, as found in mineral waters (Smith, 2005).

⬤ To illustrate just how much metal can be transported over time, even in relatively pure water, calculate how much calcium flows into an average home in a hard-water area each year. Typically, hard tapwater contains 150 milligrams per litre of calcium ions and the average water consumption per household is about 100 000 litres per year.

◔ If tapwater contains 150 mg l^{-1} of Ca^{2+} ions, i.e. 150×10^{-6} kg l^{-1} of Ca^{2+}, the weight of calcium per year = 150×10^{-6} kg $l^{-1} \times 10^5$ l y^{-1} = 15 kg y^{-1}, which would amount to 37.5 kg of calcium carbonate (1 kg calcium makes 2.5 kg calcium carbonate) if it were all converted to limescale. That is why pipes often get furred up and kettles need to be descaled. This illustrates how amounts of metals transported in solution by large volumes of water over extended periods of time can be deceptively large, even if their concentrations are quite small.

Deeper groundwaters, which are under high temperatures and pressures, may interact with hot rocks and become saline, just like buried formation waters. Such hot, watery solutions, known as **hydrothermal fluids**, are potentially corrosive (able to dissolve minerals/rocks) and may carry relatively high concentrations of metals in solution (as much as 25% of dissolved solids). Metals are often carried as **complex ions** in which metal ions combine with anions, such as chloride (Cl^-) or bisulphide (HS^-), to form anion complexes. For example, gold can form the chloride complex $[AuCl_2]^-$ and the bisulphide complex $[Au(HS)_2]^-$. However, the stability of such complexes (determining whether metals will be transported or deposited) depends critically on the composition of the solution and its temperature, pressure, acidity (i.e. pH, see Box 1.2) and oxidation conditions (Box 1.3). The circumstances and consequences of these processes of hydrothermal ore deposit formation are the subject of Chapter 4.

Metals can also be transported as organic complexes in hydrocarbons. Hydrocarbons are buoyant and migrate from petroleum source rocks, such as carbonaceous mudstones, displacing groundwaters in aquifers and penetrating fault systems (Drury, 2006). Metals with an affinity for hydrocarbons under reducing conditions, such as vanadium, molybdenum and uranium, may be transported in this way.

Box 1.2   The pH scale

The **pH** of an aqueous solution describes how acidic or alkaline it is. In fact, pH is an inverse measure of the hydrogen ion (H^+) concentration in solution — the *greater* the H^+ ion concentration, the more acidic the solution and the *lower* its pH. At pH 7, the pH of pure water, a solution is neutral (Figure 1.15) because it contains equal concentrations of H^+ and OH^- ions.

Many common liquids and natural solutions are acidic (pH <7) and some, including seawater, are alkaline (pH >7), as shown in Figure 1.15. The low pH of stomach acid may seem surprising, as might the pH of lemon juice. If you have a piece of limestone, see how readily it reacts with lemon juice.

The pH of most natural waters is in the range pH 4 to pH 9. Hard water, containing more OH^- ions than H^+ ions, has a relatively high pH value (>7) and is alkaline, whereas waters draining from peat bogs are acidic, having a low pH (<7) and a relatively high H^+ concentration, because of dissolved organic acids. Waters from abandoned mine workings that have percolated through decomposing sulphide minerals also tend to be acidic and can be an environmental hazard (Chapter 7).

Figure 1.15 The pH scale, with approximate pH for common liquids and natural waters.

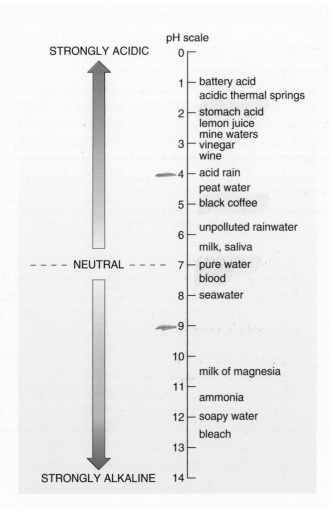

Air rarely transports material to form a metal deposit. However, the winnowing effect of the wind (removing lighter grains) may leave behind deposits preferentially enriched in heavy mineral grains.

Deposition conditions

A suitable site for deposition, combined with suitable conditions for deposition — involving changes in physical and/or chemical conditions of transportation — are essential for minerals to be deposited (Figure 1.13).

In magmas, deposition of minerals may occur within a magma chamber, or in offshoots from it, and is controlled mainly by crystallization processes, by movement of the magma and the separation of crystals (Chapter 2).

In flowing surface waters, a change in physical conditions, such as a reduction in flow, may cause deposition of mineral grains. A change in chemical conditions may lead to precipitation and sedimentation. When ions transported in hydrothermal solution encounter changed conditions, possibly through mixing with other fluids or by chemical reaction with surrounding rocks and fluids, or respond to changes in pressure, temperature, oxidation or pH conditions, they may become unstable. Any insoluble compounds that are formed will precipitate, forming crystals or encrustations.

Changes associated with oxidation and reduction (see Box 1.3) are especially important for transportation and deposition of certain metals, such as iron, that can exist in more than one oxidation state. This is because the stability of ions and their ability to remain in solution often depend on oxidation–reduction conditions. In particular, iron(II) compounds are generally far more soluble than the corresponding iron(III) compounds. Changes in oxidation conditions may therefore precipitate insoluble minerals (of iron(III), for example). Such mechanisms can be important in forming ore minerals from cool, surface waters and from hot, hydrothermal solutions (Chapters 3 and 4).

For an ore deposit of any significant size to be formed, the transporting agent needs to be available in large quantities and/or for long periods of time, under conditions (chemical and physical) favourable for the precipitation of minerals. In addition, a suitable site for deposition is essential (Figure 1.13); there must be *space* in which minerals can crystallize. Such space may be provided by pores — the gaps between the grains in a rock (Smith, 2005) — or by fissures and fractures that form when rocks are broken. Additional space may be created when wall rocks are dissolved by the passage of hydrothermal fluids. The available space for deposition determines the form of a deposit. *Dispersed* deposits often form in porous or highly fractured rocks with diffuse flow pathways. *Confined* deposits often occupy discrete fractures or fissures (to form mineral veins) in otherwise impermeable crystalline rocks or joints, especially in limestone, where dissolution often creates spaces. At the Earth's surface, the form of ore deposits produced either by escaping hydrothermal fluids or by weathering and sedimentary processes may be less tightly constrained, but can still be confined as, for example, in thin sedimentary layers.

Question 1.7

Why might you expect to find hydrothermal veins in brittle, impermeable rocks rather than soft, porous rocks?

[handwritten: Cracks → fissures veins in soft porous rock more dispersed]

Box 1.3 Oxidation and reduction

Oxidation and reduction are complementary effects in chemical reactions that typically involve, respectively, the addition and removal of oxygen atoms. However, to extend the concept of oxidation and reduction to reactions that do not involve oxygen, a broader definition is used:

- **oxidation** involves the *loss* of electrons;
- **reduction** involves the *gain* of electrons.

The mnemonic OILRIG is a convenient way of remembering this:

> Oxidation Is Loss — Reduction Is Gain.

Iron is a metal that can exist in different oxidation states, iron(II) and iron(III). Each gives rise to quite different forms of chemical behaviour, so oxidation and reduction of iron species can be very important in geological processes.

When iron(II) is *oxidized* to iron(III), it *loses* an electron:

$$Fe^{2+} - 1 \text{ electron} = Fe^{3+} \tag{1.3}$$

Similarly, when iron(III) is *reduced* to iron(II), it *gains* an electron:

$$Fe^{3+} + 1 \text{ electron} = Fe^{2+} \tag{1.4}$$

When combined with oxygen, iron(III) forms the oxide Fe_2O_3, whereas iron(II) forms the oxide FeO. Clearly, Fe_2O_3 contains proportionately more oxygen than FeO. The naturally occurring iron oxide ore mineral haematite (Fe_2O_3) contains iron(III), whereas magnetite (Fe_3O_4) contains both iron(II) and iron(III) — equivalent to $FeO + Fe_2O_3$. By contrast, in sulphide minerals, iron occurs in the reduced iron(II) state in both pyrrhotite (FeS) and pyrite (FeS_2).

A well-known example of natural oxidation is rusting. In a damp atmosphere, iron (e.g. mild steel) reacts with oxygen and water to form hydrated iron(III) oxide as follows:

$$\underset{\text{iron}}{4Fe(s)} + \underset{\text{damp atmosphere}}{3O_2(g) + 2H_2O(l)} = \underset{\text{rust}}{2Fe_2O_3.H_2O(s)} \tag{1.5}$$

$Fe_2O_3.H_2O$ can also be represented as $FeO(OH)$.

Oxidation reactions at the Earth's surface frequently involve oxygen because oxygen is a powerful oxidizing agent, is abundant in the atmosphere and dissolves in rainwater.

Energy source

Every ore-forming process, whether deep within the Earth or at the Earth's surface, requires a source of energy (principally heat or gravity) to mobilize the agent of transportation. Heat may also affect chemical processes before and during transportation and deposition. Energy may well be needed for a long period of time (perhaps 10^2–10^5 years) to maintain a system that will produce an ore deposit.

Heat energy within the Earth is ultimately derived from the decay of natural radioactive isotopes and is the source of geothermal energy (Drury, 2006). It is supplied to near-surface environments by either:

(i) conductive transfer, which causes rock temperatures to increase with depth (according to the geothermal gradient), or

(ii) convection of hot, mobile fluids — magmas or hydrothermal solutions — that have risen from hotter, deeper zones of the crust or mantle, short-circuiting the conductive transfer of heat and providing local, but often relatively short-lived sources of heat.

● What agent is most likely to be involved in ore deposit formation at the Earth's surface and in what way is energy involved in its mobilization?

○ Water is the main agent available to form ores at the Earth's surface, and its supply and movement involves the water cycle. Solar energy evaporates water to form clouds on condensation, only to be returned to the Earth as rain by gravity. It then flows over or percolates into the ground before evaporating or returning to the oceans.

1.5.2 Overview of ore-forming processes and the exploitation of ore deposits

Chapters 2 to 4 will examine the formation of ore deposits in more detail. The SPADE concept will not be considered systematically, but it nevertheless provides a framework that can aid your understanding of the geological conditions and processes involved in ore deposit formation. Although this book is by no means exhaustive in its coverage of ore deposits, it examines a range of important ore deposits formed in a variety of geological settings by:

● igneous processes, which concentrate metals in magmatic systems within the Earth and form ore minerals on solidification (Chapter 2);

● surface processes, which involve surface water as the main agent of transportation and from which deposition concentrates metals, either through physical movement of ore mineral grains or by chemical precipitation of minerals due to chemical changes in solution (Chapter 3);

● hydrothermal processes, where hot water circulating within the crust reacts with minerals, leaches and transports metals, and then concentrates metals by precipitation (Chapter 4).

Studying the geology of ore deposit formation provides essential insights into the natural constraints on the distribution and occurrence of metal resources. So where should we expect to find ores? …Everywhere? …Randomly? Do we need an understanding of geological processes to find ore deposits? Can we account for different types of metal deposit? How do the geological factors that affect the form and accessibility of a deposit also affect its price? Answers to these and many more questions about the occurrence and availability of metal resources can be resolved only through a better appreciation and understanding of their geology (Chapters 2, 3 and 4).

Geological knowledge is hugely important in the exploration for ore deposits and in mine development — topics covered in Chapters 5 and 6 of this book. Indeed, observing how geological processes concentrate minerals has aided the development of some industrial processes for concentrating ore minerals. In addition, an understanding of the geological processes that concentrate metals enables us to predict the effects of unnatural disturbances, especially pollution, on the natural environment, and to take appropriate remedial action (Chapter 7).

1.6 Summary of Chapter 1

1 The importance of metals to the industrialized world stems from the vast array of properties that they exhibit, both in their pure form and when used combined as alloys, in chemical compounds and in composite materials. The choice of a metal for a particular use depends on the suitability of its properties, its price and its availability.

2 The metal resources industry is a dynamic system. Usefulness and perceived value create the demand that supports a metal's price, and may place limits on potential sources. Price also depends on the accessibility of the ore and the cost of mineral processing and metal extraction. Supply is ultimately constrained by the availability of a metal, especially its distribution and the extent to which it is naturally concentrated. Demand is affected by substitution both for and by other materials. Price, supply and demand are all affected by economic, technological and political factors.

3 Iron production dominates world metals markets in terms of both tonnage and value. Many of the minor metals, especially manganese and nickel, which are mainly used in steel, are at least as important in terms of total production as some major metals, such as zinc and lead. Trends in metal use in the 20th century are towards weight reduction (to save energy during transportation and use), versatility, and avoidance of toxicity. The aluminium and copper industries have thrived, largely at the expense of iron and lead.

4 During the 20th century, mining has tended to move from centres of industry to more remote locations, often in developing countries, as a result of mine depletion, technological advances, and political, social and environmental pressures. The importance of mining in the USA and Western European countries has declined over the period 1930–2000, whereas mining in large developing countries such as China, Australia and some South American countries has flourished.

5 Metals are derived from ores — that is, rocks containing an unusual abundance of ore minerals and from which metals can be extracted economically. A mineral that can be used as an economic source of metals is known as an ore mineral whether or not it occurs in an ore deposit. Most ore minerals are oxides and sulphides, from which metals can be extracted by smelting.

6 Major metal constituents of ore minerals may be substituted by other metals (often in small amounts) creating impurities. Both impurities and associated minerals in ore deposits can provide valuable by-products or create costly problems for chemical processing and environmental protection.

7   The grade of a rock is the concentration of metal that it contains. The extent of an orebody is defined by the breakeven cut-off grade, which is the minimum grade that can be mined economically. The estimated reserves in a large, low-grade dispersed deposit can vary greatly according to the cut-off grade and, therefore, depend on economic conditions. In contrast, the estimated reserves in a smaller, high-grade, confined deposit are defined primarily by geological and geometric constraints. Economies of scale allow extensive dispersed deposits to be mined at lower grades than smaller confined deposits.

8   Metals are non-renewable resources, but a degree of future sustainability may be achieved by continuing trends towards increased conservation through recycling and substitution, as well as by improved efficiency in extraction and effectiveness of exploration.

9   The main *sources* of metals are rocks of the Earth's crust and mantle, from which concentration of metals by igneous, hydrothermal and sedimentary fractionation processes produces ore deposits.

10 *Pathways* are necessary for the transportation of metals from a source to a site of deposition. They may be faults, fissures or even rivers.

Q

5a

11 *Agents* that transport metals from their source to their site of deposition include magmas in igneous systems; cool meteoric water and seawater at the Earth's surface; and hot, reactive groundwaters — known as hydrothermal fluids — in subsurface environments. Physical transportation involves crystals in magmatic systems and sedimentary grains in surface waters. Chemical transportation of metals occurs in magmas, cool surface waters, and hydrothermal solutions.

12 *Deposition* of ore minerals takes place on and beneath the Earth's surface due to changes in the physical or chemical conditions that affect the transporting capacity of the agent, and where space is available.

13 Forms of *energy* involved in concentration processes include radioactive heating within the Earth and gravity. They mobilize the agents of transportation and promote chemical reactions.

14 Concentration processes involved in producing an ore deposit must normally operate either on a large scale or for a long period of time. Requirements include a Source to provide an ample supply of metals, accessible Pathways, a plentiful and/or long-lived transporting Agent, suitable conditions for Deposition and a continuing source of Energy (SPADE).

ORE DEPOSITS FORMED BY IGNEOUS PROCESSES

2

Although volcanoes are the most striking products of igneous processes, it is during the cooling and solidification of magma *within* the Earth that igneous fractionation processes can operate, providing opportunities for igneous ore deposits to form.

Magma is produced at depths where mantle or crustal rocks become hot enough to melt (Figure 2.1). A rock does not melt all at once; its constituent minerals melt at different temperatures. As a rock heats up, quartz and feldspars melt first, then micas, followed by the amphiboles, pyroxenes and olivines (depending on which minerals are present). Because of its mobility and buoyancy, the resultant magma tends to separate from its source before melting is complete and rises as a *partial* melt through the overlying rocks (Figure 2.1). If the magma reaches the surface, it cools rapidly to form fine-grained volcanic rock. Alternatively, it may accumulate at depth in a magma chamber, where it cools slowly to crystallize as coarse-grained plutonic rock. During periods of slow crystallization in a magma chamber, crystals and liquids of different chemical compositions may separate. Such processes of *fractionation* (see Section 2.1.1) not only bring about changes to magma compositions, but can also concentrate elements to form ore deposits.

Magmatic processes take place in many different global tectonic settings, as summarized in Box 2.1. They involve several different magma types, which are usually referred to according to the igneous rock type that they would form on crystallization (e.g. granitic, basaltic). Figure 2.2 identifies the main types of igneous rocks in their intrusive (coarse-grained) and extrusive (fine-grained) forms, along with a graphical representation of their approximate mineral and chemical compositions. Peridotite, the main constituent of the Earth's mantle, lies at one end of the compositional range and comprises mainly olivine, with pyroxene and minor plagioclase feldspar (see Table 1.11). At the other end of the compositional spectrum is granite, a common intrusive igneous rock of the continental crust, comprised mainly of feldspars, quartz and micas. Gabbro is the coarsely crystalline, plutonic equivalent of basalt. Together, gabbro and basalt form much of the Earth's crust in oceanic regions. Diorite is a plutonic rock, intermediate in composition between gabbro and granite (Figure 2.2), and equivalent to andesite lava. Rhyolite is a volcanic rock with the same composition as granite.

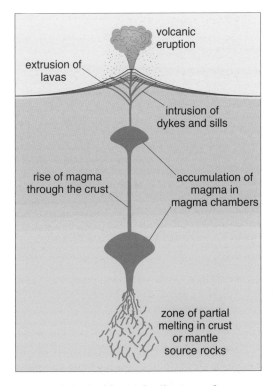

Figure 2.1 A schematic diagram of a magmatic system — from the partial melting of source rocks to the intrusion of magma to form intrusive/plutonic rocks and the eruption of magma to form extrusive/volcanic rocks.

 What is the mineralogy of gabbro, as shown in Figure 2.2?

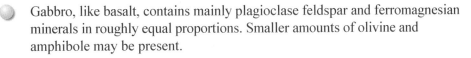 Gabbro, like basalt, contains mainly plagioclase feldspar and ferromagnesian minerals in roughly equal proportions. Smaller amounts of olivine and amphibole may be present.

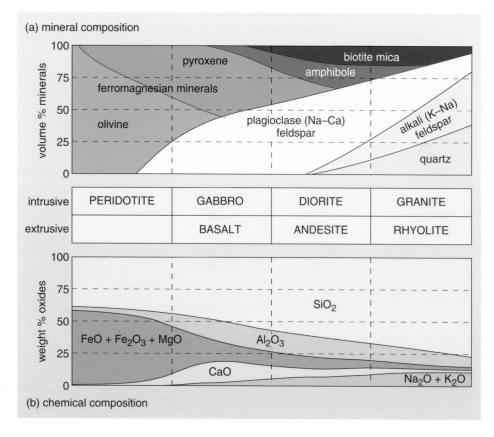

Figure 2.2 Simplified (a) mineral composition and (b) chemical composition of common igneous rocks, along with the rock names used to describe the corresponding magma types.

A comparison between mineralogical and chemical compositions in Figure 2.2 reveals a clear distinction between the *mineral*, quartz (SiO_2), a crystalline form of silica, in (a), and the *chemical constituent*, silica (SiO_2) in (b). Quartz is present in most granitic and some dioritic igneous rocks, as it is in most sandstones and metamorphic rocks, whereas silica is present as a chemical constituent in *all* silicate rocks and minerals.

Box 2.1 Global settings of magmatic activity

The origins of igneous rocks, their magma sources and their manner of formation can often be difficult to determine. However, it is possible to recognize relationships between the main magma types and the global settings in which they are more commonly found. An understanding of their occurrence and distribution is important in appreciating the general processes involved in forming ore deposits that are associated with particular types of igneous rocks.

Basaltic (gabbroic) magmas are derived mainly by partial melting of peridotite mantle in the following settings:

- at constructive plate margins beneath mid-ocean ridges where the sea floor spreads and the mantle rises (Figure 2.3a);

- within tectonic plates where an oceanic plate moves across a so-called 'hot spot' beneath the lithosphere and produces a volcanic island chain, such as the Hawaiian Islands (Figure 2.3b);

- at subduction zones where cool oceanic crust heats up on its descent into the mantle, hydrous minerals are dehydrated and water is driven off, leading to melting of the overlying mantle (Figure 2.3b).

Dioritic (andesitic) magmas are formed by a complex series of processes. These usually involve the mixing of hot, hydrous, basaltic magmas with the partial melts that they create on intruding the crust above subduction zones (Figure 2.3b).

Granitic (rhyolitic) magmas are formed mainly by partial melting of rocks deep in the crust when crustal thickening occurs during collision between continental masses and uplift raises hot crustal rocks to shallower depths (Figure 2.3c). Crustal rocks can also melt when intruded by hot basaltic magmas, especially above subduction zones (Figure 2.3b) and at continental 'hot spots' analogous to the oceanic 'hot spot' of Figure 2.3b.

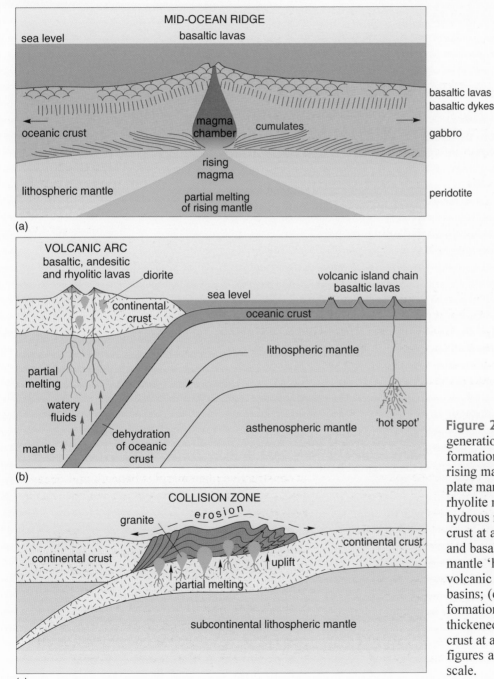

Figure 2.3 Sites of magma generation: (a) basaltic magma formation by partial melting of rising mantle at a constructive plate margin; (b) basalt–andesite–rhyolite magma formation by hydrous melting of mantle and crust at a destructive plate margin and basaltic magma formation at mantle 'hot spots' to form volcanic island chains in ocean basins; (c) granitic magma formation by partial melting within thickened and rising continental crust at a collision zone. *Note*: figures are not drawn to the same scale.

2.1 Concentration of metals by magmatic processes

The ways in which metals are concentrated by magmatic processes provide a basis for subsequent consideration of how different types of magmatic ore deposits are formed.

2.1.1 Fractional crystallization

When magma cools slowly at depth, minerals crystallize in sequence, roughly as shown in Figure 2.4. The actual sequence depends on the initial magma type and its composition. In general:

- olivine tends to crystallize before pyroxene and plagioclase feldspar in basaltic magmas;

- pyroxene and plagioclase feldspar crystallize early in dioritic magmas;

- amphibole, biotite mica and plagioclase feldspar crystallize early in granitic magmas;

- the more calcium-rich varieties of plagioclase feldspar crystallize at higher temperatures in basaltic and dioritic magmas

- the more sodium-rich varieties of plagioclase feldspar crystallize at lower temperatures and in granitic magmas, often with potassium-rich alkali feldspar.

These patterns of crystallization are illustrated in Figure 2.4b.

> With reference to Figure 2.4, from which types of magma would quartz crystallize? *Hint*: look for the magma envelopes in (a) that overlap the crystallization range of quartz in (b).

> Quartz rarely crystallizes from basaltic magmas. It crystallizes later during the crystallization of dioritic magmas, but is one of the main minerals crystallizing from granitic magmas.

Consider the crystallization of a basaltic magma. While the magma is hot, and before crystallization is well advanced, both mineral grains and melt can move independently. The early crystallizing minerals, olivine and pyroxene, are significantly denser (Figure 2.4b) than the basalt magma (density ~2.9 t m^{-3}). These dense minerals sink under gravity in the magma chamber and accumulate at its base to form **cumulate** layers rich in ferromagnesian minerals and therefore of different composition from the original magma. This combination of **fractional crystallization** and crystal settling clearly has considerable potential for concentrating elements in cumulate layers of rock.

Cumulate layers of mainly ferromagnesian minerals are relatively rich in iron, magnesium and some important trace metals. However, metals that are 'locked' in silicate minerals are difficult (and thus expensive) to extract. Fortunately, a number of oxide ore minerals also crystallize at high temperatures from basaltic magmas and are very dense. They include ilmenite ($FeTiO_3$, density 4.7 t m^{-3}), magnetite (Fe_3O_4, density 5.2 t m^{-3}) and chromite (($Fe,Mg)Cr_2O_4$, density 4.6–4.8 t m^{-3}). Such oxide ore minerals not only contain higher concentrations of commercially important metals than silicate minerals, but the metals can be more readily extracted from them. They are more normally found only as accessory minerals

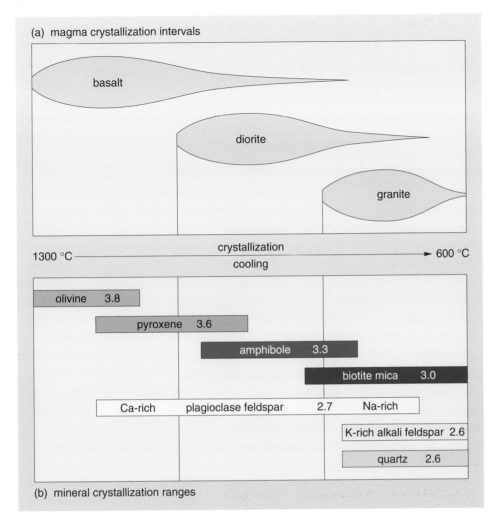

Figure 2.4 Simplified crystallization sequences for the common magma types: (a) crystallization intervals for basaltic, dioritic and granitic magmas; (b) crystallization ranges for the main minerals in igneous rocks. The magma temperature decreases and crystallization proceeds from left to right across the diagram. The widths of the magma envelopes reflect the amounts of corresponding minerals (vertically beneath) that are crystallizing. Numbers are approximate mineral densities in t m^{-3}.

thinly dispersed (at <1%) in most igneous rocks, but they may be sufficiently enriched in some cumulate layers to form ore deposits of a type known as **magmatic segregation deposits** (Section 2.2).

- Crystal settling is an important fractionation process that can form magmatic segregation deposits. What properties of the magma and crystals enable it to operate most efficiently?

- There must be a large density contrast between the crystals and the magma, and the magma must be very fluid so that the crystals can sink easily. Gravity settling is most effective in hot, basaltic magmas because they are very fluid and crystallize ferromagnesian minerals such as olivine and pyroxene, which are dense enough to settle under gravity. Granitic magmas are much more viscous, so it would be more difficult for minerals, even dense ones, to settle. In addition, there is little density contrast between a granitic magma and the minerals crystallizing from it.

However, fractional crystallization also takes place in granitic magmas, but it is accompanied by a different mechanism of separation, a process called *side-wall crystallization*. This process involves early-formed crystals (plagioclase feldspar, amphibole and biotite mica) forming at the (cooler) sides of the magma chamber and, with progressive crystallization, they extract the denser (early-crystallizing) components from the magma, which becomes less dense and convects upwards. The convecting magma progressively crystallizes as it rises to the top of the magma chamber; as a result its silica content increases and its ferromagnesian constituents decrease.

Although granitic magma can be derived from basaltic magma by fractionation processes, it requires a large proportion of cumulate minerals to be removed. Only small volumes of granite could be formed in this way. Large bodies of granitic magma are more often formed by the partial melting of continental rocks (Box 2.1).

Igneous rock compositions depend first on the minerals that melted to produce magma and then on subsequent fractionation processes acting prior to and during crystallization. Strong natural constraints systematically determine the composition of the resulting igneous rocks — not only their typical major element compositions (Figure 2.3), which in turn determine their mineral content, but also their trace element content. Typical abundances of selected trace metals in common igneous rocks are given in Table 2.1.

Question 2.1

Table 2.1 lists typical abundances of some trace metals that occur in igneous rocks. Ore deposits of each trace metal are likely to be associated with the rock type in which the metal is most abundant. For each metal in the table where the 'rock type' is missing, insert the most appropriate rock type. Calculate the missing minimum concentration factors necessary to achieve the corresponding average minimum exploitable grades and add your answers to the right-hand column.

Gabbro to Granite   *Gabbro to Granite*
Increasing concentration – incompatible | Decreasing concentration – Compatible

Table 2.1 Typical abundances of some economically important trace metals in a range of common intrusive igneous rocks.

Trace metal	Peridotite /ppm	Gabbro /ppm	Diorite /ppm	Granite /ppm	Igneous rock type in which abundance is greatest	Average minimum exploitable grade/ppm	Minimum concentration factor
chromium, Cr	2 000	200	30	10	*peridotite*	300 000	*150*
copper, Cu	20	70	50	10	gabbro	5 000	*71*
lithium, Li	0.5	10	22	40	*granite*	20 000	*500*
nickel, Ni	2 000	130	30	5	*peridotite*	10 000	*5*
niobium, Nb	5	15	25	40	granite	1 000	*25*
platinum, Pt	0.05	0.01	0.005	0.001	peridotite	5	100
tantalum, Ta	0.25	0.75	1.5	2.5	*granite*	500	200
tin, Sn	0.5	1.5	2	3.5	*granite*	5 000	1 430
titanium, Ti	5	10 000	5 000	1 000	gabbro	30 000	3
tungsten, W	0.5	1.0	1.5	2.0	*granite*	5 000	*2500*
uranium, U	0.005	1	2	3.5	granite	350	100
vanadium, V	60	400	100	30	*gabbro*	20 000	*50*

Note: this table is to be completed as part of Question 2.1.

As fractional crystallization proceeds, the remaining magma becomes enriched in constituents that cannot easily enter the crystallizing minerals. Some trace elements, which neither enter the structures of early-crystallizing minerals, nor form high-temperature accessory minerals, unlike chromium in chromite or titanium in ilmenite, become increasingly concentrated in the diminishing amount of melt remaining. These are known as **incompatible elements** because their ionic size and charge prevent them substituting into any common silicate minerals (Section 1.2).

- Which elements in Table 2.1 may be called incompatible?

- Lithium (Li), niobium (Nb), tantalum (Ta), tin (Sn), tungsten (W) and uranium (U) are incompatible because their concentrations increase (reflecting magma enrichment by progressive fractionation) from gabbro through to granite compositions.

Q 5c

Most of these incompatible metals form ions with high charges (lithium is an exception, forming a small ion with a single charge), so they cannot readily substitute for major elements (see Figure 1.9) in common silicate minerals. When sufficiently concentrated (though still at trace abundances) in granitic magmas, incompatible elements may themselves form accessory minerals, such as cassiterite (SnO_2), zircon ($ZrSiO_4$), uraninite (UO_2) and thorite ($ThSiO_4$). More highly fractionated granitic magmas may also become enriched in water and form **pegmatites**. These are coarsely crystalline rocks that may be mineralized and rich in incompatible metals, such as Li, Nb, Sn, Ta, U and W (Section 2.3).

Q 6f

Elements that behave in the opposite manner to incompatible elements, in other words those that readily enter the structures of early-crystallizing minerals, such as olivine and pyroxene, become depleted in the remaining melt, and are called **compatible elements**.

- Which elements in Table 2.1 may be called compatible elements?

- Chromium, nickel and platinum are compatible elements because they are richer in peridotite than gabbro, in gabbro than diorite, and in diorite than granite.

These elements, therefore, are likely to become enriched only in basaltic magma systems. Magmatic deposits of chromium, nickel and platinum will tend to occur in cumulate layers of gabbro and peridotite rock. Likewise deposits of copper, titanium and vanadium would tend to occur in cumulate layers of gabbros.

2.1.2   Separation of aqueous fluid

Volcanoes emit gases as well as lava and ash. In fact, it is the release of gases dissolved in the magma that provides much of the energy for explosive volcanic eruptions. These gases include carbon dioxide (CO_2), sulphur dioxide (SO_2), hydrogen chloride (HCl), and hydrogen fluoride (HF), but water vapour (H_2O) usually predominates.

Deep within the Earth, water occurs mainly in **hydrous minerals**, such as micas and amphiboles, which contain hydroxyl (OH^-) ions in their crystal structure. Much of this water was initially acquired when low-temperature hydrous minerals (especially clays) were formed at the Earth's surface, either by weathering or by interaction between seawater and rocks of the ocean floor. During burial, these minerals were converted by metamorphism to other hydrous minerals, such as micas and amphiboles, which are stable at higher temperatures. When dehydration or melting of such minerals occurs deep in the crust or mantle, the chemically bound water is released, along with other volatile products. At depth, under great pressure, the water readily dissolves in the magma to produce a water-rich or hydrous magma.

- At which magma production sites (see Box 2.1) are hydrous magmas most likely to form?

- Above subduction zones (Figure 2.3b). As cool hydrated oceanic crust heats up on descending into hot mantle, watery fluid derived from dehydration of hydrous minerals rises into the overlying mantle. These aqueous fluids assist with partial melting, and dissolve in the magma produced.

When magma rises and cools it starts to crystallize. However, if it contains 2–4% dissolved water, and most of the minerals crystallizing early (Figure 2.4) are **anhydrous minerals** (i.e. without combined water), then the magma becomes progressively enriched in water. The enrichment increases as crystallization of anhydrous minerals proceeds. When the magma cannot accommodate any more water, it becomes *water-saturated*. Any further enrichment either by continuing crystallization or by reduction in pressure as it rises to higher crustal levels will cause bubbles of watery fluid to separate from the magma (Figure 2.5a). These bubbles of watery fluid will tend to rise and accumulate at the top of the magma chamber (Figure 2.5b) in a similar way to bubbles of gas rising in a bottle of sparkling water, but at extremely high temperatures and pressures.

Whereas compatible elements tend to substitute into crystallizing minerals and incompatible elements tend to stay in the magma, some metals prefer to reside as ions or, more likely, as ionic complexes, in aqueous solution. The removal of such trace metals from the magma by the aqueous fluid is a form of **scavenging**. In addition to dissolved metal ions, the hydrothermal fluid also contains reactive 'volatile' constituents, such as HF, HCl and CO_2, with which metals often form ionic complexes. When such fluids or brines escape, they may react with minerals in already crystallized parts of a pluton or in surrounding rocks. This process of chemical exchange between the rock and fluid, known as **hydrothermal alteration**, does two things: it changes the composition of the fluid itself and may affect its ability to hold metals in solution; it likewise changes the composition of the rock through which it passes.

The separation of watery fluid from hydrous magmas rising in the crust causes expansion and build up of pressure which leads to fracturing of surrounding rocks (Figure 2.5c). In addition, on reaching very high levels in the crust, at subcritical temperatures a watery fluid transforms or 'flashes' explosively to steam (Drury, 2006), with shattering consequences! Such explosive events in high-level magmas result in severe fracturing of the surrounding rocks, creating pathways for the escape of metal-rich fluids (Figure 2.5c). These effects are particularly important in the formation of **porphyry ore deposits** (Section 2.4).

Above the critical temperature (374 °C for pure water; up to 600 °C for highly saline brines), water exists only as a supercritical fluid; below it, at subcritical temperatures, water exists as liquid and vapour.

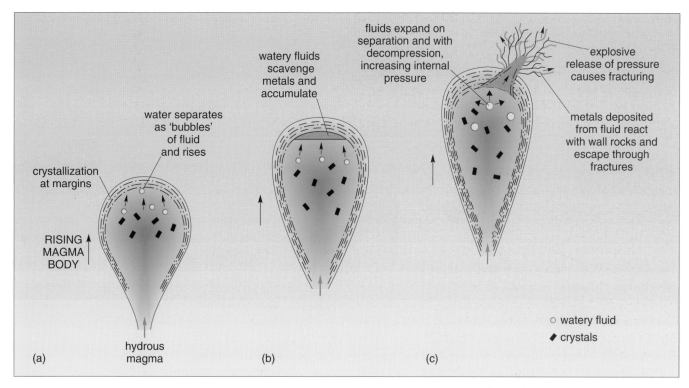

Figure 2.5 Schematic diagrams showing stages in the emplacement of a body of hydrous magma as it rises to high levels in the crust: (a) the hydrous magma cools, starts to crystallize and becomes saturated with water, which separates out as bubbles of watery fluid; (b) the aqueous fluids scavenge soluble metals and accumulate near the top of the magma chamber; (c) during ascent and decompression, separation of watery fluids brings about expansion and fracturing enables fluids to escape. At a very high level, the reduction in confining pressure transforms water to steam, which instantly occupies a much larger volume, causing explosive fracturing of the surrounding rock and further pathways for escaping fluids.

2.2 Magmatic segregation deposits

Magmatic fractionation processes can produce two main types of ore deposit from basaltic magmas: chromite deposits and sulphide deposits.

2.2.1 Chromite deposits

The main chromium ore mineral, chromite ($(Fe,Mg)Cr_2O_4$), is dense, and crystallizes early from chromium-rich basaltic magmas. Indeed, the concentration of chromium in cumulate layers of peridotite can be ten times that in gabbro (Table 2.1). Such layers, ranging from centimetres to a few metres in thickness, and composed almost entirely of chromite, can sometimes be traced laterally for a kilometre or more, and are often developed repeatedly.

Several possible explanations have been put forward as to how these layers form. A differential crystal settling process was once proposed on account of the density of chromite (4.5–4.8 t m^{-3}) being greater than that of olivine (3.8 t m^{-3}). It was thought that the motion of convecting magma would hold the lighter silicate minerals in suspension while the denser chromite grains settled to form a chromite layer. When convection slowed, the lighter silicate minerals would then settle to form a silicate-rich layer. However, it would be difficult for convection to be maintained over very large areas and it is now thought more likely that the layers form when chromite crystallizes alone without silicate minerals. The preferred explanation involves *magma mixing*, whereby the magma composition, having already evolved along paths crystallizing predominantly silicate minerals, is shifted to a new composition as a result of the mixing with a new pulse of the original magma, from which chromite-only crystallization then occurs. A chromite deposit, however, often comprises a series of chromite layers, alternating with silicate minerals, as shown in Figure 2.6, which demands repeated pulses of magma injection and mixing.

The largest chromite deposits of this kind are **stratiform chromite deposits**, formed as layers (Figure 2.6) within extremely large, layered igneous complexes of basalt to peridotite composition, which can be tens to

Figure 2.6   Alternating layers of chromite and silicate minerals in the Bushveld layered igneous complex.

hundreds of kilometres across and several kilometres thick. The best known of these are the Bushveld Complex of southern Africa (by far the largest — see Box 2.2), the Great Dyke of Zimbabwe and the Stillwater Complex of Montana, USA. These enormous igneous bodies were intruded into stable continental crust in Precambrian times. In each of them, the chromite layers extend over very large areas, and reserves amount to billions of tonnes. They contrast in size with the much smaller **podiform chromite deposits**, which occur as discontinuous pods (lens-shaped bodies) that individually rarely exceed a few million tonnes but are locally richer in chromite and deposits are tens of metres thick. Podiform chromite deposits are more widely distributed worldwide than stratiform chromite deposits. Although likely to be formed by similar magma mixing processes, their scale and occurrence is quite different. Podiform deposits formed within oceanic crust at spreading centres occur within *ophiolite complexes*, which are slices of oceanic crust emplaced tectonically onto continental crust, usually as a result of plate collision events. They formed in magma chambers of the oceanic crust, probably at constructive plate margins. Examples of podiform chromite deposits include the Vourinos Complex in Greece and the Zhob Valley ophiolite in Pakistan; major deposits also occur in the Urals, in the Philippines and Turkey.

- Although 98% of the world's chromite resources are in stratiform deposits, this kind of deposit accounts for only half the world's present chromite production. How can you explain this observation?

- Levels of production depend largely on economic factors, whereas the presence of deposits and the occurrence of resources depend mainly on geological factors. It would be surprising if production levels were closely matched to levels of resources — and chromite deposits provide a particularly stark contrast. Stratiform chromite deposits are very large (especially the Bushveld Complex) and contain vast resources. Podiform deposits are more common but much smaller, yet locally thicker and richer in chromite. Consequently they are worked in many different parts of the world.

2.2.2 Sulphide deposits

Copper and nickel sulphides are found in layers in large igneous intrusions, such as the Sudbury Complex in Ontario, Canada. The Sudbury deposits are especially famous because it is thought likely that the igneous activity was caused by a meteorite impact (about 1850 Ma ago). However, the formation of stratiform sulphide deposits differs significantly from that of chromite deposits. In basaltic magmas, sulphide minerals do not *crystallize* at high temperatures. Instead, sulphur remains dissolved in the magma, so another mechanism must operate to form magmatic sulphide deposits.

As basaltic magmas with a high sulphur content cool, they can become saturated in sulphur, and then the sulphur can no longer be held in 'solution'. In the same way that an aqueous fluid separates when hydrous magmas become saturated (Section 2.1.1), a sulphur-rich liquid separates to form globules of molten sulphide, which is mainly iron sulphide. This separation phenomenon occurs because the silicate and sulphide melts do not mix, and is known as **liquid immiscibility**.

- The iron sulphide liquid is much denser than the magma, so how does it behave on separation?

- Just as with crystal settling, the dense iron sulphide liquid sinks and accumulates as a layer towards the bottom of the magma chamber.

Unlike settling crystals, globules of dense liquid can coalesce to form larger bodies that displace the lighter magma. Figure 2.7a–b shows how this might happen, using water (magma), snooker balls (dense crystals) and mercury (molten sulphide) as analogues. Once it had cooled and crystallized, the resulting stratiform sulphide deposit would be capped by a mixture of sulphides and silicates beneath a cumulate layer composed entirely of silicates (Figure 2.7c).

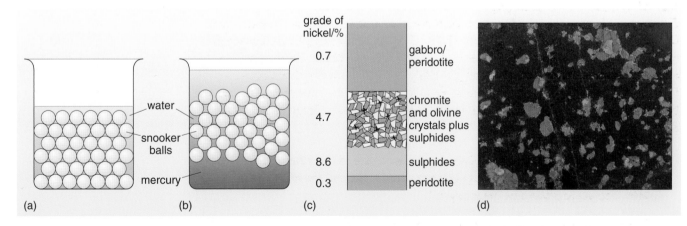

Figure 2.7 The 'snooker ball' model illustrating the concentration of sulphide melt by liquid immiscibility and gravity settling towards the base of a magma chamber. (a) Snooker balls (dense crystals) immersed in water (magma). (b) When mercury (the sulphide melt), which is considerably denser than both water and snooker balls, is added, it sinks, displacing both the water and the snooker balls. The snooker balls do not float on top of the mercury because the pressure of balls above (that sink in the water) depresses them. (c) A schematic section (with typical grades of nickel) through a magmatic sulphide segregation deposit associated with peridotite layers (cumulate silicates) in a layered basaltic intrusion. (d) Blobs of sulphide minerals, mainly pyrrhotite and chalcopyrite, with minor pentlandite, in a sample of gabbro from the Sudbury Complex.

Q 6 c

Before they crystallize, globules of molten sulphide *scavenge* from the magma the more electronegative metals, such as Cu, Ni and Co, which have affinities for sulphur (Figure 1.8). As it cools, a sulphide melt crystallizes mainly as pyrrhotite (FeS), which is the iron(II) sulphide that is stable at high temperatures. Any copper and nickel form the sulphide minerals chalcopyrite ($CuFeS_2$) and pentlandite (($Ni,Fe)_9S_8$) respectively. Crystallized blobs of sulphide, mainly pyrrhotite and chalcopyrite, with minor pentlandite, are illustrated in Figure 2.7d, a sample of sulphide-bearing rock from the Sudbury Complex. The sulphide melt also scavenges highly electronegative precious metals, such as gold and platinum. On cooling, these metals may form sulphides, native metals or even metal alloys in the sulphide layers.

Platinum Group elements

Ore-bearing stratiform sulphide deposits of this kind also occur within the Bushveld and Stillwater Complexes, where platinum ores are mined in their own right from thin sulphide-rich layers. In contrast, at Sudbury, platinum is only a by-product of copper and nickel sulphide mining.

Box 2.2 The Bushveld Complex — possibly the most valuable ore deposit in the world?

The Bushveld Complex is a huge, saucer-shaped igneous intrusion (Figure 2.8b) that is over 300 km across and between 6 km and 8 km thick. It occupies an area of 67 000 km^2 just north of Pretoria in South Africa (Figure 2.8a). The lower part of the intrusion is mainly peridotite; the upper two-thirds is mainly gabbro (Figure 2.8c). Between these major divisions, there is a zone of strongly layered rocks with individual cumulate layers rich in pyroxene, calcium-rich plagioclase feldspar, chromite and platinum. At higher levels, layers of cumulate magnetite that are important for their high vanadium content (grading 0.5–2% V_2O_5) account for 50% of the world's vanadium supply. The shape of the intrusion and the presence of granite (formed by the melting of crustal rocks) overlying the middle part of the intrusion, results in the ore deposits being exposed mainly at the eastern and western margins of the Complex (Figure 2.8a and b).

Fourteen chromite seams, varying from a few centimetres to 2 metres in thickness and extending laterally for many kilometres, lie within the strongly layered zone, mostly near its base. Accessible chromite reserves at depths shallower than 300 m at the eastern and western margins amount to over 2 billion tonnes, but ten times this amount would be available if mining were extended to lower-grade ores and to a depth of 1200 m. The Bushveld Complex contains about 75% of world chromite resources.

Near the top of the strongly layered zone, a thin sheet less than 1 m thick comprises mainly coarsely crystalline pyroxene. At its upper and lower margins are thin, centimetre-thick layers containing chromite. These are also rich in sulphides, and more importantly, rich in platinum and other precious metals. Platinum occurs as native metal, as natural alloy, and as sulphide, arsenide and antimonide minerals. It occurs in association with gold and other precious metals, such as ruthenium, rhodium, palladium, osmium and iridium (see Periodic Table at the back of the book), which have similar properties to platinum and are known collectively as *platinum group elements* (PGEs). This sheet, known as the Merensky Reef (Figure 2.8c) after Hans Merensky, an early prospector, is one of the best-documented parts of the Bushveld intrusion. It is mined as a whole unit because the narrow, centimetre-thick layers would be impossible to mine separately. The grade of platinum reaches 7.5–11 g t^{-1}, which is well above the cut-off grade for platinum of 5 g t^{-1}.

The grades of copper (0.11%) and nickel (0.18%) sulphides in the Merensky Reef are much lower than in the Sudbury ores, but even these abundances are sufficient for copper and nickel to be recovered as by-products of PGE mining. Several hundred metres below the Merensky Reef, another chromite layer, 0.5–2.5 m thick, is a major source of PGEs, with platinum grades of 3.5–19 g t^{-1}.

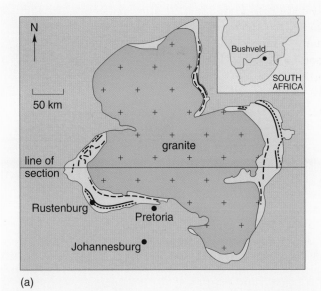

(a)

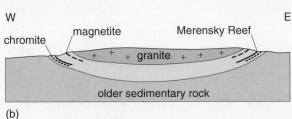

(b)

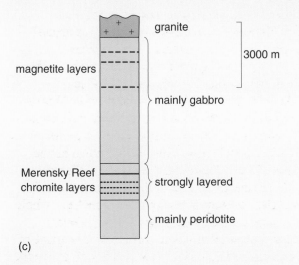

(c)

Figure 2.8 The Bushveld Complex: (a) plan view, showing the extent of economic horizons; (b) W–E cross-section; (c) idealized vertical section.

What, then, could be the value of Bushveld ores? Reserves of PGE in the Bushveld Complex are believed to exceed 63 000 tonnes, which is well over 88% of the total world reserves of these metals, and a very large amount in comparison to the world's total annual extraction of 450 tonnes in the early 2000s. With the mid-2005 price of platinum around US$900 per troy ounce (the normal unit for pricing precious metals — there are 32 150 troy ounces per metric tonne) or US$28 900 per kilogram, perhaps the Bushveld Complex may be justifiably regarded as one of the world's most valuable deposits.

⬤ What was the value of the PGE reserve (assuming it all has the same value as platinum) in mid-2005?

◗ $6.3 \times 10^7 \text{ kg} \times \text{US\$}2.89 \times 10^4 \text{ kg}^{-1}$
$= \text{US\$}1.8 \times 10^{12}$, nearly 2 trillion dollars!

Question 2.2

(a) The similarities and differences between the processes that gave rise to chromite-rich and PGE-rich layers in the Bushveld Complex are described below. To show your understanding of these processes, fill in the missing words from the following:

chromite; crystallized; dense; precious metals; gravity; immiscible; magma; ore; sulphide.

The ……… minerals in both the chromite-rich and PGE-rich layers are ……… and form sequences of thin layers over a wide area. They formed by ……… settling following repeated injection and mixing of ……… pulses during crystallization of the intrusion. The ……… layers contain mainly minerals that ……… from the magma, whereas the Merensky Reef contains ……… minerals that originally separated as an ……… melt that scavenged ……… from the magma.

(b) The reserves of PGEs in the Bushveld Complex amount to 63 000 t. Assuming the reserves account for 80% of the total PGEs (the remaining 20% being non-economic) in the intrusion (total mass 1500×10^9 t), what is the average concentration of PGEs in the whole intrusion? This represents the initial (undifferentiated) magma composition. What degree of concentration was necessary to produce ores averaging 10 g t^{-1}?

$63000\,\text{t} \times \dfrac{100}{80} = 78\,750\,\text{t} \times \dfrac{\text{kg}}{1000} \times \dfrac{\text{g}}{100}$

$= 7\,875\,050\,000 = 7.9 \times 10^{10}\,\text{g}$

in $1500 \times 10^9\,\text{t}$

$\text{Concentration} = \dfrac{7.9 \times 10^4\,\text{t}}{1.5 \times 10^{12}\,\text{t}} = 5.3 \times 10^{-8}\,\text{t} = 0.053\,\text{g t}^{-1}$

of 10 g t^{-1} $\dfrac{10}{0.053} = 189$ times

2.3   Pegmatite ore deposits

Pegmatites are very coarse-grained igneous rocks, usually of granitic composition, and composed principally of quartz, potassium feldspar and muscovite mica (Figure 2.9a). Some pegmatites are mineralized, but few are mined today. Their inclusion here is partly to illustrate a particular form of magmatic enrichment, and partly because they can host the ore minerals of rare metals, including beryllium (Figure 2.9b), caesium, cerium, lithium, niobium, rubidium, tantalum, thorium, tin, tungsten, uranium and zirconium. These metals often have specialized uses, as shown in Table 2.2. The same minerals sometimes occur as *accessory minerals* in granitic rocks, but in pegmatites they can be abundant enough to form ore deposits.

Question 2.3

Some of the metals found in the pegmatite ore minerals listed in Table 2.2 also appear in Figure 1.9. Which are they, and how do their ionic charges and ionic radii compare to those of the major metals sodium, calcium, potassium, iron, magnesium and aluminium? What is the implication of these observations for ionic substitution in rock-forming minerals?

Most pegmatite deposits are small compared to the majority of ore deposits exploited today. Some rare metals, such as rare earth elements and niobium, are now more easily obtained from other sources (such as carbonatites, which are unusual igneous rocks that crystallized from carbonate-rich magma). Localities still important for mining pegmatite ores include the Greenbushes Pegmatite, Western Australia, for lithium in spodumene and the Tanco Pegmatite at Bernic Lake in Manitoba, Canada, for tantalum, lithium and niobium.

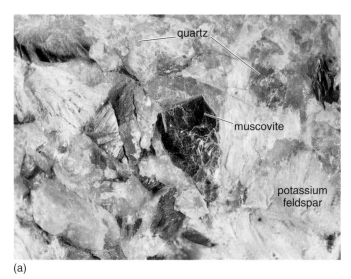

(a)

(b)

Figure 2.9   (a) Pegmatite rock containing large crystals of quartz, potassium feldspar and muscovite mica. Field of view 10 cm across. (b) A 6 cm long crystal of the semi-precious gemstone, aquamarine, a pale-blue variety of beryl, the main ore-mineral of beryllium, set in pegmatite.

Q
5f

Pegmatites commonly occur as lenses or sheet-like bodies; they range from a few centimetres across and a few metres in length, to a few metres across and hundreds (occasionally thousands) of metres in length. Usually they are *unmineralized* (i.e. without ore minerals); less commonly they contain concentrically arranged zones of minerals (Figure 2.10) and may be *mineralized* (i.e. contain ore minerals). Pegmatite zonation involves variations in mineralogy and texture, so different zones may be distinguished by their mineral content and/or grain size. Figure 2.10 features zonation that progresses from a granitic border through more coarsely crystalline zones of quartz and potassium feldspar to a core region containing quartz and, sometimes, exotic minerals, such as beryl, tourmaline and spodumene crystals.

Table 2.2 Some metals that can be obtained from pegmatites: their minerals, uses and properties. (*Note*: m.t. = melting temperature.)

Metal	Mineral/formula	Important uses	Notable properties
beryllium, Be	✓ beryl, $Be_3Al_2(SiO_6)_{18}$ (Figure 2.9b)	brake discs for jet aircraft; windows of X-ray tubes	low density; high m.t. (1279 °C); resistant to metal fatigue; a good heat insulator; transparent to X-rays; toxic
caesium, Cs	pollucite, $(Cs,Na)_2Al_2Si_4O_{12}.H_2O$	atomic clocks and light-sensitive detectors	nuclei of caesium atoms have different energy states
cerium, Ce	monazite, $CePO_4$	coatings for high-definition TV tubes; lighter 'flints'	phosphorescence; high-friction alloy
lithium, Li	✓ spodumene, $LiAlSi_2O_6$	low-density alloys; batteries; coolant in nuclear reactors	low density; high thermal conductivity; low m.t. (181 °C)
tantalum, Ta	✓ tantalite, $FeTa_2O_6$	military warheads; electronic capacitors (as in mobile phones); surgical implants	high density; machinable; high resistivity; very high m.t. (2996 °C); resistant to corrosion
tin, Sn	✓ cassiterite, SnO_2	tinplate; float glass; alloys (bronze, pewter, solder, gunmetal)	low m.t. (232 °C); resistant to corrosion
tungsten, W	wolframite, $FeWO_4$	abrasive and cutting tools (tungsten carbide); high-speed steel; darts; light bulb filaments	high density; very high m.t. (~3400 °C); low thermal expansion
uranium, U	uraninite, UO_2	fuel for nuclear reactors	fissile isotopes

⬤ How does the pegmatite zonation in Figure 2.10 provide clues to pegmatite formation and the concentration of incompatible elements?

◯ Pegmatites crystallize in cavities from the margins inwards. Anhydrous silicate minerals, such as plagioclase feldspar, alkali feldspars and quartz, form the outer zones. Hydrous and incompatible element-bearing minerals tend to form at the core. These observations correspond with the initial crystallization of anhydrous minerals, causing an increase in the proportion of water and incompatible elements in the remaining magma, which crystallize last.

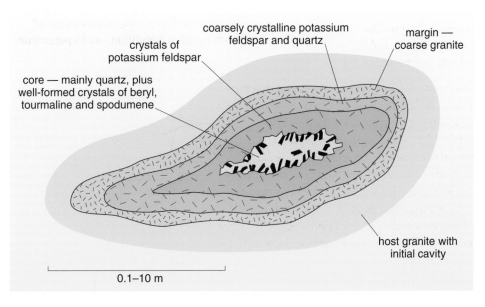

coarsely crystalline potassium feldspar and quartz

crystals of potassium feldspar

margin — coarse granite

core — mainly quartz, plus well-formed crystals of beryl, tourmaline and spodumene

host granite with initial cavity

0.1–10 m

Figure 2.10 Schematic representation of the internal structure of a mineralized zoned pegmatite, showing concentric textural and mineral zonation. Minerals rich in incompatible elements (if present) are concentrated at the core.

This process is a form of fractional crystallization that takes place within a body of pegmatite magma. But how is the pegmatite magma formed? Figure 2.11 shows how crystallization of anhydrous minerals from a 'normal' hydrous granitic magma (H_2O ~0.2%) concentrates water in the remaining melt to produce a water-rich pegmatite magma. Similar enrichment of incompatible elements and volatiles is also possible until they either enter crystallizing minerals or escape in fluids.

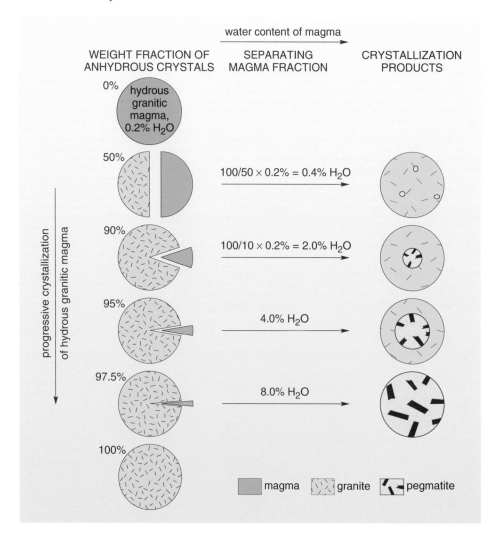

Figure 2.11 Formation of pegmatite from 'normal' hydrous granitic magma by enrichment of water in the magma remaining after crystallization of anhydrous minerals. When the amount of melt remaining halves, its water content doubles. After 97.5% crystallization, the water content of the remaining 2.5% melt has increased 40 times to 8%. The greater the enrichment of the water in the separated magma fraction, the greater the proportion of pegmatite formed on crystallization.

Question 2.4

Use Figure 2.11 to help you to estimate the concentration of lithium in the melt remaining after 97.5% crystallization of a granitic magma having an initial lithium concentration of 10 ppm. Assume that lithium behaves incompatibly, like water, and does not enter crystallizing minerals.

Experimental work has shown that a pegmatite magma containing high concentrations of water (over 5%) and 'volatile' incompatible elements, such as fluorine and boron, has very different properties from 'normal' hydrous granitic magma. Whereas 'normal' hydrous granitic magma is viscous, pegmatitic magma is very mobile, and crystallizes at much lower temperatures. It can also penetrate fractures, thus developing its sheet-like form. Internal zonation of individual pegmatites (Figure 2.10) represents an opportunity for further incompatible element enrichment once the pegmatite magma has reached its final destination.

2.4 Porphyry ore deposits

Porphyry is a textural term used to describe an intrusive igneous rock comprising relatively large crystals set in a matrix (or groundmass) of finer-grained crystals. Porphyry ore deposits acquired their name because porphyritic texture is a distinctive feature of some plutonic igneous rocks with which they are associated. Porphyry ore deposits are large-scale, low-grade, dispersed deposits that contain varying amounts of copper and/or molybdenum ore minerals, along with lesser amounts of gold, silver and tungsten that are often mined as by-products. No porphyry deposits were mined before 1905. They became viable only with the development of large-scale mining methods, such as powered shovels and rail track to transport rock, together with improved methods of processing and separation of ore minerals (Chapter 6). Today, porphyry deposits provide over 50% of the world's copper and 70% of the world's molybdenum. Many such deposits are located in the Cordilleran mountain ranges of North and South America, and the islands of the western Pacific.

The Bingham Canyon Mine in Utah, USA (near Salt Lake City), was the first porphyry copper deposit to be mined and even today it ranks as one of the largest ore deposits in the world (Figure 2.12). The deposit is about 2.5 km long, 1.7 km wide and over 1 km deep. Since Bingham opened, over a billion tonnes of ore, yielding an average of 0.9% Cu, have been mined from it and yet it still has ore reserves of 1.7 billion tonnes that exceed the cut-off grade of 0.7% Cu.

Figure 2.12 An oblique view of the Bingham Canyon open pit porphyry copper mine, Utah. The pit is about 2 km across, though spoil heaps and tailings ponds occupy a much greater area.

Porphyry copper deposits are generally found in association with small, 1–2 km diameter igneous intrusions of diorite or granodiorite composition. (As its name suggests, granodiorite is a rock type intermediate between granite and diorite.) Although pyrite (FeS_2) is the dominant sulphide mineral, the ore minerals are mainly copper sulphides, such as chalcopyrite ($CuFeS_2$) and bornite (Cu_5FeS_4), which are dispersed throughout large volumes of rock in a complex network of tiny veinlets called a **stockwork**. Figure 2.13 shows a typical porphyry copper stockwork in which intense fracturing and recrystallization have almost obliterated the original porphyritic texture of the host rock. These effects resulted from the passage of metal-bearing aqueous fluids (of the kind described in Section 2.1.2), which not only deposited ore minerals in veins and pore spaces, but also reacted with the surrounding rock, changing its mineralogy — a process known as *wall-rock alteration*.

Figure 2.13 Typical example of porphyry copper stockwork showing mineralized veins containing copper sulphides occupying the fractures. The wall-rock alteration around the veins has almost obliterated the porphyritic texture of the host rock. The field of view is 12 cm across.

Mineralized porphyry intrusions are generally emplaced as hydrous, partially crystalline magmas (typically containing about 3% H_2O) and reach shallow depths (usually between 1 km and 2 km) in the crust. The reduction in pressure as the magma rises, and the increasing concentration of water in the magma, due to crystallization of mainly anhydrous minerals, cause the magma to become water-saturated. 'Bubbles' of watery fluid then separate from the magma (Section 2.1.2) and rise to the top of the magma chamber (Figure 2.14a). Metals that form soluble ionic complexes, such as copper, can be scavenged by the aqueous fluid. Separation of fluids is accompanied by an increase in volume, which creates an overpressuring of the magma chamber and eventually the fracturing of surrounding rocks.

Q
5g

The shattering of the crystalline 'shell' of the intrusion (Figure 2.14a) allows water vapour to escape and the magma to rise further (Figure 2.14b). The sudden loss of water from the magma *raises* its crystallization temperature, causing it to crystallize more rapidly, so that early formed, coarse-grained crystals are set in a fine-grained groundmass: a typical porphyritic texture.

On escaping through newly formed fractures and permeating the surrounding rock, the hot, aqueous fluids react with silicate minerals, giving rise to wall-rock alteration and deposition of ore minerals (such as copper sulphides). Fluids at subcritical temperatures at very shallow depth may transform explosively from liquid to steam, which involves a huge expansion. Repeated fracturing of rock and escape of aqueous fluids produces a thoroughly altered, fractured and mineralized stockwork (Figure 2.13). The extensive alteration of the surrounding rocks is useful in locating porphyry mineralization because the distinctive alteration 'halo' produced by the mineralizing fluids (shown in Figure 2.15a) is usually much larger than the mineralized region itself (compare with Figure 2.15b).

Q
5h

Characteristically, a high-temperature potassium feldspar alteration zone centred on the porphyry intrusion gives way outwards to a zone of micaceous alteration and then to a lower-temperature zone characterized by chlorite, which is a flaky, green mineral. Beyond that, lower temperature alteration produces clay minerals from feldspars. The distribution of ore minerals is also zoned, as illustrated in Figure 2.15b. The main orebody commonly takes the shape of a steep-walled cylinder, often

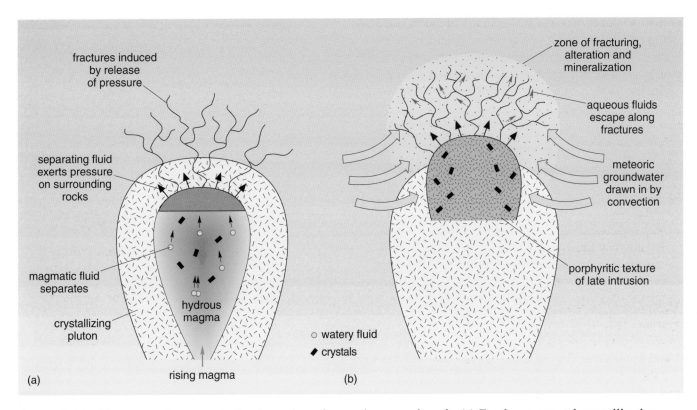

Figure 2.14 The magmatic stages in the formation of a porphyry ore deposit. (a) Emplacement and crystallization of hydrous granodioritic magma and separation of watery fluid. Consequent expansion produces fracturing and escape of fluids. At a high level, transformation of the fluid to steam gives rise to explosive fracturing. (b) Rapid crystallization of the porphyritic intrusion and the escape of aqueous magmatic fluids through fracture zones. Heat from the intrusion convects hydrothermal fluids derived from the magma itself and from meteoric groundwater drawn in from surrounding rocks.

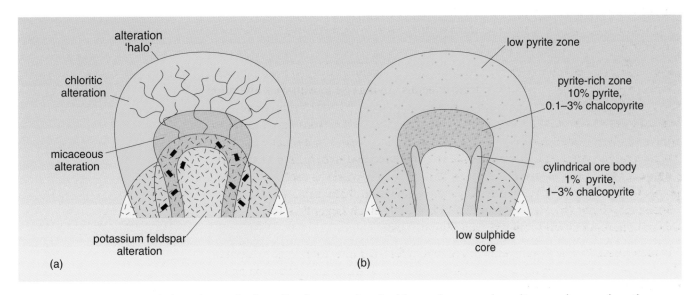

Figure 2.15 Patterns of alteration and mineralization associated with porphyry ore deposits superimposed on the porphyry intrusion featured in Figure 2.14, showing: (a) zonation of alteration products to form a 'halo'; (b) the distribution of sulphide mineralization typical of a porphyry copper deposit.

centred on the porphyry intrusion, but not confined to it. Outside it, a pyrite-rich zone extends roughly to the boundary between the zone of potassium feldspar alteration and the surrounding zone of micaceous alteration. In the zone of chloritic alteration, the mineralization is variable, but mainly non-economic.

Intrusions that give rise to porphyry-type deposits and supply the magmatic fluids are also a source of heat. This causes convection, drawing in and heating up meteoric groundwater from the surrounding rocks (Figure 2.14b). These fluids may mix with hot magmatic fluids and/or react with wall-rocks, and ore minerals may be deposited. Therefore, most porphyry ore deposits are complex, produced by successive mineralizing systems. Although initiated by magmatic processes, they are, for the most part, hydrothermal systems. The early (higher temperature) products of magmatic fluids are 'overprinted' by (lower temperature) products of meteoric fluids.

An important factor that often determines whether or not a porphyry deposit is economic may arise when the porphyry deposit is exposed by erosion. Near-surface weathering of primary sulphide minerals and leaching by percolating groundwater releases soluble metal ions into solution. At depth, reaction between these metal-rich solutions and primary sulphide minerals can form an enriched zone of secondary minerals (see Section 3.3.2), with ore grades enhanced to perhaps five to ten times the grade of the primary ore.

Porphyry molybdenum deposits have many of the features (large tonnages, low-grade dispersed mineralization, alteration haloes) seen in porphyry copper deposits, although they tend to be associated with intrusions of granitic rather than granodioritic composition. Molybdenum porphyry deposits in the western USA account for half the world's molybdenum reserves, and include the once-famous Climax deposit in Colorado. The cut-off grade for molybdenum is about 0.1% molybdenite, MoS_2 (quoted in terms of the main molybdenum ore mineral), with grades usually in the range 0.1–0.5% MoS_2. Tin porphyries are also known in Bolivia and Alaska, but such deposits grading 0.2–0.3% Sn (in which cassiterite, SnO_2, is the main ore mineral) are currently uneconomic.

Porphyry copper deposits are the best-known porphyry ore deposits, having become increasingly important as a source of copper during the 20th century. Molybdenum porphyries are the main source of molybdenum. The global distribution of porphyry copper and molybdenum deposits is closely linked to volcanic arcs above subduction zones (Figure 2.16), particularly the continental arcs of the Andes and the North American Sierras, and the oceanic arcs of the western Pacific. This distribution is an important consideration when exploring for new copper and molybdenum deposits.

The conditions for the development of porphyry deposits accompany the subduction of oceanic lithosphere. At destructive plate margins (Figure 2.3b), heating and dehydration of the hydrous minerals within the oceanic crust drive off watery fluids. When these rise into the overlying mantle, melting occurs and the resulting hydrous magmas rise and interact with overlying crustal material to form a range of magma compositions. It is when these hydrous magmas are emplaced at a high level in the crust that porphyry ore deposits are formed (Box 2.3).

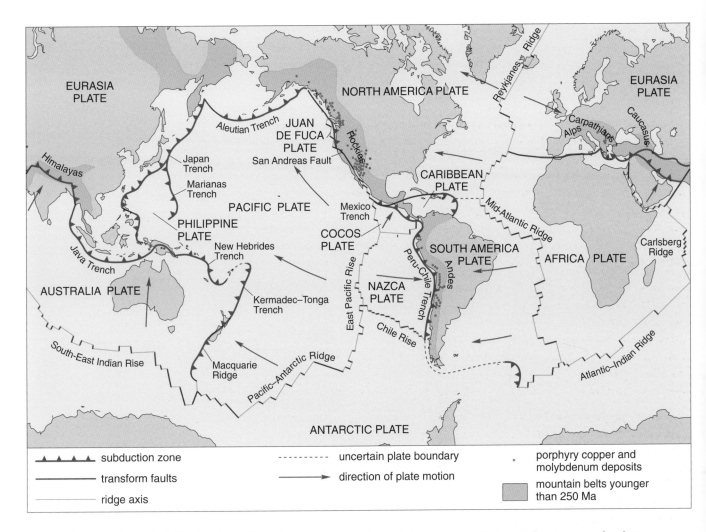

Figure 2.16 The global distribution of porphyry copper and molybdenum deposits in relation to tectonic plate boundaries.

Box 2.3   The Chilean porphyry copper belt — taking the lead in world copper production

The Andean mountain chain has long been one of the world's most important mining areas. The Incas worked gold and silver for ornamental purposes and made bronze weapons long before the Spanish invaded in the early 16th century. The Andes lie along the western margin of the South American continent, forming a volcanic arc, which is part of the destructive plate margin (Figure 2.3b) along which the oceanic Nazca Plate is being subducted (Figure 2.17a).

Many ore deposits within the Andes are related to Cretaceous–Tertiary age igneous intrusions of dioritic or granodioritic composition. Porphyry copper deposits in the Western Cordillera are the most important economically, but related hydrothermal vein deposits also contain economic lead, zinc, copper and silver. In the Eastern Cordillera, porphyry and vein deposits contain tin, tungsten and silver. Bolivia is a leading exporter of tin; and mining of porphyry copper deposits has made Chile the world's leading copper

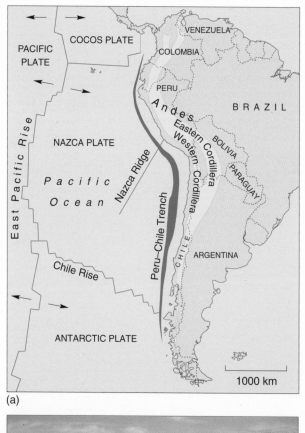

(a)

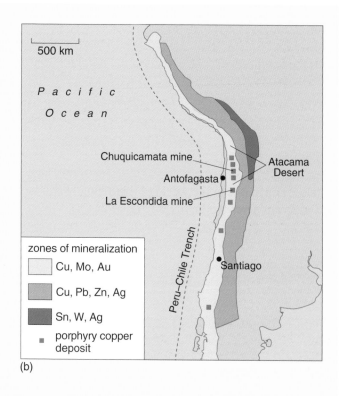

(b)

(c)

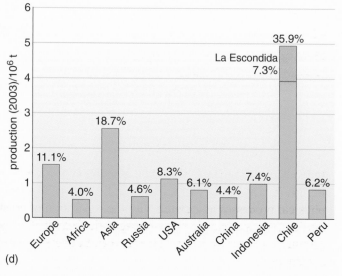

(d)

Figure 2.17 (a) The setting of the Andean chain in its plate tectonic context. (b) Regional zoning of metals in the central Andes and the location of Chuquicamata and La Escondida mines in relation to other Chilean porphyry copper deposits. (c) The Chuquicamata open pit. (d) World copper production in 2003, highlighting the contribution of La Escondida.

producer (Figure 2.17d). In 2003, Chile not only produced 4.9 Mt of copper, but also 33 000 t of molybdenum, 1300 t of silver and 3.9 t of gold, largely as by-products of porphyry copper mining.

Chuquicamata mine in northern Chile (Figure 2.17b) is about 150 km from the coast, at a height of 3000 m, and in one of the driest parts of the Atacama Desert. It is one of the largest sources of copper in the world, producing about 600 000 t annually, from one of the largest open pits in the world (3.7 km long by 1.8 km across and over 0.5 km deep; Figure 2.17c). With 500 Mt of ore, grading 1.75% Cu, already removed,

reserves still stand at 1.5 billion tonnes, grading 1.1% Cu and 0.12% Mo. Current plans are to extend mining underground. In recent years the Escondida mine has outstripped the Chuquicamata mine as the world's largest producer (Figure 2.17d).

The granodiorite porphyry at Chuquicamata is highly fractured to form a stockwork of primary copper ore containing 0.5–1.0% Cu, mainly in the form of the sulphides chalcopyrite ($CuFeS_2$), bornite (Cu_5FeS_4) and enargite (Cu_3AsS_4). Zones of enriched secondary mineralization locally grade up to 15% Cu.

Question 2.5

Even in regions favourable for porphyry ore formation, unmineralized diorites, granodiorites and granites are in the majority. The right circumstances are required for a porphyry ore deposit to form. Decide whether the following factors would *favour* or *hinder* the formation of porphyry ore deposits and briefly explain your answers:

(a) a low proportion of water in the initial magma;

(b) crystallization of magma at deep levels in the crust;

(c) a high content of copper (and/or molybdenum) in the magma;

(d) eruption of magma at the Earth's surface;

(e) crystallization of anhydrous minerals from the magma.

2.5 Summary of Chapter 2

1 Igneous processes take place in magmatic systems and involve crystals, liquids (i.e. magma, sulphide melt and water) and gases. Chemical and physical processes associated with the separation of crystals or immiscible liquids from magma give rise to magmatic fractionation, which not only produces different types of igneous rock but may concentrate metals to form ore deposits.

2 Igneous rocks span a range of compositions — from peridotite to gabbro (basalt) to diorite (andesite) to granite (rhyolite) — the formation of which depends on the source of the magma and the extent to which magmatic fractionation has occurred. Different types of ore deposit are associated with particular types of igneous rocks: magmatic segregation deposits are associated with peridotites and gabbros, pegmatite deposits with granites, and porphyry deposits with diorites, granodiorites and granites.

3 Magmatic segregation deposits separate from hot fluid basaltic magmas when either dense early-formed crystals or dense immiscible liquids (sulphide melt) sink towards the floor of a magma chamber and form cumulate layers.

p63

Basalt

&

6d

Settling of crystals may produce chromite ore deposits; settling of sulphide-rich immiscible liquids may produce ore deposits rich in copper, nickel, gold or PGEs. Development of the multiple layering that is typical of many magmatic segregation deposits requires periodic injections of new magma and mixing with the already fractionated magma.

4   Pegmatites form from granitic magma after the crystallization of anhydrous minerals has enriched the remaining melt in water and sometimes incompatible elements, which makes it particularly fluid. Pegmatites are not often mineralized, but when they are, they can be enriched in ore minerals of rare metals, including beryllium, caesium, lithium, niobium, rare earth elements (such as cerium), tantalum, thorium, tin, tungsten, uranium and zirconium, many of which infrequently form other kinds of mineral deposit.

5   Porphyry deposits are formed when crystallizing hydrous dioritic to granitic magmas that formed above subduction zones rise to shallow depth. When the magma becomes water-saturated, due to decompression and crystallization of anhydrous minerals, watery fluids separate and scavenge the melt for metals such as copper and molybdenum. Overpressuring due to separation of fluids causes fracturing of the surrounding rocks, as does the boiling of subcritical fluid at a high level in the crust. The fractures provide pathways for distribution of both metal-rich magmatic fluids and convecting meteoric fluids from surrounding rocks. The fractures also provide sites for the deposition of ore minerals, as do adjacent zones of wall-rock alteration. Porphyry deposits provide much of the world's copper and molybdenum, as well as substantial quantities of tin, silver and gold as by-products. They are typically low-grade but extremely large deposits.

ORE DEPOSITS FORMED BY PROCESSES AT THE EARTH'S SURFACE

3

Processes acting at the Earth's surface are more familiar than those acting below ground. Clays, sands and gravels, formed quite recently by rivers, on beaches, offshore and as glacial deposits, can form industrial mineral resources (Argles, 2005); but what of metals and ore deposits? It may not be obvious that ore deposits are being formed at the Earth's surface today, yet most of the processes that concentrated metals (as ore minerals) in the past remain active.

3.1 Surface concentration processes

Weathering and erosion of rock, transportation and deposition of derived products all constitute surface processes (Figure 3.1). Weathering, which is the breakdown of rocks *in situ*, takes on different forms:

- **physical weathering** involves processes such as frost shattering and simply breaks rocks into fragments;

- **chemical (including biochemical) weathering** involves, for example, the reaction of rainwater and percolating solutions on rocks, breaking down susceptible minerals and taking soluble material into solution (Box 3.1).

⬤ Which type of weathering is the more likely to *concentrate* metals — physical or chemical weathering? Why?

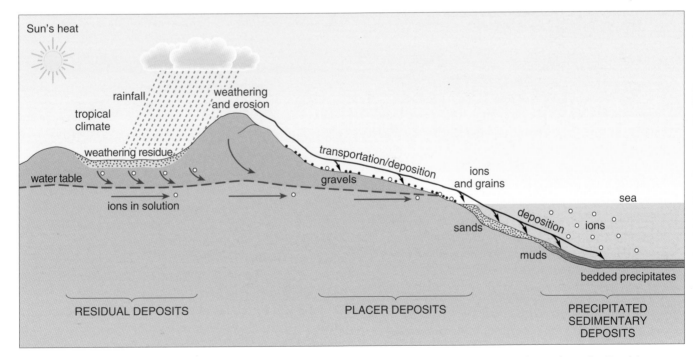

Figure 3.1 The main processes of the rock cycle that are involved in the concentration of metals at the Earth's surface. Arrows represent transportation by surface and underground waters.

Chemical weathering is the more likely to concentrate metals because it involves selective decomposition of minerals and the removal of some chemical constituents in solution — a form of chemical fractionation — whereas physical weathering only breaks down rock into smaller fragments. The insoluble products of chemical weathering that remain in place at the surface are known as **residual deposits** (Figure 3.1 and Section 3.3.1). Chemical weathering also liberates the more resistant mineral grains, including some ore minerals, which subsequently may be transported and concentrated by physical processes.

Box 3.1   Natural waters and chemical weathering

Rainwater contains dissolved carbon dioxide, which makes it mildly acidic (pH ~5.6), and dissolved oxygen, which makes it oxidizing. As noted in Section 1.5, acidic solutions (containing an excess of H^+ ions over OH^- ions) are capable of reacting with and decomposing minerals in rocks, especially carbonate minerals in limestones and calcareous sediments, as follows:

$$CaCO_3(s) + H^+(aq) = Ca^{2+}(aq) + HCO_3^-(aq) \quad (3.1)$$
limestone   acid solution   hard water

This process is a form of chemical weathering, which also affects silicate minerals. For example, potassium feldspar can break down to produce the clay mineral, kaolinite:

$$2KAlSi_3O_8(s) + 2H^+(aq) + H_2O(l) =$$
potassium feldspar   acid rainwater

$$Al_2Si_2O_5(OH)_4(s) + 2K^+(aq) + 4SiO_2(aq) \quad (3.2)$$
kaolinite   silica in solution

Bacterial decay of plant matter in soils produces organic acids, which are often more important than carbon dioxide in acidifying soil moisture and seepage, particularly in warm, humid climates. When sulphide minerals, especially pyrite, in rocks break down they further increase acidity. High acidity, high temperatures and high rainfall tend to accelerate the chemical breakdown of minerals that are unstable at the Earth's surface, making chemical weathering more important in tropical regions than in polar or temperate climates.

Some minerals are more susceptible to decomposition by chemical weathering than others. Those that form and are stable at high temperatures and pressures deep in the Earth tend to be least stable under conditions at the Earth's surface: thus olivine and

calcium-rich plagioclase feldspar break down easily whereas muscovite mica, and more especially quartz, tend to be very resistant to chemical weathering.

The oxidizing nature of rainwater can also be a significant factor in the weathering of minerals. Iron is present as iron(II) in many minerals, such as olivine, pyroxene, amphibole and biotite mica, but when released into solution it is transformed by the oxidizing action of rainwater into compounds such as hydrated iron(III) oxide that are generally insoluble:

$$4Fe^{2+}(aq) + 6H_2O(l) + O_2(aq) =$$
iron(II) ions   oxidizing solution

$$4FeO(OH)(s) + 8H^+(aq) \quad (3.3)$$
hydrated iron(III) oxide

How does the oxidation reaction in Equation 3.3 affect the pH of the solution?

H^+ ions are produced, which lower the pH of the solution and increase its acidity. Oxidation reactions often involve changes in the acidity of a solution.

Variations in the oxidation conditions of surface and groundwater solutions occur naturally. Rainwater, free-flowing surface waters and water percolating into the ground all contain dissolved oxygen and are oxidizing. However, as these waters seep through soils and rocks, the oxygen gets used up by bacteria that break down organic matter (from plants) and by reaction with minerals that contain metals in a reduced state, so groundwater conditions become more reducing with depth. In carbon- or sulphur-rich environments, groundwater can become very reducing indeed. This is also true of environments in which organic material (high in carbon) is decaying, such as in swamps and in stagnant waters of the sea floor.

Fractionation also occurs during transportation and deposition; with very different consequences for physical and chemical processes.

1 *Physical* transport depends on the energy of the environment (i.e. the speed of movement of the transporting medium — water or air), which determines how easily grains can be moved and subsequently deposited. Small, light clay particles and silt grains, for example, can be transported more easily and at lower energies than dense grains and larger sand grains and pebbles. Thus, transported grains can be separated according to their size, density and changes in the speed of flow: a process known as **sorting**. As the speed of flow declines, larger and/or heavier grains are the first to be deposited, followed by progressively smaller and/or lighter grains. Sorting is important in forming concentrations of dense ore minerals, known as **placer deposits** (Figure 3.1 and Section 3.2).

2 *Chemical* transport in surface waters involves ions in solution and tiny, charged particles or *colloids* (Section 3.4). Clays, silica and iron(III) hydroxide normally form insoluble particles but can be transported in colloidal suspension. A change in chemical conditions, such as pH or oxidation state (as described in Section 1.5), or mixing with saline waters, such as seawater, can affect both the stability and solubility of ions and neutralize the charge on colloidal particles, so bringing about precipitation and deposition of **chemical sediments**. Such processes can be important in forming some bedded sedimentary ore deposits (Figure 3.1 and Section 3.4).

3.2   Ores formed through physical transport and deposition by surface waters: placer deposits

Physical transportation of sediment by water can sort sediment according to density and grain size.

● What property of the transporting medium most influences the degree of sorting?

○ The *energy of transportation* is the most important factor.

Strictly, the energy of transportation determines what grains can be transported, so it is a *change* in the energy of transportation that deposits and sorts grains. For example, a high-energy environment such as a fast-flowing stream may transport a wide range of grain sizes ranging from clay minerals to pebbles and rock fragments. A slackening of the current, and hence a decrease in the energy of transportation, causes the larger and heavier grains to be deposited, whereas the smaller, lighter particles remain in suspension or move as bedload. Clay minerals are not deposited until the energy of transportation is very low, as in lakes, lagoons, estuaries and the deeper parts of the oceans.

An increase in the energy of transportation, especially in turbulent conditions, can also be an effective means of sorting. For example, if sediment containing quartz and clay minerals is stirred up, perhaps by waves on beaches or by rapids in rivers, the lighter clay minerals may be removed, leaving the larger and denser grains behind. This process is known as **winnowing**. Consequently, a change in the energy of transportation combined with efficient sorting can fractionate mixtures of minerals and produce concentrations of particular minerals.

Selective deposition from flowing water may not only concentrate sediment grains of a particular size, but also grains of a particular density. Ore minerals are generally much denser than most rock-forming silicate minerals, so are concentrated because they are deposited first. They are frequently trapped in locations where flow rates rapidly diminish, and are left behind by winnowing. Such accumulations of ore minerals are known as *placer deposits*.

● What properties of an ore mineral would favour the formation of a placer deposit?

○ High density to assist sorting, and durability to resist both chemical decomposition and physical disintegration.

Minerals prone to chemical attack, such as iron and copper sulphides that are easily oxidized, are unlikely to survive weathering, transportation and subsequent deposition. Soft or easily fractured minerals, especially well-cleaved ones, become worn or broken down during transportation to produce very fine grains that are not easily concentrated by sorting. Hard, poorly cleaved ore minerals, which resist breakdown by weathering, are the most durable and likely to survive transportation as sand-sized **detrital grains**. Ore minerals in placer deposits must therefore be chemically stable during the chemical breakdown of their host rock and physically stable during transport and concentration by physical sorting processes.

Table 3.1   Selected properties of some ore minerals.

Mineral	Formula	Density*/t m^{-3}	Hardness†	Cleavage
barite	$BaSO_4$	4.5	3	good
zircon	$ZrSiO_4$	4.6–4.7	7.5	none
ilmenite	$FeTiO_3$	4.7	5.5	none
molybdenite	MoS_2	4.9	1.5	good
bornite	Cu_5FeS_4	5.1	3	poor
columbite	$FeNb_2O_6$	5.2–7.9	6	weak
cassiterite	SnO_2	6.8–7.1	6.5	poor
gold	Au	15.0–19.3	2	none

*Densities of common rock-forming minerals range from about 2.5 to about 3.0 t m^{-3}.

†As measured by Moh's scale, which ranges from 1 (softest: gypsum) to 10 (hardest: diamond).

Question 3.1

Table 3.1 lists eight ore minerals with details of their density, hardness and cleavage. Which *five* might be found in placer deposits and why?

Comparison!

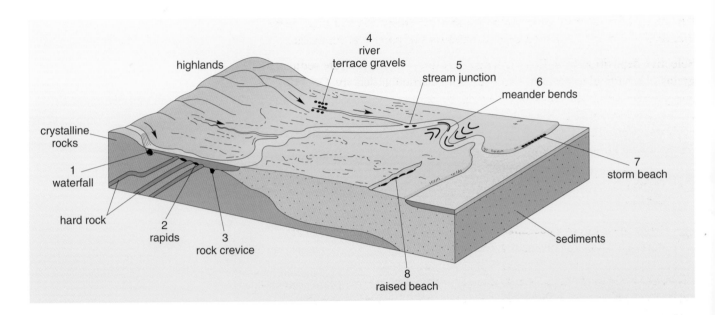

Figure 3.2 illustrates the locations where placer deposits may be found. Sites 1–4 are sediment traps in rivers, where heavy mineral grains can settle, to become inaccessible to rapidly flowing currents. At site 5, a fast-flowing stream slows as it meets a larger, more sluggish stream; at site 6, on the inside of a river meander, the current slackens, allowing selective deposition of heavier mineral grains. Sites 1–6 are all locations of *alluvial* deposits; sites 7 and 8 are *coastal* deposits. Site 7 is a storm beach, where winnowing by wave action leaves behind heavy mineral grains. Where sea level has fallen relative to the land, abandoned beaches become raised beaches (site 8), so beach placer deposits may occur inland.

Table 3.2 lists the most important **heavy minerals** (mostly dense oxide minerals and native metals) mined from placer deposits. The most common placer minerals are magnetite, ilmenite and rutile. These are the main heavy mineral constituents of *black sands*, as some beach placer deposits are called. Their densities (Table 3.2) exceed considerably that of the dominant quartz grains (density 2.65 t m^{-3}). The mineral content of a placer deposit depends on the source rocks from which it was derived and the efficiency of sorting during deposition. Notice that Table 3.2 suggests that sorting is more efficient in beach environments, as these deposits tend to contain lower density placer minerals. The higher density placer minerals tend to be more important in alluvial environments.

The hardest known substance, diamond, is also denser (3.5 t m^{-3}) than most silicate minerals and can be found concentrated in alluvial and beach placer deposits. Diamonds discovered in the 1860s in gravels of the Orange River, South Africa, led to the discovery of the igneous source of the diamonds upstream at Kimberley, and later, downstream in beach deposits along the western coast of South Africa and Namibia. The value of diamonds makes placer mining attractive even at extremely low concentrations.

Figure 3.2 Typical locations of placer deposits in alluvial and coastal environments. See text for explanation of numbered sites.

magnetite 5.2
ilmenite 4.7
rutile 4.2

zircon 46-4.7
monazite 4.8-5.5
magnetite 5.2

Q 8 b

69

Table 3.2 Ore minerals commonly recovered from placer deposits.

Metal/element	Ore mineral	Density/t m^{-3}	Main environment
carbon	diamond, C	3.5	beach sand and alluvial
titanium	rutile, TiO_2	4.2	beach sand
zirconium	zircon, $ZrSiO_4$	4.6–4.7	beach sand ✓
titanium	ilmenite, $FeTiO_3$	4.7	beach sand
rare earth elements	monazite, $CePO_4$	4.8–5.5	beach sand ✓
iron	magnetite, Fe_3O_4	5.2	beach sand ✓
niobium	columbite, $FeNb_2O_6$	5.2–7.9	alluvial
tin	cassiterite, SnO_2	6.8–7.1	alluvial
tantalum	tantalite, $FeTa_2O_6$	7.9–8.2	alluvial
gold	native metal, Au	15.0–19.3	alluvial
platinum	native metal, Pt	14.0–19.0	alluvial

Q8a

Many heavy minerals were formed originally as accessory minerals in igneous rocks.

Which types of igneous rock would be the likely source of placer deposits containing (a) cassiterite, (b) zircon, and (c) magnetite? (*Hint*: refer back to Section 2.1.1.)

These accessory minerals occur in igneous rocks as follows: (a) cassiterite in granites, (b) zircon in granites, (c) magnetite in gabbros.

Some metals, such as gold and tin (as cassiterite), were mined from alluvial deposits long before they were mined from any other type of ore deposit. This highlights an important reason for mining placer deposits: as they mostly occur in loose sediments, they are easily worked and the ore minerals are easily separated. Nowadays, some alluvial placer deposits are worked with high-pressure water jets, especially in Brazil and Malaysia. Beach placer deposits are mined in bulk by **dredging** — often in artificial lagoons (see Figure 3.3). Numerous occurrences of rutile–zircon–ilmenite sands occur in both eastern and western Australia (see Box 3.2), making Australia a world leader in heavy mineral production (with 54% of rutile, 43% of zircon and 24% of ilmenite world production in 2003).

Some '*fossil*' placer deposits (i.e. placer deposits which have undergone burial and been consolidated since their initial accumulation) have proved to be of immense value. The best known is the Witwatersrand Goldfield in

South Africa, where Precambrian 'quartz pebble' conglomerates have provided over one-third of the world's gold (as well as much silver and uranium) since mining started in 1886. It ranks as one of the world's most valuable ore deposits. There is controversy about the origin of the gold because much of it appears to have had a hydrothermal origin, but its distribution in braided channel deposits of river deltas suggests that its original deposition was controlled by sediment sorting prior to hydrothermal remobilization.

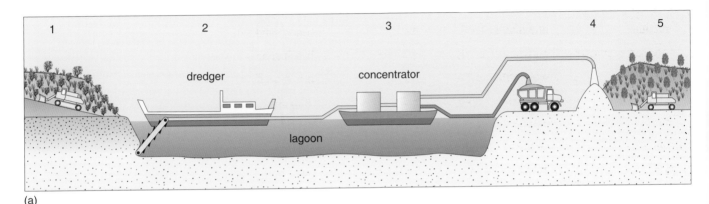

(a)

(b)

Figure 3.3 Mining unconsolidated coastal placer deposits by dredging. (a) Working in an artificial lagoon provides water to facilitate handling of loose material that needs no crushing; such operations are extremely flexible. 1 *Preparation* — ahead of the slowly advancing mining plant, the vegetation is cleared and the topsoil removed for later use. 2 *Dredging* — the dredger advances at a rate of 2–3 metres per day into the mining face of the dune. As the sand face is undermined, it collapses into the pond forming a slurry which is sucked up and pumped to a floating concentrator. 3 *Concentration* — the heavy minerals are separated from the sand using a gravity process and stockpiled as heavy mineral concentrate for transportation to the smelter site for processing. 4 *Stacking* — using the tailings, the dunes are reshaped as the first step in the rehabilitation programme. 5 *Rehabilitation* — a thin layer of topsoil is spread over the bare sand providing a 'kick-start' to the processes through which the dunes can recover naturally. (b) Dredging operations in the Zulti North lease area, Richards Bay Minerals, South Africa.

Box 3.2   The 'black sand' deposits of eastern Australia

Though not the largest of placer deposits, the 'black sands' of North Stradbroke Island (off Brisbane, along the eastern coast of Australia) provide a good example of beach placer deposit formation. The geography of the island is shown in Figure 3.4. A long, sandy beach borders the eastern margin of the island and is separated by a swamp from a series of sand dune ridges that rise to over 200 m.

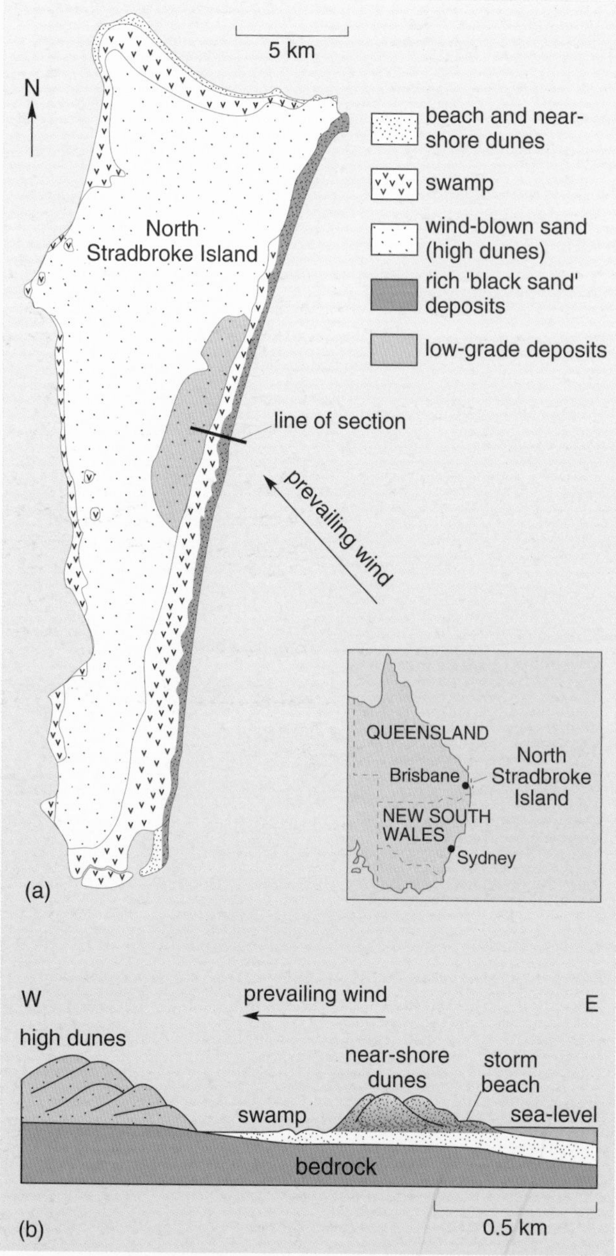

The accumulation of the 'black sands' is due to summer storms, which blow onto the island from the southeast. In this high-energy environment, sand is moved along the shore by incoming waves to form a storm beach. The turbulence of breaking waves stirs the sand and the lighter quartz grains are returned to the sea in the backwash, leaving the dense minerals on the storm beach. This is one form of winnowing. Another form occurs at low tide, when onshore winds blow light sand grains from the lower beach to form dunes, which cover and preserve storm beaches (see cross-section, Figure 3.4b). Exceptionally strong winds blow sand from these near-shore dunes even further westwards adding to the high dunes in the centre of the island. Sorting by wave action is more efficient than sorting by wind action and produces the highest-grade heavy mineral deposits.

Zircon, rutile and ilmenite are the main ore minerals, but monazite (Table 3.2), although only present in tiny amounts, is a valuable ore mineral for rare earth elements (see Periodic Table inside back cover), especially cerium. These heavy minerals are most enriched in the storm beaches, though they only occur in small tonnages. Higher tonnages of lower-grade deposits are available from the near-shore dunes and the high dunes. The estimated resources (before mining began) are shown in Table 3.3.

Table 3.3 Estimated resources of heavy minerals.

Location	Quantity of ore (sand)/t	Grade of heavy minerals/%
storm beach	3000	12
near-shore dunes	2 million	8
high dunes	400 million	1.7

Since mining started in the 1940s, 15% of the island has been mined; there are resources to last another 25 years. The ultimate source of the heavy minerals is thought to be crystalline rocks, such as granites, basalts and metamorphic rocks of Australia's interior. The weathering products, carried to the sea by rivers, were diverted northwards along the shore by the prevailing waves and currents.

Figure 3.4 The distribution of beach placer deposits on North Stradbroke Island, Australia, (a) in plan view and (b) in cross-section.

3.3   Ores formed by chemical leaching and deposition from groundwaters

3.3.1   Residual weathering deposits

In tropical climates, warm and humid conditions promote chemical weathering of surface rocks (Figure 3.1). If erosion is minimal, the products of weathering may accumulate as thick residual soils, which are known as **laterites**. Such soils can be developed on many common rock types, especially on permeable rocks through which surface water can drain. Laterites consist mainly of kaolinite and the insoluble hydrated oxides of aluminium (e.g. gibbsite, $Al(OH)_3$) and iron(III) (e.g. goethite, $FeO(OH)$): the latter gives these soils their deep brick-red colour. Laterites that have developed on iron-rich rocks, such as gabbro, may contain as much as 50% iron(III) oxide, but that is rare. Owing to their accessibility, some laterite deposits have been worked for iron in the past, but their iron content is generally too low and they are too thin to be mined economically for iron today.

An important type of ore deposit associated with laterite formation is developed on weathered peridotite in which nickel is an abundant trace element (~2000 ppm). The nickel is leached from the upper layers of the lateritic soil and deposited as hydrated nickel silicate minerals around the partially weathered blocks of bedrock beneath (Figure 3.5). Economic deposits of this kind, grading 1–3% Ni, are known in many tropical areas where there are outcrops of peridotite rocks, as in the Pacific islands of New Caledonia, where nickel mining started as long ago as 1876. Nickeliferous laterites account for about 65% of global nickel resources — far more than in magmatic nickel sulphide deposits

Figure 3.5 Schematic section and chemical profile through a nickel-bearing laterite deposit of New Caledonia. The richest nickel deposits lie below the residual laterite within the zone of weathered peridotite. Metal concentration profiles show variation in composition of some major element oxides and nickel.

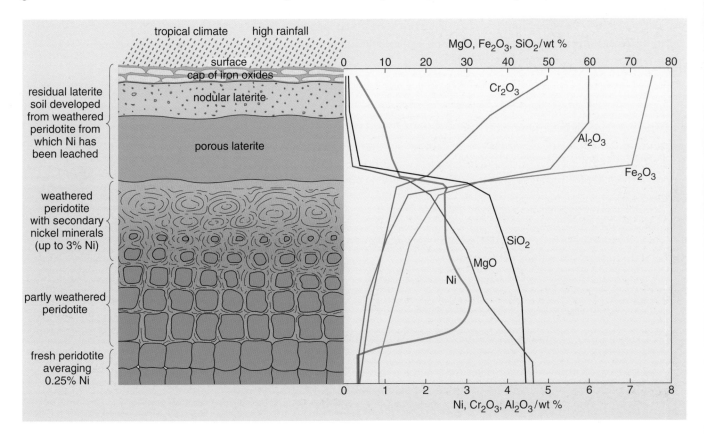

(Section 2.2.2). Cobalt, at grades of only 0.12%, and copper at around 0.3%, are often valuable by-products of some lateritic deposits.

- Why are lateritic deposits economic to mine at relatively low grades?

- They occur at shallow depths, often as poorly consolidated material, and can be worked easily from the surface. In some deposits, other metals, such as cobalt and copper, may be valuable by-products.

Several metals, including nickel, chromium, cobalt, copper, titanium and gold, may be obtained from residual deposits, but by far the most important metal in terms of quantity mined is aluminium. Although aluminium is the third most abundant element in the Earth's crust after oxygen and silicon, and the most abundant metal at 8.4% Al, it is usually combined with other elements in silicate minerals, such as feldspars and micas, from which its extraction would be prohibitively expensive. So, in what natural form is aluminium most concentrated, and most easily extracted?

Figure 3.6 Mining reddish-brown, earthy bauxite in a shallow pit, Huntly, Australia.

Box 3.1 showed how chemical weathering can produce the clay mineral kaolinite from feldspars. The aluminium content of kaolinite, expressed as alumina (Al_2O_3), is 40%, a marked enrichment compared with 18–28% Al_2O_3 in feldspars, but it is not economic to extract aluminium from kaolinite (a silicate mineral). In warm tropical climates, chemical weathering may progress further; kaolinite breaks down and silica is leached out leaving behind insoluble hydrated aluminium oxide minerals, such as gibbsite:

$$Al_2Si_2O_5(OH)_4(s) + H_2O = 2Al(OH)_3(s) + 2SiO_2(aq) \qquad (3.4)$$

kaolinite   gibbsite   silica in solution

Laterite rich in hydrated aluminium oxides is called **bauxite**, which takes its name from the village of Les Baux, near Arles in southern France, where it was first worked commercially. It occurs as a poorly consolidated, earthy, often nodular deposit, pale red–brown to white in colour and is worked in shallow pits (Figure 3.6).

The ability of surface waters to dissolve silica (Section 2.1) more readily than hydrated aluminium oxides, as reflected in Equation 3.4, applies only over a restricted range of pH values (see Figure 3.7).

- Over what range of pH values shown in Figure 3.7 is silica effectively more soluble than alumina?

Q7f

- The solubility of silica is much higher than alumina between pH 4 and pH 10 because the insoluble hydrated oxide of aluminium (see caption, Figure 3.7) is stable over this pH range. Therefore silica, when released by weathering solutions, is more easily dissolved than alumina because the pH of rainwater (Figure 1.15) and most near-surface groundwater lies within this range.

Notice that alumina is soluble in very acidic waters (pH <4). This explains how acidic solutions (Box 3.1), including acid rain produced by industrial emissions of SO_2, can leach aluminium from soils and bedrock to produce surface waters that are toxic to both fish and plant life.

If silica is more easily dissolved than alumina by surface waters, why isn't bauxite more common? Firstly, *extreme* chemical weathering is required to break down silicate minerals completely, allowing silica as well as the more soluble metals (Na, K, Ca and Mg) to be removed in solution. For that to happen, it is necessary for all the conditions that produce thick lateritic soils to be satisfied, such as a hot climate and heavy rainfall, with periodic changes from wet to dry conditions encouraging migration of moisture in the soil, and with minimal erosion by surface run-off. Secondly, quartz (the mineral composed of silica) is plentiful in many rocks, and relatively resistant to solution by weathering, making such rocks unsuitable.

Another problem is that iron and titanium also tend to form insoluble oxides during weathering. Even if a laterite is rich enough in alumina to be a bauxite, it must also be sufficiently low in impurities to be exploitable because the industrial processing of bauxite for aluminium extraction demands usually at least 50% Al_2O_3, less than 5% SiO_2, a maximum of 20% Fe_2O_3 and less than 3% TiO_2. Therefore, bauxite source rocks must have relatively high aluminium content but low iron and titanium contents.

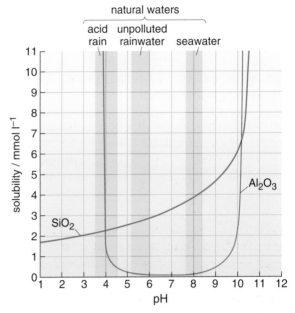

Figure 3.7 The variation in solubility of alumina and silica in aqueous solution over a range of pH conditions. In acidic solution (pH <4), aluminium can form the soluble $Al^{3+}(aq)$ ion. In intermediate-pH solutions (pH 4–pH 8), the solubility of the aluminium is low because it forms the insoluble hydrated oxide, $Al(OH)_3$. Above pH 8, it forms the soluble $[Al(OH)_4]^-$ ion.

Question 3.2

Complete Table 3.4 to estimate the proportion of alumina that might be formed in the insoluble residues after intense chemical weathering of some common igneous rocks. Then decide which of the given rock compositions would be the most suitable to form bauxite ore.

Table 3.4 Estimation of alumina contents of insoluble weathering products for a range of igneous rock types.

	Calculation	Peridotite	Gabbro	Diorite	Granite
% Al_2O_3 in rock	A	4.0	14.1	16.0	14.0
% Fe_2O_3 + TiO_2 in rock	B	14.1	15.0	9.1	2.9
total % of insoluble oxides (residue)[†]	A + B	18.1			
% Al_2O_3 content of insoluble residue[†]	$\dfrac{A \times 100}{A + B}$	22.1			

[†]These calculations assume that Al_2O_3, Fe_2O_3 and TiO_2 are the only insoluble products, that decomposition of primary minerals is complete and that all silica and soluble metals (Na, K, Ca and Mg) are lost in solution.

Box 3.3   The bauxite deposits of Jamaica

Large-scale mining of bauxite in the small, subtropical island state of Jamaica dates from the early 1950s and, by the 1960s, Jamaica was providing an astonishing 60% of the world's bauxite. Currently, it supplies about 10% of world production and has the third largest reserves after Australia and Guinea (Table 3.5).

Geologically, most of Jamaica is made up of limestones of Tertiary age that outcrop around a central mountain range (Figure 3.8a). High rainfall, reaching 2000 mm per year in the mountains, has dissolved the limestone creating a deeply pitted land surface that is riddled with caves and underground streams. The numerous bauxite deposits average 6 m in thickness and reach thicknesses of up to 30 m in pockets occupying depressions in the limestone topography (Figure 3.8b and c), especially where the limestone is strongly faulted. The fractured limestone provides good drainage, which minimizes surface run-off and hence erosion of the bauxite.

A major question arises: how can bauxite deposits be formed by chemical weathering of the bedrock if only a tiny amount of alumina (0.2%) is contained in the limestone? One possible explanation might be that a huge thickness of limestone had been dissolved away. A more likely explanation is that the alumina originated from another source, most probably from the weathering of volcanic ash, which had fallen on the island and collected on the limestone in surface hollows.

Ore grade bauxite is restricted to deposits containing 46–50% Al_2O_3, 3.5–4% SiO_2, 17–22% Fe_2O_3 and 2.4–2.6% TiO_2, although considerable variation occurs within a single deposit. Hydrated aluminium oxide ore minerals (e.g. gibbsite, $Al(OH)_3$), are accompanied by lesser amounts of gangue minerals, especially kaolinite, haematite, hydrated iron oxides and insoluble accessory minerals.

In 2003, Jamaica's bauxite production was 13.4 Mt, about half of which was refined to alumina on the island. No smelters have been built on Jamaica because aluminium production requires huge amounts of electrical energy, which is not readily available. Reserves amount to 2000 Mt, a figure that depends more on limitations set for impurities by the refineries than on the cut-off grade for aluminium.

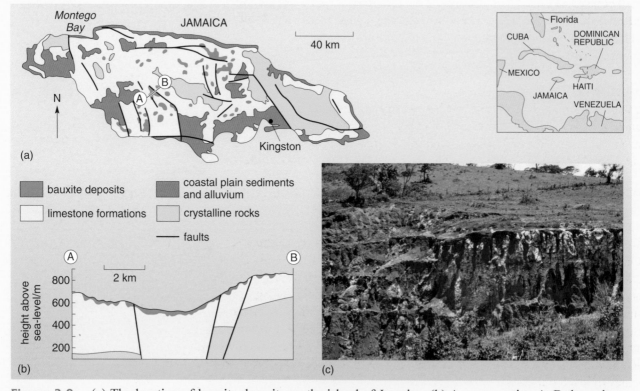

Figure 3.8   (a) The location of bauxite deposits on the island of Jamaica. (b) A cross-section A–B through a bauxite field in the middle of the island, showing the occurrence of bauxite in pockets. (c) Exposure of bauxite (red–brown) in Jamaica showing the deeply pitted surface of the underlying limestone (creamy white).

An important factor in bauxite formation is the opportunity for water to penetrate the rock. Granite may not be ideal in this respect, unless it is highly fractured or previously altered (by hydrothermal fluids), because it is normally impermeable. In contrast, volcanic ash usually has higher porosity and permeability, allowing easy access to surface waters.

Most bauxite deposits occur in tropical regions. The most important reserves are in equatorial South America, the Caribbean and Australia (Table 3.5). Currently, world reserves amount to 23 billion tonnes, a huge figure compared with the world annual production of 146 Mt in 2003, of which Australia supplied about 38%. Curiously, some non-tropical countries such as Greece and China also have significant bauxite reserves (Table 3.5). Such deposits have formed where volcanic ash or wind-borne dust from desert regions came to rest on limestones. Permeable limestones provide an ideal trap for such precursors of residual deposits as they provide good drainage that minimizes run-off of surface water and hence erosion (see Box 3.3). Because bauxite forms at the Earth's surface and the deposits are often earthy and poorly consolidated, they are vulnerable to erosion, therefore most bauxite deposits are geologically young; very few are older than 100 Ma.

Some bauxite deposits contain metals other than aluminium as by-products. The most valuable of these is probably gold; indeed, a bauxite deposit at Boddington, southeast of Perth, contains 1.8 g t^{-1} gold and is one of Australia's largest sites of gold production. Gold-bearing laterites can now be worked economically by *in situ* liberation and heap leach methods (see Chapter 6) down to grades of 0.6 g t^{-1}, especially where deep, subtropical weathering has liberated gold from sulphide minerals to depths of 100 m to 300 m in West Africa and Australia.

3.3.2 Secondary enrichment deposits

Mineral deposits themselves, particularly sulphides, can also be affected by chemical weathering. Under near-surface conditions, sulphide minerals react chemically with oxidizing rainwater. For example, oxidation and hydration of chalcopyrite forms insoluble iron(III) hydroxide (that itself breaks down to the mineral goethite, FeO(OH)) and soluble copper and sulphate ions as follows:

$$4CuFeS_2(s) + 10H_2O(l) + 17O_2(aq) = 4Fe(OH)_3(s) + 4Cu^{2+}(aq) + 8SO_4^{2-}(aq) + 8H^+(aq) \qquad (3.5)$$

chalcopyrite   rainwater   iron(III) hydroxide   soluble ions

At the surface of a copper–iron sulphide deposit, as indicated in Figure 3.9, insoluble iron(III) hydroxide forms a residual deposit, composed largely of the hydrated iron oxide, goethite, which produces a reddish-brown to bright orange (rusty) surface layer, called iron cap or **gossan**. This colourful capping is a distinctive diagnostic tool that has revealed many a sulphide mineral deposit to prospectors (Figure 3.9b). Decomposition of sulphides is aided by a natural biochemical reaction involving bacteria, such as *Acidithiobacillus ferrooxidans*, which help in the oxidation process and are now used in modern ore processing schemes to leach out metals.

So, what happens to the soluble ions that are released to infiltrating meteoric water? In the *oxidizing* conditions above the water table (Figure 3.9a), copper

Table 3.5 Major world reserves of bauxite. (Source of data: *USGS Mineral Commodity Summaries*, 2005)

Country	Bauxite reserves/Mt
Guinea	7 400
Australia	4 400
Jamaica	2 000
Brazil	1 900
India	770
Guyana	700
China	700
Greece	600
Surinam	580
others	3 950
total	23 000

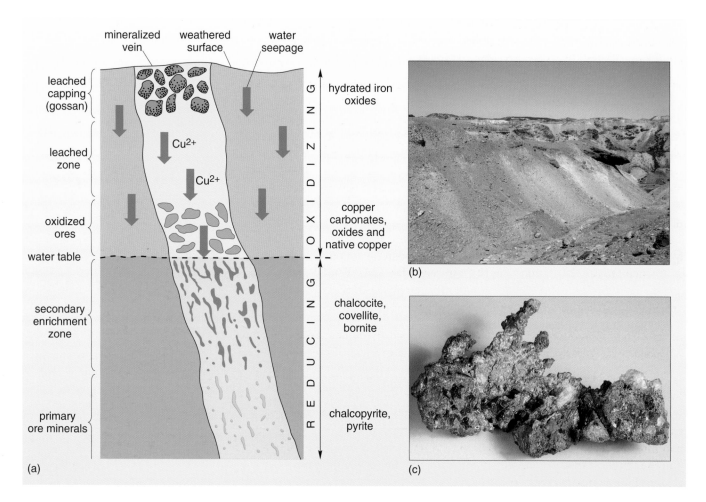

Figure 3.9 (a) Generalized section through a chalcopyrite-bearing mineral deposit, where leaching of soluble (copper) ions in oxidizing groundwater occurs above the water table and secondary enrichment of (copper) sulphide minerals in reducing groundwater occurs beneath the water table. (b) Rusty weathering of gossan at the surface of a sulphide deposit; pale-coloured leached zone beneath. (c) Native copper (red–brown) encrusted by copper carbonate (green).

ions may combine with bicarbonate (HCO_3^-) ions dissolved in rainwater to form colourful copper carbonate minerals, such as green malachite ($CuCO_3.Cu(OH)_2$) and blue azurite ($2CuCO_3.Cu(OH)_2$). Copper may also be deposited in its native form (Figure 3.9c) close to the water table and, depending on chemical conditions, as the oxide, cuprite (Cu_2O), and the hydrated copper silicate, chrysocolla.

However, most metal ions remain in solution until reaching the water table, below which groundwater conditions tend to be *reducing* (Figure 3.9). The metal ions then react with the primary (original) sulphide ore minerals to produce new secondary ore minerals. In a copper-rich sulphide deposit, these secondary minerals include the sulphides covellite (CuS), chalcocite (Cu_2S) and bornite (Cu_5FeS_4) — for example:

$$CuFeS_2 + Cu^{2+}(aq) = 2CuS(s) + Fe^{2+}(aq) \qquad (3.6)$$

primary chalcopyrite   secondary covellite

(Fe_2O_3) and magnetite (Fe_3O_4), occur in high concentrations in extensive deposits from which iron can be extracted relatively easily.

Early in the Industrial Revolution of Western Europe, 'black band' iron ores rich in siderite ($FeCO_3$) were mined alongside coal from Carboniferous Coal Measure sequences. Coal-forming swamps in Carboniferous times had provided reducing conditions in which iron(II) was transported in solution. Precipitation of siderite had occurred when swamp waters mixed with oxidizing waters carrying bicarbonate ions.

The natural coexistence of coal and iron ore was an important factor in the development of the iron smelting industry during the Industrial Revolution. The main problem with these 'bog' iron ores was their small volume — supplies were unable to match the growing demand. In Europe, the heart of the Industrial Revolution, new sources were provided in Britain mainly by Jurassic ironstones located along a belt from Northamptonshire through Lincolnshire to Cleveland, and in central Europe by ironstones of the Alsace–Lorraine and Salzgitter areas. Bedded units, 10–15 m thick and extending for tens of kilometres, were worked extensively in Britain until the 1970s.

However, these Jurassic ironstones were a problem for smelting because they contain high amounts of calcium, silica and phosphorus. These ores are no longer worked because purer, richer, more easily smelted ores became available from overseas. These deposits were found initially near Lake Superior in North America in the late 19th century, but ores of the same type are now worked extensively in many other parts of the world, including the Krivoy Rog–Kursk area of the Ukraine; the Hamersley Range of Western Australia (see Figure 3.11); and in China and Brazil. Some of these deposits extend for hundreds of kilometres and may be as much as 500 m thick. Most formed as sediments between 2750 Ma and 1900 Ma ago in Precambrian times. As shown in Figure 3.12, they comprise fine layers, each of which is several millimetres thick and rich in the iron oxide minerals haematite and magnetite, alternating with layers of

Q8g

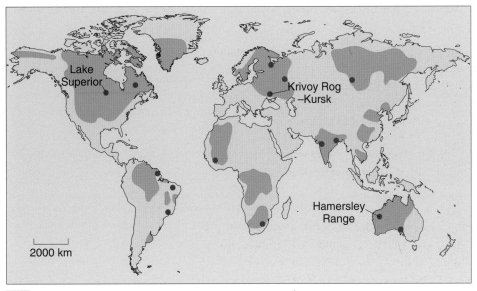

Figure 3.11   Distribution of Precambrian banded iron formation deposits and ancient stable cratons.

cratons   • BIF deposits

precipitated silica (chert). For this reason they are known as **banded iron formation** (BIF) deposits. Sedimentary structures suggest that their deposition was in a low-energy environment; ripple marks and sun cracks indicate shallow water. The absence of detrital grains suggests that deposition may have been by chemical precipitation far from land, or possibly near a low-relief land surface with little erosion.

Before about 2200 Ma ago, free oxygen did not exist in the Earth's surface environments and seawater would have contained abundant soluble Fe(II) ions. Photosynthetic blue–green bacteria had become locally profuse in shallow seas, producing oxygen by photosynthesis. In these shallow seas, the free oxygen would locally oxidize the soluble Fe(II) ions to form insoluble Fe(III) and precipitate iron(III) oxides and hydroxides as layers. Some authorities believe that the finest banding is indeed diurnal. The restriction of BIF deposits to this particular period of Earth history suggests that a rather special combination of atmospheric and oceanic — and possibly even biological — conditions was responsible for BIF deposition. BIF deposits are largely confined to relatively stable areas of ancient continental crust that are more than 2000 Ma old, known as *cratons* (Figure 3.11).

The amount of iron occurring in BIFs worldwide may be as much as 10^{14} tonnes, but only a small proportion of this is currently economic. BIFs in which oxide minerals dominate average 30–35% iron, but silicate- and carbonate-bearing BIFs contain only 25–30% iron. Economic, high-grade BIF deposits (Box 3.4), enriched to levels exceeding 60% iron, occur where silica has been leached out and replaced by haematite and goethite, a process akin to residual and secondary enrichment (Section 3.3.1). World resources of iron ore are estimated to exceed 800 billion (8.0×10^{11}) tonnes, and contain more than 230 billion (2.3×10^{11}) tonnes of iron. This greatly exceeds the annual worldwide production of iron ore, which currently approaches 1.25×10^9 tonnes, therefore iron resources would seem to have a relatively long lifetime.

Sedimentary deposits similar to BIFs contain the majority of manganese ores worldwide. The potential of another source of manganese is considered in Box 3.5.

1 cm

Figure 3.12 Sedimentary iron ore: alternating bands (2–8 mm wide) of chert and iron oxide in a polished specimen of banded iron formation.

Box 3.4 Iron ores of the Hamersley Range, Western Australia

Iron ore reserves in the Hamersley region of Western Australia (Figure 3.13a) amount to 13.5 Gt, and inferred resources a further 13.5 Gt. This is all the more remarkable because for many years they had been overlooked. In Australia in the late 19th century, iron ore was seen as being of 'no great value', but before the Second World War an embargo was put on Australian exports of iron ore by the Commonwealth Government because it was thought that reserves were running out and the country should conserve its stocks! In addition, the state government prevented prospectors from retaining rights to any discovery, thereby removing incentives for exploration. It was

not until the early 1960s that these regulations were lifted. Intensive exploration followed, which established much of the known reserve during the following ten years.

Many surface rocks in the Hamersley Range weather to an orangish- or reddish-brown colour (Figure 3.13b), revealing large areas composed of Precambrian banded iron formations that are between 2750 Ma and 2300 Ma old. The highest-grade ores form units 2–15 m thick, which are separated by shales, chert and iron carbonate-bearing sediments. The most productive deposits have undergone secondary enrichment and consist largely of haematite

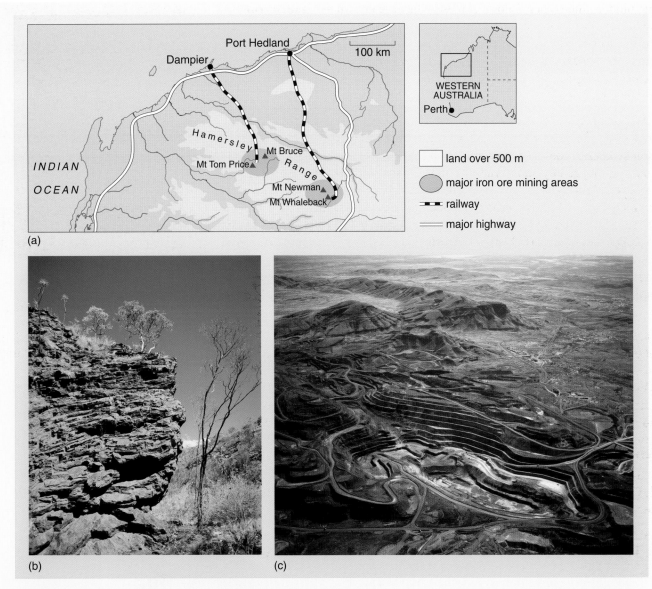

Figure 3.13 (a) The location of iron ore deposits in the Hamersley Range of Western Australia. (b) Banded iron formation (BIF) exposed as a rusty weathering outcrop in the Hamersley Range, Western Australia. (c) Mount Tom Price iron ore mine, Hamersley Range, Western Australia.

with variable amounts of goethite. The ore mined today contains more than 60% iron, with impurities less than 4% SiO_2, less than 2% Al_2O_3 and less than 0.1% P_2O_5. Secondary enrichment appears to be related to the present erosion surface, but the same surface was exposed when extensive laterization took place in early Tertiary times and, in parts of Australia, extensive weathering occurred very much earlier (before the Permian). Even more remarkably, fragments of enriched ores are found in 1800 Ma old conglomerates, which indicates a much earlier episode of enrichment.

In the early 2000s, Australia was the world's third largest iron ore producer behind China and Brazil. It produces about 200 Mt of ore per year, most of it from the Hamersley region, where it is worked by BHP Billiton and Rio Tinto. One of the largest deposits, at Mt Tom Price, an orebody 8 km by 1.2 km in area, contained an initial reserve of 900 Mt of ore, grading 64% iron. The workings at Mt Tom Price, mined since 1965, are shown in Figure 3.13c.

Question 3.3

(a) The importance of iron to the industrialized world is due mainly to its versatility, particularly to its use in steels. It also has a relatively low price. Give three reasons why iron can be produced cheaply.

(b) Suggest why the substitution of iron and steel products might have beneficial consequences, even if the cost of iron ore is relatively low and supplies are plentiful.

Box 3.5 Manganese nodules

Although more of a curiosity than a resource at present, **manganese nodules**, with the appearance of 'burnt baked potatoes', occur in abundance scattered over the surface of some deep ocean floors (Figure 3.14a) where sedimentation rates are slow. They are composed of hydrated iron and manganese oxides, built up in layers around a nucleus, forming an often concentrically banded internal structure (Figure 3.14b). Similar layers also encrust rock surfaces on the ocean floor, but manganese nodules are loose on the surface and could be dredged up. However, although they may occur over huge areas, they occur at great water depths and form only a very thin layer.

Manganese is usually the most abundant metal (16%) in the nodules, being enriched more than a hundred times relative to its average abundance in continental crust. However, there are large reserves of sedimentary manganese deposits similar to BIFs that contain over 35% Mn. Manganese nodules are therefore very unlikely ever to become manganese ores. Their content of other metals, particularly nickel (0.5%), cobalt (0.3%), copper (0.3%), lead (0.1%) and zinc (0.1%) may be more attractive, but dredging is not yet an economic proposition, although the yield of nodules could be as much as 15 billion tonnes in the northeast tropical Pacific Ocean between California and Hawaii.

Ownership is another problem, as most nodules reside in international waters outside national 200-mile limits. Lack of international agreement on ocean-floor mining management and the distribution of royalties, along with depressed mineral prices and new discoveries of metals elsewhere, have 'undermined' hopes of profitable exploitation, and interest has generally waned. In addition, the dredging of large areas of the sea floor would disturb sediments and organisms living on or within the ocean floor, and would attract environmental opposition.

(a)

(b)

Figure 3.14 (a) A view of manganese nodules lying on the ocean floor.
(b) A cross-section through a manganese nodule, showing concentric layering.

3.5   Summary of Chapter 3

1   A variety of processes at the Earth's surface can concentrate metals to form ore deposits. Dense minerals resistant to weathering are concentrated by physical transport and deposition to form placer deposits. Chemical processes concentrate metals through the removal of soluble material, which leaves behind insoluble residual deposits, and by precipitation of dissolved material, which forms bedded sedimentary deposits on the sea floor and secondary enrichment deposits beneath the land surface.

2   Chemical transport and precipitation of metals in surface and near-surface waters are controlled largely by changes in pH and/or the oxidation state of the environment. These conditions are often influenced by the reducing properties of decaying organic matter. Rainwater is oxidizing and slightly acidic due to dissolved atmospheric gases. With progressive seepage and reactions with rocks and organic matter, groundwater becomes more reducing.

3   Placer deposits are concentrations of hard, dense, chemically stable ore mineral grains liberated by chemical breakdown and erosion of crystalline source rocks. They are transported by surface waters to form alluvial placer deposits in rivers and beach placer deposits along coasts. Gold and cassiterite are recovered from alluvial deposits; heavy oxide minerals, such as rutile and ilmenite, and accessory minerals, such as zircon and monazite, are recovered from beach deposits. Some 'fossil' placer deposits of Precambrian age are among the world's most important gold and uranium deposits. Recent, unconsolidated placer deposits can be mined by dredging or with high-pressure water jets.

4   Residual deposits are the insoluble residues that result from intense weathering of surface rocks in tropical climates, where rainfall is high and intermittent, drainage is good, and erosion is minimal. Lateritic soils rich in insoluble oxides of iron and aluminium are a common form of residual deposit. Sometimes they contain ore deposits of nickel, cobalt, copper and gold, which are minable to quite low grades because they are easily accessible and poorly consolidated. Volumetrically, the most important form of laterite is bauxite, the aluminium ore, which is composed largely of hydrated aluminium oxides. The best rocks to be sources of bauxite are those accessible to percolating rainwater and low in impurities, such as iron and titanium, which would form insoluble weathering products. Under warm, humid climatic conditions, silica produced during chemical weathering is more soluble than alumina in surface waters.

5   Weathering of sulphide mineral deposits by oxidizing rainwater often leads to the formation of secondary enrichment or supergene deposits. Copper and silver especially may be leached from sulphide minerals at and near the Earth's surface. The metal-rich solutions migrate downwards to the water table, where they may react with primary ore minerals under reducing conditions to form enriched secondary ore minerals.

6   Chemical (or biochemical) precipitation in shallow seas was responsible for deposition of Precambrian banded iron formations, which form

extensive iron-rich deposits. The ultimate source of iron is not always clear: it is most likely to have been transported in solution in the Fe(II) state, until oxidized in shallow seas, where oxygen was being produced by photosynthesis (involving blue–green bacteria), which caused iron(III) oxides to precipitate. Economic grades often exceed 60% iron, usually enhanced by leaching and secondary enrichment.

ORE DEPOSITS FORMED BY HYDROTHERMAL PROCESSES

4

Hydrothermal ores are probably the most widespread and diverse of all ore deposits. They often form easily recognizable, confined deposits, well suited to small-scale extraction. Most of the ore deposits worked in the 18th–20th centuries in upland areas of the UK were of hydrothermal origin. Anyone who has sifted through old mine dumps in the Pennines, Wales, the Lake District, southwest England and parts of Scotland would probably be familiar with the hydrothermal minerals galena (PbS), sphalerite (ZnS), chalcopyrite ($CuFeS_2$), pyrite (FeS_2) and barite ($BaSO_4$). Most of these were extracted from veins similar to those illustrated in Figure 4.1, but often developed on a larger scale.

5 cm

(a)

5 cm

(b)

Figure 4.1   Examples of hydrothermal vein deposits: (a) a mineral vein with silvery arsenopyrite along the margins and white quartz in the centre; (b) a banded hydrothermal vein with zones of white quartz, reddish-brown sphalerite, dark-grey galena and creamy dolomite from North Wales.

Figure 4.2   Hot water fountains to at least 10 m, expelled under great pressure from a geyser in New Zealand.

What, then, distinguishes hydrothermal deposits from other types of mineral deposit? Essentially, they are deposited by hot watery fluids in voids and fissures within the Earth's crust. These fluids are visible only where they escape as hot springs or, if under pressure, as geysers (Figure 4.2). They are essentially the same as the geothermal fluids that are sometimes exploited for their energy content (Drury, 2006). Minerals deposited from hydrothermal solutions include ore minerals, but, more commonly, they are worthless gangue minerals, such as calcite or quartz. Quartz veins are commonly found in metamorphic rocks, whereas calcite veins are frequently associated with limestones. Mostly, such veins are **barren**, that is, unmineralized.

Hydrothermal systems will form vein deposits in open fractures; disseminated deposits in porous and permeable rocks; and replacement deposits in rocks susceptible to dissolution (Figures 4.3a, b and c respectively). Where hydrothermal fluids escape from the Earth's crust, they may form encrusted chimney-like deposits around underwater vents, or mounds and terraces where they escape onto the land surface as geysers or hot springs.

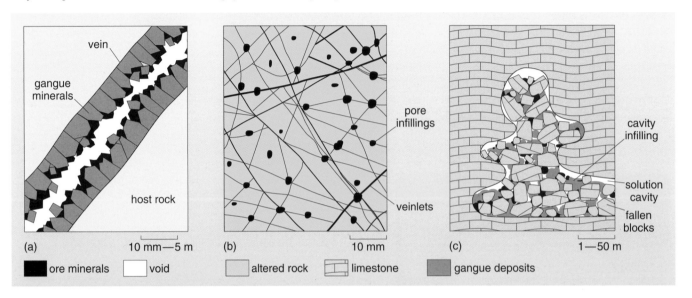

There is a huge diversity of hydrothermal ore deposits, reflecting the variability in their environments of formation. This chapter will focus only on selected deposits formed at and near the Earth's surface on land and in submarine environments. These highlight many of the essential principles of hydrothermal ore formation, the fundamentals of which are considered next.

Figure 4.3 Schematic forms of hydrothermal mineralization: (a) a simple vein (sometimes open at the centre), formed by deposition in a fissure. With periodic enlargement, a vein may become more complex and banded, as the minerals deposited can change with time (see Figures 4.1a and b); (b) disseminated mineralization in fractures of a stockwork and in surrounding porous altered rock; (c) solution cavities in limestone containing infill of ore minerals and gangue (calcite especially).

4.1 The anatomy of a hydrothermal system

A mineralizing hydrothermal system has several essential components which are discussed here in a slightly different order from the mnemonic 'SPADE' (Section 1.5). The physical and chemical aspects of a hydrothermal system are shown schematically in Figure 4.4.

4.1.1 The main components of a hydrothermal system

Agent — the hydrothermal fluid

Hydrothermal fluids consist largely of water, but they also contain dissolved solids and sometimes small amounts of other fluids, such as hydrocarbons. As noted in Section 1.5.1, water may have several different origins:

- *meteoric water*, which is derived from rainfall, enters rocks by infiltration and is low in dissolved constituents;
- *seawater*, which is saline, contains about 3.5% of dissolved constituents (mainly Na^+, K^+, Mg^{2+}, Ca^{2+}, Cl^- and SO_4^{2-}), enters rocks either by infiltration and convection within the sea floor or as *formation water* trapped in marine sediments;
- *magmatic water*, which comes from magmas, may contain as much as 20–25% of dissolved constituents.

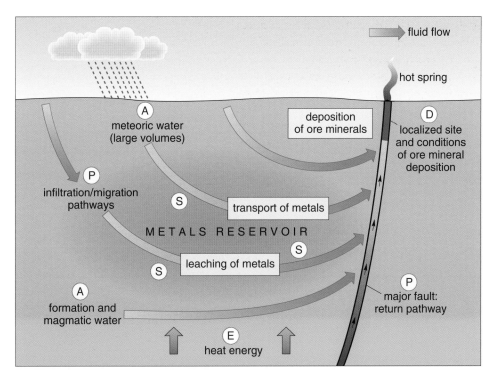

Figure 4.4 The anatomy of a hydrothermal system in schematic form. Physical components are ascribed to the mnemonic 'SPADE' — *sources* of metals (S), *pathways* (P), *agents* (A), site of *deposition* (D) and *energy* source (E). Chemical processes are shown in boxed text.

Hydrothermal fluids may originate from any one of these sources or from a mixture of sources. Although magmatic water may emanate from areas of igneous activity, the hot springs of volcanic regions on land are often entirely meteoric in origin, whereas the waters circulating in oceanic crust and trapped in buried marine sediments are dominantly of seawater.

Only magmatic waters are likely to start out with very high concentrations of trace metals. Separation of aqueous fluid from magma, as with porphyry ore-forming systems (Section 2.4), happens in a very reactive environment, and some metals preferentially enter the aqueous solution as it separates from the magma. However, hydrothermal fluids often acquire metals through the dissolution or the breakdown of minerals and through leaching of rocks (Section 1.5). In general, the richer the chemical 'cocktail' in a hydrothermal solution, the more reactive it is likely to be. So, compared to meteoric water, seawater has a 'head start' chemically, while magmatic fluids are generally the most reactive of all.

Sources — the metals reservoirs

Any rocks through which hydrothermal fluids can pass are potential sources of metals. If they contain metals in a leachable form, they are described as **fertile**. In shales, especially black shales, formed as carbonaceous mudstones (Section 3.4), cations of metals such as Cu, Zn, Pb, U and Mo are often rather loosely attached (adsorbed) to organic material or clay minerals, and may be scavenged when saline formation waters are expelled. In addition, hydrothermal fluids may react with minerals (e.g. metal sulphides by oxidation), thereby leaching or exchanging metal ions with the host rock. Potential source rocks that cannot supply metals to a hydrothermal fluid are described as **infertile**. One example would be a sandstone that is composed almost entirely of silica, and contains few trace metals. The mineralogy and chemistry of source rocks therefore exert an important control on the availability of metals (by both their fertility and their composition) and hence on the type of mineralization developed in a hydrothermal system.

Black Shales

Q 6

Pathways — linking fertile source rocks to sites of deposition

Voids and cavities in rocks may contain fluids, but, as with water supplies (Smith, 2005) or hydrocarbon accumulations (Drury, 2006), these spaces must be interconnected for the fluid to migrate (Figure 4.4). Rock formations with connected pores (e.g. sandstones) or well-developed joint or fracture systems (e.g. limestones) can therefore provide permeable pathways. In impermeable rocks, such as shales or igneous rocks, the flow of fluids is concentrated along fractures and joints, which open up at times of tectonic activity. Fracturing may also arise as a result of magma intrusion; expansion associated with hydrothermal fluids decompressing or outgassing on their way to the surface; or to large-scale tectonic movements of the crust.

- Why is the repeated activation of fractures important for the formation of hydrothermal vein deposits?

- Hydrothermal systems require open pathways for fluids to migrate and to supply material for continuing deposition. However, deposition tends to seal fractures, preventing further passage of fluid. Thus, repeated activation of fractures is necessary to maintain open pathways and ensure continuing mineral deposition in a hydrothermal system.

The internal structure of many hydrothermal veins — with mineral zonation parallel to the margins, often symmetrical about a central zone, and sometimes with open cavities (Figures 4.1a and 4.3a) — indicates repeated or prolonged opening of fractures and periodic deposition from fluids as conditions or fluid composition changed.

Pathways facilitate the emergence of fluids from source rocks, provide channels for the flow of metal-charged fluids over long distances, and constrain those fluids to zones where deposition might occur (Figure 4.4).

Energy — the driving force

To maintain a hydrothermal system, the mere presence of water is not enough. A long-term supply of water is necessary to maintain flow (Figure 4.4), and energy — gravitational or geothermal — is required to drive the flow.

- In what ways does water move below the Earth's surface?

- It flows downwards under gravity, it convects upwards when heated, and it can be squeezed out of pores in rocks on compaction.

Infiltrating meteoric water flows under *gravity* to the water table, below which an aquifer is saturated in water. Movement of groundwater within an aquifer is controlled by the *hydraulic gradient* (Smith, 2005), which reflects both recharge and leakage from the aquifer. Deeper-seated groundwater may move by *convection*, whereby water heated by hot rocks expands, its density decreases and it becomes buoyant as it is displaced by surrounding cooler, denser water. As the heated water rises, it cools, is itself displaced by warmer water from below and eventually sinks, so forming a circulating convection system. Lastly, *compaction* expels formation waters from wet, clay-rich sedimentary rocks as they are compressed on burial by younger sediments.

Geothermal heat is supplied to a hydrothermal fluid from surrounding rocks, which become progressively hotter with depth. Depending on the *geothermal gradient*, the depth at which a particular temperature is reached varies from place to place. With a normal, continental geothermal gradient ($25\,°C\,km^{-1}$), temperatures reach only 250 °C at 10 km depth, but in an active volcanic area, where hot magma is close to the surface, gradients are much higher and temperatures may reach 250 °C or more within 1–2 km of the surface.

Convection plays a major role in focusing large volumes of fluids through pathways to localized sites of mineral deposition (Figure 4.4). The buoyancy of heated water provides the driving force and hot water migrates wherever there is an easy escape route. For instance, faults and highly permeable strata often facilitate fluid flow so that it is channelled to a location where minerals can be deposited.

Deposition — the site and conditions where ore minerals can accumulate

Without space in which ore minerals can crystallize, hydrothermal ore deposits cannot develop. 'Space' includes *in situ* replacement of existing minerals, especially as a result of alteration or dissolution by corrosive hydrothermal fluids themselves. The form of the available space determines the form of an ore deposit. *Dispersed deposits* (Section 1.3), which can involve small ore-mineral grains, selective mineral replacement or stockworks (Figure 4.3b), usually form low-grade ores as a result of diffuse fluid flow or only small amounts of available space. *Confined deposits* often occur as individual veins that contain concentrations of ore minerals (e.g. Figure 4.3a), and follow geological features — a sedimentary layer or a fault — or even occupy cavities dissolved out of limestone (Figure 4.3c) either through hydrothermal corrosion or dissolution by rainwater. The form of a hydrothermal deposit also depends on whether the site of deposition is at or beneath the Earth's surface, and whether surface deposition is on land or beneath water.

Changes in chemical conditions are necessary for deposition of ore minerals. They may arise through reaction of the fluid with surrounding rocks or by mixing with other physically or chemically different fluids. Reduction of pressure may release gases and affect the chemistry of the fluid. Consequently, deposition from hydrothermal fluids frequently occurs at relatively high levels in the crust (Figure 4.4) and at locations where they escape from the crust, on land or under water.

4.1.2 Hydrothermal fluid compositions

How can we determine the composition of hydrothermal fluids? Direct sampling presents some challenges. Although geysers and hot springs emerge at the Earth's surface, they may only represent near-surface circulations of meteoric water; they may be hot and rich in silica or calcium carbonate, but might not represent deeper mineralizing hydrothermal circulations. In recent times, however, investigation of active geothermal systems for their geothermal potential has enabled hydrothermal fluids to be intercepted and sampled in deep boreholes at many localities. Contrasting fluid compositions are listed in Table 4.1, including data from a geothermal well near the Salton Sea in California (see Box 4.1, overleaf) and from a well in the Broadlands geothermal field in New

Zealand. Alongside them are the compositions of seawater and of an ancient hydrothermal fluid obtained from **fluid inclusions**, the bubbles of fluid that become trapped in hydrothermally deposited minerals (see Box 4.2). Many hydrothermal fluids turn out to be highly saline solutions, or *brines*, that are rich in alkali metal (especially Na^+ and K^+) and Cl^- ions, with lesser amounts of metals such as Mg, Fe, Pb, Zn, Au and Ag and dissolved gases such as hydrogen sulphide, carbon dioxide and methane.

Box 4.1   The Salton Sea — modern hydrothermal fluids

One of the first major discoveries of metal-rich fluids deep in the Earth's crust took place in 1962 during exploratory drilling for geothermal power on the Colorado River delta near the edge of the Salton Sea, a large brackish-water lake about 70 m below sea level in southern California (Figure 4.5). This location lies on part of the San Andreas Fault within a thermally active crustal zone at the northern extension of the East Pacific Rise.

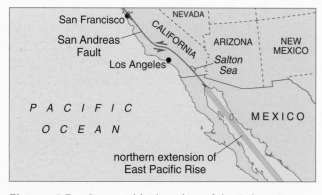

Figure 4.5   Geographical setting of the Salton Sea.

One of the boreholes reached a depth of 1.6 km and tapped a highly saline hydrothermal brine at a temperature of 300–350 °C. Surprisingly, this solution contained 25% of dissolved salts (compared with only 3.5% in seawater), including very large amounts of Na^+ K^+, Ca^{2+} and Cl^- ions, as well as many other metals at concentrations far in excess of those in seawater (Table 4.1). The mineralizing potential of the fluid was dramatically illustrated by the deposition of silica containing fine-grained metal sulphides with an overall composition of 20% copper, 7% silver and 7% iron. These deposits accumulated at the ground surface at a rate of more than one tonne per month. However, zinc, lead and manganese concentrations in

the deposits were low, despite their unusually high concentrations in the brine (Table 4.1). The Salton Sea geothermal field is still under development as a power source. It has been estimated that mineral recovery from a 1000 MW power plant on the site could provide as much as 20% of the manganese requirements for the United States.

The Salton Sea brine originated as meteoric water that percolated through evaporites bordering the Salton Sea and dissolved alkali metal chlorides. This reactive fluid then leached trace metals from buried metal-rich, fertile shales to produce the metal-rich hydrothermal fluid (Table 4.1).

Question 4.1

To appreciate the compositional differences between the modern hydrothermal fluids from Broadlands and the Salton Sea, use Table 4.1 to answer the following:

(a) Which three metals are the most concentrated in the Salton Sea brine and how do their concentrations compare with seawater and Broadlands fluid?

(b) Which metals in the Salton Sea brine have concentrations more than 1000 times those of seawater?

(c) Briefly describe the Salton Sea brine, given that seawater could be described as a saline solution, low in trace metals, and somewhat alkaline (pH 8.2).

(d) Briefly describe the composition of the Broadlands fluid. Is it as saline as seawater?

(e) On compositional grounds, which of the fluids — from Broadlands or the Salton Sea — would be the more suitable for supplying a geothermal plant?

Table 4.1 Compositions of natural waters: seawater, modern hydrothermal fluids from Broadlands and the Salton Sea, and an ancient hydrothermal fluid from a fluid inclusion in fluorite.

Ions	Concentration in seawater/mg l^{-1}	Concentration in modern hydrothermal fluids/mg l^{-1}		Concentration in ancient hydrothermal fluid/mg l^{-1}
		Broadlands	Salton Sea	
Na^+	10 500	980	50 400	40 400
K^+	380	200	17 500	3 500
Ca^{2+}	400	2.4	28 000	8 600
Mg^{2+}	1 290	0.02	54	5 600
Fe^{2+}	0.002	—	2 290	—
Mn^{2+}	0.002	—	1 400	450
Cu^{2+}	0.003	—	8	9 100
Pb^{2+}	0.000 13	—	102	—
Zn^{2+}	0.005	—	540	10 900
Ba^{2+}	0.02	—	235	—
Sr^{2+}	8	—	400	—
Rb^+	0.12	2.2	135	—
Li^+	0.18	12.6	215	—
Ag^+	0.000 104	—	1.4	—
SO_4^{2-}	2 650	6.5	5	1 200
Cl^-	19 500	1 668	155 000	87 000
S^{2-} (as H_2S)	—	—	16	—
Total dissolved salts	34 400	3 000	250 000	167 000
pH	about 8.2	8.6	6.0	—

The compositions of the fluids from the Broadlands and Salton Sea geothermal systems are clearly very different (Question 4.1 and Table 4.1). Before we explain why the Salton Sea fluid is so much more saline than seawater, whereas the Broadlands water is much less saline than seawater, let's consider whether or not the fluids from either system could produce mineralization.

The only way to identify the fluid that produced a specific type of mineral deposit is to sample it — but accessible deposits are generally no longer part of an active hydrothermal system. However, minerals in hydrothermal deposits often trap tiny pockets of fluid during crystallization. These fluid inclusions (Box 4.2) not only reveal the composition of the hydrothermal fluid from which they were deposited, but also the temperature at which the host mineral crystallized — which is essential for understanding how mineral deposits were formed. Table 4.1 shows the composition of an ancient hydrothermal fluid from a fluid inclusion in fluorite (a common gangue mineral), which has a composition that is much closer to the Salton Sea fluid than it is to seawater.

Box 4.2   Fluid inclusions — microsampling of hydrothermal fluids

Most fluid inclusions are small (2–50 µm in diameter) and require a powerful microscope to be seen. They look like bubbles and are most easily visible in transparent mineral grains. The spectacular example illustrated in Figure 4.6 contains not only a liquid but also a crystal and a bubble of gas (vapour). How did this inclusion become so complicated?

At the time it was trapped, the fluid was hot and homogeneous: it contained neither solid particles nor gas bubbles. The size of the space it occupied depended on the prevailing pressure and temperature. On cooling, the trapped liquid contracted much more than the mineral surrounding it. The liquid could no longer fill the pocket completely, so a space formed — a bubble occupied by vapour. During cooling, the solubility of the dissolved salts decreased, and crystallization occurred — hence the crystal of halite (NaCl) in Figure 4.6.

A branch of study has grown up to measure and interpret the compositions of fluid inclusions. By heating an inclusion until the liquid just redissolves the salt crystal, and expands to consume its own vapour bubble, the inclusion can be assumed to be at the temperature at which trapping occurred. Fluid inclusion trapping temperatures range from about 600 °C down to about 50 °C for different types of hydrothermal system. Fluid inclusions

also vary greatly in their composition, and may even contain hydrocarbons — which can sometimes be useful for evaluating the maturation conditions of petroleum formation (Drury, 2006).

The composition of the fluid inclusion given in Table 4.1 is comparable with Salton Sea brine. It, too, contains high levels of dissolved salts (almost 17% in total), with Na^+ and Cl^- ions dominant. However, compositions of fluid inclusions are as variable as those of geothermal brines.

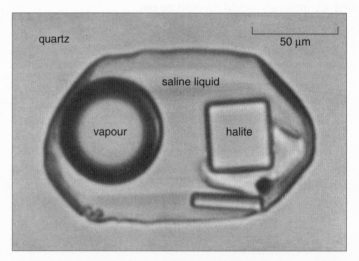

Figure 4.6   An inclusion of saline fluid trapped in a crystal of quartz as it grew in a hydrothermal vein. The round bubble of vapour and the cubic crystal of halite formed on cooling.

So why are the hydrothermal fluids of the Salton Sea so rich in dissolved material, even compared with seawater? Although they started out as meteoric (almost pure) water they became highly saline by percolating through evaporite deposits rich in soluble salts, such as alkali halides (e.g. halite, NaCl) and calcium sulphate (gypsum, $CaSO_4.2H_2O$). Hot solutions, if already rich in dissolved solids, particularly ions such as Cl^- and SO_4^{2-}, can be very corrosive, capable of dissolving and reacting with more minerals, so increasing their metal content even further. The ultimate metal content of a hydrothermal fluid, therefore, depends not only on the initial composition of the fluid (whether meteoric or seawater), but also on the composition of the rocks through which it passes.

This helps explain the contrasting compositions of the Salton Sea brine and the geothermal water at Broadlands (Table 4.1). Both have meteoric sources, but the water at Broadlands passed mainly through volcanic rocks containing little soluble material, whereas the Salton Sea fluid acquired a high concentration of dissolved salts from evaporites. The lower salinity of the Broadlands water suggests it was the less reactive of the two examples.

anion ~ a negatively charged ion

Notice from Table 4.1 that Cl^- ions are often the main anions in hydrothermal solutions. In fact, most metals (except silver and mercury) are soluble in chloride-rich solutions, which explains why many hydrothermal brines can carry large amounts of metals. However, many of the more familiar ore minerals, such as the sulphides, galena, sphalerite and chalcopyrite, are extremely insoluble. It is easy to see how they would *precipitate* from a hydrothermal solution, but it is more difficult to understand how Pb^{2+}, Zn^{2+} and Cu^{2+} ions could be *transported* together with S^{2-} ions without the sulphides precipitating prematurely.

The answer is likely to be in the chemical mode of transport. Sulphur can be transported as soluble ions. Under oxidizing conditions, sulphur could be transported as the sulphate ion, SO_4^{2-}, which can coexist in solution with many metals (although only sparingly so for barium and lead). Then, if reduction of sulphate to sulphide occurred, for example due to reaction with organic material, sulphide minerals would precipitate out.

Another way in which sulphur and metals can be transported in solution is as complex ions. Metals such as Ni, Cu, Zn, Pb, Pt, Hg and Au are able to form complex ions, especially with the bisulphide anion, HS^-, in reducing conditions. The resulting complex ions, such as $[Zn(HS)_3]^-$, $[PbS(HS)]^-$ and $[HgS(HS)]^-$, are often soluble, and may be transported in solution *without* precipitation of sulphide minerals. Studies of active hydrothermal systems show that gold is sometimes present as the complex ions $[Au(HS)_2]^-$ or $[AuCl_2]^-$, depending on the conditions and the fluid composition. In reducing solutions, gold may be present as the $Au^+(aq)$ ion, but a significant concentration of hydrogen sulphide (H_2S, the gas which smells like rotten eggs) in solution forms bisulphide ions (HS^-) (Equation 4.1). These combine with the $Au^+(aq)$ ions to form the stable and soluble complex ion $[Au(HS)_2]^-$ (Equation 4.2):

$$H_2S(aq) = H^+(aq) + HS^-(aq) \tag{4.1}$$

$$Au^+(aq) + 2HS^-(aq) = [Au(HS)_2]^-(aq) \tag{4.2}$$

If confining pressure is reduced, and especially if boiling occurs, H_2S gas is released from solution. The $[Au(HS)_2]^-$ complex then becomes unstable, and metallic gold is precipitated.

In brief, precipitation of hydrothermal minerals may take place for a number of reasons, including:

- temperature change (cooling), which may reduce the solubility and stability of dissolved ions and ionic complexes;

- pressure change (reduction), especially at high levels, when dissolved gases are released and/or boiling occurs, thereby changing the chemistry of the fluid;

- chemical reaction with wall rocks and mixing with other fluids, bringing about changes in pH and/or the oxidation condition of the fluid.

Question 4.2

Why is the HS^- ion likely to be important in the formation of sulphide ore deposits?

4.1.3   The scale and duration of hydrothermal processes

A combination of circumstances is required to form a substantial hydrothermal deposit. To acquire their complement of metals, large volumes of hydrothermal fluids must generally pass through large volumes of crustal rocks to scavenge metal ions (Figure 4.4). Then they must be focused, probably by convection, through constrained pathways, to deposit ore minerals in a relatively small volume. Even small concentrations of metals leached from source rocks can be sufficient to produce ore deposits at the site of deposition, providing sufficient fluid is available and flow is maintained for a long period of time.

Consider first the *volume of water* that might be required to form a hydrothermal ore deposit.

●   If a hydrothermal zinc deposit contains 5 Mt of ore, with an average grade of 3% zinc, what volume of hydrothermal fluid, capable of depositing 200 milligrams of zinc per litre of the fluid, would be involved in forming the deposit? (*Note*: this is quite a lot of dissolved zinc.)

◐   The quantity of zinc in the deposit is 5×10^6 t $\times 0.03 = 1.5 \times 10^5$ t. If one litre of fluid deposits 200 mg of zinc, then the total volume of fluid required to form 1.5×10^5 t of zinc would be:

$$\frac{1.5 \times 10^5 \times 10^6 \text{ g}}{0.2 \text{ g l}^{-1}} = 7.5 \times 10^{11} \text{ l} = 7.5 \times 10^8 \text{ m}^3$$

10^9 m^3 = 1 km^3, so the volume of water would be 0.75 km^3.

(margin note) $1 \text{ t} = 10^6$ g; 10^3 l = 1 m^3

This volume of water could be equivalent to a sizeable lake, 25 km^2 in area and 30 m deep — alternatively, a seepage of rainfall amounting to 75 mm per year for 100 years over an area of 100 km^2. Hence, for geologically realistic times of thousands or tens of thousands of years, it would not be difficult to supply enough hydrothermal fluid from a region of 10 km × 10 km to form this size of deposit. But, of course, it would be necessary to channel all this water to a localized site of deposition. A persistent heat source to aid convection and prolonged access to structural pathways would help to focus fluids over long periods of time.

Now consider the *size of the source region* supplying the zinc.

●   The average crustal abundance of zinc is 70 ppm, but not all of it in rocks may be leachable. If an average of, say, 25 ppm were leached from rocks accessible to fluids, how extensive would the source region have to be?

◐   To produce 1.5×10^5 t of zinc would require leaching of

$$\frac{1.5 \times 10^5 \text{t}}{25 \times 10^{-6}} = 6 \times 10^9 \text{ t of crust.}$$

Converting this to volume, and assuming a crustal density of 2.75 t m^{-3} ($= 2.75 \times 10^9$ t km^{-3}), the volume of crust is

$$\frac{6 \times 10^9 \text{ t}}{2.75 \times 10^9 \text{ t km}^{-3}} = 2.2 \text{ km}^3$$

This volume of crustal leaching could represent a sedimentary layer, 220 m thick, extending over an area of 10 km^2 or, alternatively, fluid pathways might need to access about 10% of a 2.2 km thick portion of crust over that same area.

Therefore, so long as a sufficiently large volume of source rock is accessible to fluids for a sufficiently long period, a relatively small percentage of leaching would be sufficient to produce an ore deposit.

Question 4.3

Why do you think the majority of hydrothermal deposits are barren?

4.2 Exhalative hydrothermal ore deposits

Hydrothermal fluids that emerge from the Earth's crust, either onto the land surface or onto the ocean floor, are termed **exhalative**.

● In what ways do these two environments differ, and what are the consequences for mineral deposition?

○ On land, hydrothermal fluid *escapes into the air*, perhaps as a geyser (Figure 4.2), or more gently as a hot spring (Figure 4.7a). The water then flows or seeps away if it does not evaporate first. Dissolved material may be precipitated to form surface encrustations: gases and steam escape into the atmosphere.

Hydrothermal fluids, emerging from the ocean floor, *mix with seawater*. Changes in temperature and fluid chemistry bring about the precipitation of minerals that encrust surfaces or become dispersed in suspension. Under the high pressures of the deep ocean floor, gases remain in solution.

Another important difference between land and ocean-floor environments is the chemical and mineralogical composition of the underlying crust. Continental crust has an average composition rather like granodiorite. It differs markedly from that of oceanic crust, which is rather like basalt. Thus, the rocks and the minerals with which the hydrothermal fluids have been in contact have quite different compositions, and different metals are available to be leached.

Oceanic crust is dominated mineralogically by ferromagnesian minerals, whereas continental crust comprises mainly quartz, plagioclase feldspars and micas. Seawater heated within the ocean floor alters ferromagnesian minerals to chlorite and clay, releasing iron and trace elements such as copper, zinc and manganese. In continental crust, hydrothermal fluids alter alkali feldspars and micas to clay minerals and release traces of barium and lead from those minerals. Thus, crustal compositions and availability of trace metals strongly influence the composition of hydrothermal fluids and the mineralogy of corresponding deposits. The low abundance of elements such as tin, tungsten, lead and silver in the basaltic rocks of the ocean floor — because they do not substitute in ferromagnesian minerals — results in these metals tending to be rare in oceanic hydrothermal deposits.

There is a third difference between land-surface and ocean-floor environments.

● How does the water that occupies spaces in the underlying rock differ between terrestrial and ocean-floor settings?

On land, groundwater is derived from rainfall and is low in dissolved salts (initially, at least), whereas within the ocean floor, infiltrating solutions start out as seawater, which is saline.

4.2.1 Land-based hot spring-related deposits

Spectacular evidence for active hydrothermal systems is provided by active geysers, which release hot water and steam from within the Earth. There are many examples in Iceland; North Island, New Zealand (Figure 4.2); and Yellowstone Park, Wyoming, USA, where groundwater is heated by magma at relatively shallow depth. As hot hydrothermal waters rise to the surface, they decompress: supercritical fluids (above 374 °C for pure water) may **flash** to steam whereas subcritical fluids boil to produce steam (Drury, 2006). Either of these mechanisms can cause geysers to erupt. Less active hydrothermal systems produce hot springs and mud pools (Figure 4.7a and b).

On land, hydrothermal fluids often consist of meteoric water that has percolated deep into the crust through aquifers and fractures. On penetrating to depths of 2 km or more, temperatures of 200–300 °C may be attained in thermally active areas. When convecting back to the surface they transfer heat and disrupt subsurface temperature distributions, as shown in Figure 4.8.

Figure 4.7 Surface expressions of hydrothermal fluids in geothermally active areas: (a) hot springs — hot water escapes gently; (b) mud pools — gases (mainly steam) bubble through hot mud; (c) terraces — dissolved silica (or sometimes calcium carbonate) has precipitated from cooling thermal waters to form a cascade of terraces.

(a)

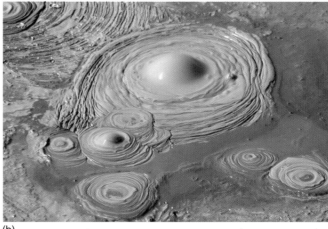
(b)

(c)

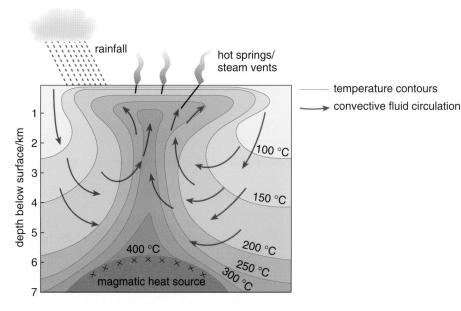

Figure 4.8 Hydrothermal fluid circulation feeding a hot spring system in a volcanic region where a magma chamber occurs at 6–7 km depth. Convected fluids affect temperature variation with depth.

Shallow hydrothermal fluids are frequently acidic and oxidizing, and able to react with feldspars and micas to form clay minerals — an effect known as **argillic alteration**. Although a hydrothermal process, this effect occurs at low temperatures and resembles extreme surface weathering (as described in Section 3.1). Just as with weathering reactions, the breakdown of one mineral and the formation of others by hydrothermal alteration may release those trace elements that cannot be accommodated in the alteration products. Even cool fluids may scavenge trace elements from the rocks that they alter. The metals involved would depend on the initial rock composition and its mineralogy, as well as on the temperature and composition of the fluid.

Hydrothermal brines cool rapidly once they emerge, and gases escape, changing the fluid chemistry. This leads to the precipitation of dissolved material as encrusted layers, sometimes forming mounds and terraces (Figure 4.7c). The most common hot spring deposits are either precipitated silica (*sinter*), or precipitated calcium carbonate (*travertine*). Although these deposits may be prominent at the surface, the main site of mineralization is below ground, in the feeder channels, where chemical interaction with wall-rocks occurs, fluids cool and gases are released as fluids approach the surface.

- What effect may decompression and boiling of fluids have? (*Hint*: think back to the behaviour of similar fluids in porphyry ore systems (Section 2.3).)

- Both the rapid decompression and flashing of supercritical fluids and, at a high level, the transformation of subcritical fluids to steam by boiling, result in sudden increases in volume, which can be powerful enough to shatter rocks. As a result, fragmented rocks, sometimes called hydrothermal explosion breccias, are commonly associated with hot springs, geysers and sinter terraces.

As well as producing steam, boiling releases other gases that are dissolved in the fluid. The change in the solution chemistry may cause complex ions in solution to break down and precipitate the metals they carry to form insoluble minerals, such as mercury, bismuth and antimony sulphides, and sometimes, gold and silver as native metals. These metals are often derived from volcanic source rocks and can be carried in solution as chemical complexes such as $[AuCl_2]^-$ and $[Au(HS)_2]^-$ (Section 4.1.2). Another mechanism of precipitation may be by reaction with iron(II) in solution after its release from decomposing ferromagnesian minerals in wall rocks. This could explain the common association of gold with pyrite:

$$4[Au(HS)_2]^-(aq) + 4Fe^{2+}(aq) + O_2(g) = 4FeS_2(s) + 4Au(s) + 2H_2O(l) + 4H^+(aq) \qquad (4.3)$$

soluble gold   iron (II)   pyrite   gold

Q9e

Box 4.3 Gold deposits in Nevada

Hot spring-related hydrothermal gold deposits in Nevada, USA, have made headlines, not only for the 'Gold Rush' of the 1860s, but also for the surge in gold mining since 1980. Nevada is also notable as an active geothermal region.

Several different forms of gold-bearing deposits occur in Nevada, developed as summarized in Figure 4.9. The richest deposits, containing several hundred grams per tonne of gold and even more of silver, are sometimes called 'Bonanza' ores, like the famous

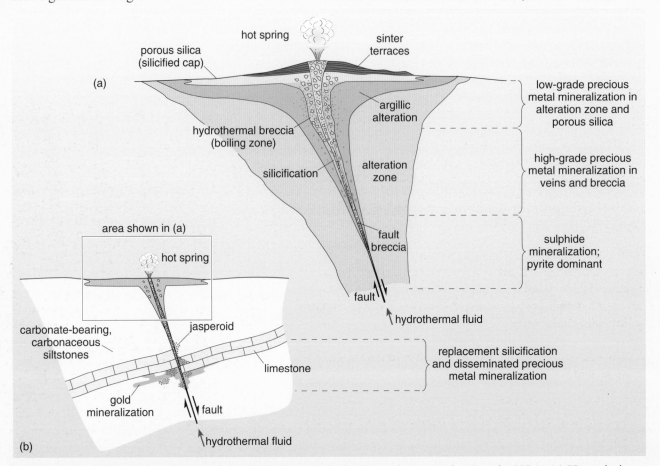

Figure 4.9 A schematic representation of gold-bearing hydrothermal systems in Nevada, USA. (a) Hot solutions escaping along a fault alter surrounding rocks, and deposit silica, sulphide minerals and gold in veins, fault breccias, stockwork and hydrothermal breccias; sinter terraces are formed around hot springs at the surface. (b) At deeper levels, the hydrothermal system is more constrained and, on intersecting a band of limestone, replaces it with iron-rich silica to form jasperoid, a red–orange flinty rock. The precious metals in veins and replacement deposits are mainly silver and gold.

Comstock Lode, worked in Nevada from 1860 to 1880. They are usually found in quartz vein systems that formed at depths of 100–350 m in feeders to hot spring systems and are associated with pyrite and sulphides of antimony, arsenic and mercury.

In the near-surface parts of hot spring systems, precious metal mineralization occurs at much lower grades throughout a stockwork of veins and in zones of hydrothermal alteration and brecciation. Breccias, composed of angular, broken fragments, may form by fault movements or by explosive hydrothermal activity. Faults often provide major channels (pathways) for migration of hydrothermal fluids towards the surface, and sites for mineral deposition. Fault intersections are particularly favourable areas to prospect for hydrothermal deposits because of greater fluid flows and the capacity for fluids to interact with rocks that have already been affected by earlier fluids.

Low-grade disseminated deposits also occur in zones of argillic alteration (Figure 4.9a), where fluids have penetrated and reacted with wall rocks to form clays. These disseminated deposits are much more extensive than the vein deposits, and have become important because gold at only a few g t^{-1} (or ppm) is economic to mine on a large scale by modern methods. In such deposits, gold is so fine grained that it cannot be seen, nor can it be 'panned' by prospectors. Two developments led to their discovery and the explosion of mining since 1980: detection of the gold by geochemical methods of exploration and a rise in the price of gold, allowing its economic extraction by cyanide leaching (Chapter 6).

4.2.2   Submarine massive sulphide deposits

Submarine hydrothermal activity was only suspected until it became possible to image and sample the ocean depths. Such observations at mid-ocean ridge sites in the late 1970s discovered active vents in the deep ocean floor from which hydrothermal fluids were pouring. These fluids emerge at temperatures in excess of 300 °C and precipitate particles of metal oxides and sulphides which make them appear like clouds of black smoke (Figure 4.10) — hence their name, **black smokers**.

Several questions arise. How do these black smokers form? Where do the fluids originate? Why are they so hot? Beneath mid-ocean ridges, basaltic magma is formed by partial melting of hot mantle rising from great depth (Section 2.1) and contains very little magmatic water.

- What other source of water is available, and how might it be heated?

- Seawater is the obvious source of water. The intrusion of basaltic magma into the oceanic crust provides a continual source of heat.

In magmatically active ocean floor (as at constructive plate margins), seawater penetrates fissures in basaltic lavas made permeable by the fragmentation and alteration that occur on eruption into seawater. The hot oceanic crust heats the permeating seawater, which becomes a highly reactive fluid that alters minerals and leaches metals from the oceanic crust.

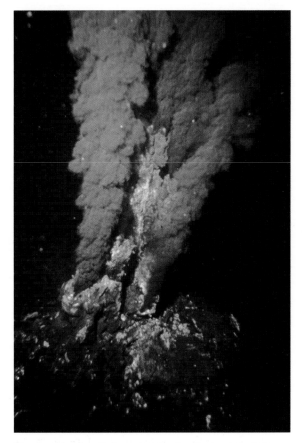

Figure 4.10   Submarine hydrothermal activity — a black smoker chimney.

This hot fluid, now rich in metals such as iron, manganese, copper and zinc, returns to the ocean floor by convection (Figure 4.11).

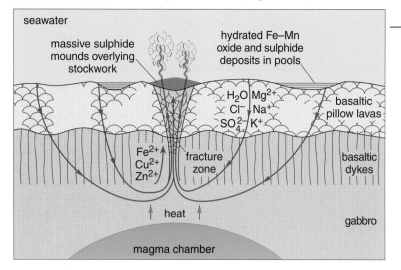

Figure 4.11 Convective circulation of hydrothermal fluids above 'hot spots' caused by igneous activity beneath the ocean floor. The initial salinity of the seawater enhances its reactivity to alter hot basaltic rocks and leach metals from surrounding rocks before returning to the ocean floor.

On emerging from the ocean floor, these hot, metal-charged fluids mix with cold seawater, precipitating particles of sulphide and insoluble sulphate minerals to form a 'smoker'. Around the smoker vent, the accumulation of insoluble minerals — mainly anhydrite ($CaSO_4$), barite ($BaSO_4$) and metal sulphides — typically forms a cylindrical chimney-like deposit (Figure 4.12). Within the ocean floor, the fluids deposit sulphides in the fractures that provide pathways to the surface. This forms a mineralized stockwork beneath the sulphide-rich mounds that build up through accumulation of collapsed chimneys. The mounds and stockworks form **massive sulphide deposits**, which are often 50 m across. More rarely, deposits reach hundreds of metres across and tens of metres in thickness and contain several million tonnes of high-grade sulphide minerals. Remains of ancient hydrothermal vents, including fragments of the chimneys, are often found in massive sulphide deposits.

Figure 4.12 The development of black smoker chimneys, sulphide mounds and mineralized stockwork where hydrothermal fluids emerge from the ocean floor. The sulphide mounds are often 50 m or more across.

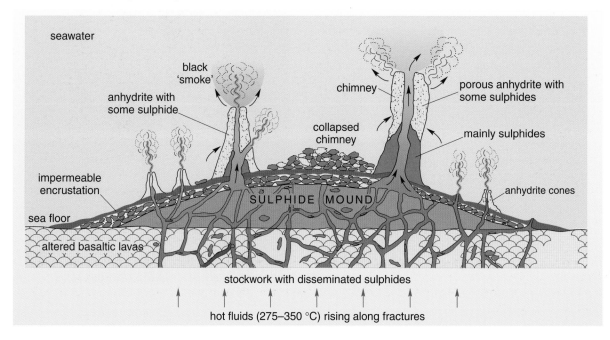

Box 4.4   Red Sea hot brine pools and metalliferous muds

The Red Sea (Figure 4.13a) is bordered by continental crust that had been joined until 30 million years ago, when it started to break up. It is floored by basaltic oceanic crust that has been forming along its axial zone, where the structure is a submarine *rift valley*. The Red Sea is probably the best example of active continental break-up heralding the birth of a new ocean.

Along the axial rift zone of the Red Sea there are many hydrothermal features typical of oceanic spreading ridges, such as black smokers and basins containing hot brine pools, many of which contain metalliferous sediments (Figure 4.13b). One such basin is the Atlantis II Deep, 14 km by 5 km in area, which contains over 200 Mt of metalliferous sediment that is rich in manganese and iron oxides, and sulphides of iron, copper and zinc (Figure 4.13b). Of this, 90 Mt (grading 2% Zn, 0.45% Cu and 38 g t^{-1} Ag) has formed during the last 15 000 years.

Could the Atlantis II Deep be a renewable resource, providing a sustainable supply of metals? Not really,

because it amounts to only 6000 t y^{-1}, of which just 120 t is zinc — somewhat short of the 9.0 Mt of zinc metal consumed globally in 2003!

Brines trapped in these deep basins are rather like hydrothermal fluids. Their salinity reaches concentrations of 30% NaCl and temperatures are as high as 60 °C. The high salinity is thought to have been derived by seawater percolating through evaporites on the flanks of the Red Sea. These solutions also pass through hot basaltic crust from which they leach metals at temperatures above 250 °C. Through convection they discharge into the axial basins. Although hot, the high density of the brines and the lack of large-scale circulation in the basins cause them to be trapped, pooling beneath cool seawater (Figure 4.13b). Precipitation of metals occurs when the hot fluids cool, to form soft, muddy metalliferous sediments. Sulphide and sulphate minerals precipitate from the lower brines, and Fe–Mn oxides from the upper brines.

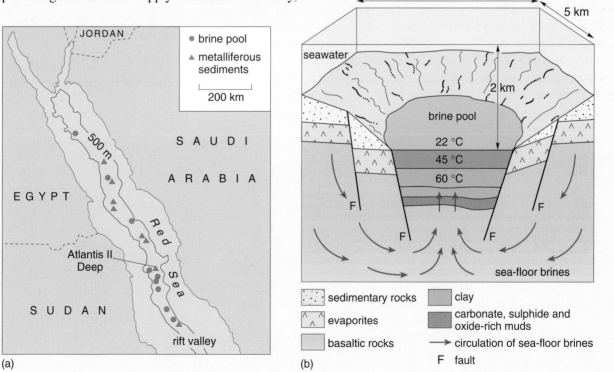

Figure 4.13   (a) Location of hot brine pools along the Red Sea rift valley. (b) A section across a brine pool in the Atlantis II Deep, showing temperature/density stratification of the brines and layers of metalliferous sediments. Although the brines are hot, they form pools because they are denser than the surrounding seawater owing to their high content of dissolved salts.

A surprising feature of black smokers is that colonies of organisms live in and around the chimneys from which the hot hydrothermal brines emerge. These fluids might be expected to be a most unhealthy chemical cocktail, but some forms of organism actually thrive in these conditions and, indeed, are found nowhere else on Earth. They include organisms thought to be related to some of the earliest forms of life on Earth, so black smokers have been regarded by some as possible 'crucibles of life'.

Mineral deposits being formed in association with active black smokers are not confined to massive sulphide mounds, veined stockworks or encrusted chimneys (Figure 4.12). The sulphide-rich black 'smoke' also disperses particles of oxide and sulphide minerals to accumulate in ocean-floor depressions (Figure 4.11). If these metalliferous sediments are buried, they can be preserved to form ore deposits. Sulphide layers from a deposit formed in this way, about 450 Ma ago, at Parys Mountain, Anglesey, are shown in Figure 4.14.

Figure 4.14 Pyrite mineralization in dark, metalliferous sediment — from the sulphide deposit at Parys Mountain, Anglesey. Field of view 18 cm across.

Submarine, exhalative sulphide deposits are not confined to sea-floor spreading centres; any hydrothermal fluid charged with metals that vents into a submarine environment (fresh or saline) has ore-forming potential. In the geological record, such deposits are known from many sedimentary sequences where evidence of volcanic activity is absent. These include lead–zinc deposits in Ireland, which contain fossil hydrothermal vents similar to those described above. There, relatively cool fluids, probably formation waters from buried sedimentary source rocks, emerged from the sea floor while 320 Ma Carboniferous limestones were being deposited.

Some ancient massive sulphide deposits occur in sequences of ocean-floor basaltic rocks originally formed at constructive plate boundaries. These are known as Cyprus-type deposits, after the deposits occurring in the ophiolites of Cyprus (named *Kupros* by the Greeks, their name for copper). About 1 Mt of copper was mined from Cyprus in 5000 years from some 20 sites, but Cyprus is now insignificant as a producer on the world scene. Although Cyprus-type deposits are not large — at most a few hundred metres across and tens of metres thick, containing only a few million tonnes of reserves — they are spread widely across the world and are particularly rich in copper and zinc sulphides, which together form 5–15% of the deposit. The remainder of these deposits — indeed, the dominant part — is iron sulphide, largely pyrite (FeS_2), which is usually considered a gangue mineral.

Another form of massive sulphide deposit — the Kuroko type — is named after deposits in Japan, where there are over a hundred occurrences in eight districts along an 800 km zone. In contrast to the Cyprus type, Kuroko-type deposits tend to be associated with *rhyolitic* lavas that formed in subduction-related volcanic arcs. Although they formed through similar exhalative processes, the source rock compositions, and the shallower depth of water into which fluids were expelled, are different in such volcanic arc settings.

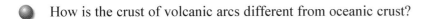 How is the crust of volcanic arcs different from oceanic crust?

The ocean floor is of basaltic composition (Box 2.1), formed by ocean ridge volcanism as a result of *dry* melting of peridotite mantle. By contrast, volcanic arc crust is broadly of dioritic composition, and formed from magmas generated by *hydrous* melting of peridotite mantle and the crust above, irrespective of whether it was oceanic (basaltic) or continental (granodioritic) crust originally.

Volcanic arc crust is compositionally more variable than ocean-floor crust, and contains higher levels of incompatible elements. Consequently, the elements concentrated in Kuroko-type deposits are more varied than in Cyprus-type deposits. They include lead, silver and gold, as well as copper and zinc, and the deposits often contain large quantities of barite, gypsum and pyrite.

One Cu–Zn deposit in the UK may be likened to Kuroko-type deposits — the Parys Mountain deposit in Anglesey, which is the location of the sulphide mineralization shown in Figure 4.14. It is also associated with rhyolitic volcanic rocks. The deposit was mined in open pit and underground in the late 18th and much of the 19th centuries, but was closed by the 20th century. Evaluation of the Parys Mountain deposit in the 1980s revealed 4.8 Mt of ore remaining, grading 3% Pb, 6% Zn, 1.5% Cu, 6.9 g t^{-1} Ag and 0.4 g t^{-1} Au. It has the potential to be the largest base metal mine in the UK with a planned output of 0.25 Mt y^{-1}, but because of depressed metal prices in the 1990s, the prospect has yet to be developed. Further evaluation in 2005 has confirmed the potential of the mine.

Of much greater importance individually are massive sulphide deposits of Precambrian age, such as the Golden Grove deposit in Western Australia and the Kidd Creek deposit of Canada (see Box 4.5). Known as primitive-type deposits, these are usually much larger than the Kuroko type. They may have been formed by similar processes, but at a time when global processes operated on a different scale.

Box 4.5 Kidd Creek massive sulphide deposit

The Kidd Creek deposit of Ontario, Canada, is a massive sulphide deposit occurring in ancient (2700 Ma old) Precambrian volcanic rocks of the Canadian Shield. The orebody was not discovered until 1959. It had been hidden by swamp and thick glacial till from earlier prospectors, who sought gold in the area. It was found by modern geophysical exploration techniques. Trial drilling proved over 8% Zn, 1.2% Cu and over 100 g t^{-1} Ag. The orebody turned out to be over 600 m long and up to 150 m wide, extending to a depth of at least 1500 m. Alongside it, a stockwork deposit of mainly chalcopyrite in fragmental rhyolite (Figure 4.15a and b) represents a feeder zone for hydrothermal fluids beneath the massive sulphide deposit.

- What do these dimensions suggest about the shape and orientation of the orebody? Bear in mind that massive sulphide mounds normally form on the sea floor as extensive but relatively thin layers.

- The narrowest dimension of the Kidd Creek orebody is its width; the greatest, its depth. It is tabular in form and must have been tilted by tectonic forces, so it is now in an almost vertical orientation rather than the horizontal orientation as it was formed.

Because of the physical form of the deposit (Figure 4.15b), initial mining at Kidd Creek was as an open

pit. Underground mining started in the 1970s and the open pit was worked out and abandoned by 1979.

From 1966 to 1989, 85 Mt of ore were mined, grading 7.2% Zn, 2.2% Cu, 0.28% Pb and 102 g t^{-1} Ag. At the beginning of 1990, reserves were estimated at 45 Mt, grading 5.1% Zn, 3.5% Cu, 0.16% Pb and 67 g t^{-1} Ag.

- How much copper is likely to be extracted in total from Kidd Creek, and how does this compare with all the copper mined on Cyprus?

- $(85 \text{ Mt} \times 0.022) + (45 \text{ Mt} \times 0.035) = 3.4 \text{ Mt}$ copper. This compares with about 1 Mt copper in total from some twenty mine sites in Cyprus.

Although the massive ore at Kidd Creek contains pyrite, sphalerite, chalcopyrite and galena, which are minerals typical of Kuroko deposits, and the association of basalts, andesitic and rhyolitic lavas (Figure 4.15a) suggest a volcanic arc setting, it is a much larger primitive-type deposit of Precambrian age.

Question 4.4

Why was more copper mined in less than 25 years from Kidd Creek than in 5000 years from many individual deposits in Cyprus?

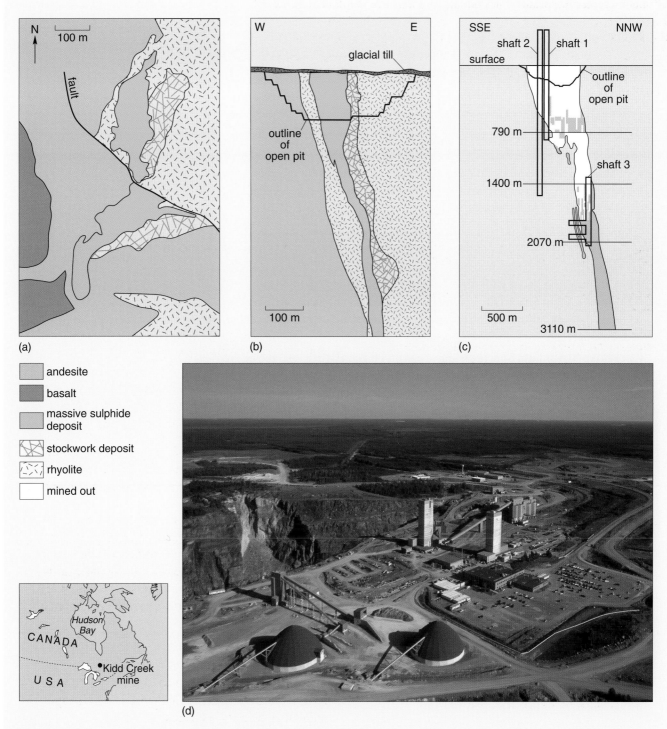

Figure 4.15 The Kidd Creek massive sulphide deposit: (a) plan view; (b) in cross-section; (c) the extent of mining in 2005; (d) mining operations, with two shafts and the open pit behind. *Note*: (b) and (c) are drawn to different scales.

4.3 Summary of Chapter 4

1   Hydrothermal systems involve the movement of hot, aqueous fluids, often in large volumes, through pathways in the crust, as a result of convection driven by geothermal heating, magma intrusion or by compaction due to burial.

2   Forming a hydrothermal ore deposit also requires:

- an extensive and fertile source of ore mineral components (e.g. metals and sulphur);

- a fluid of suitable composition to extract and transport those components;

- a suitable site where chemical and physical conditions favour the precipitation of ore minerals, where prolonged fluid flow is focused, and space is available for deposition.

3   Compositions of hydrothermal fluids, and the ores they may produce, depend on the source of the fluid and the assemblage of source rocks that it leaches. Therefore different types of deposit, in terms both of form and typical ore minerals, are associated with different geological environments. However, the principles that govern the concentration of metals — leaching of large volumes of rock; transportation of soluble components; localized precipitation of ore minerals — are always the same.

4   Exhalative hydrothermal activity can be seen on the Earth's surface at the present day, both on land (associated with hot springs) and on the ocean floor (associated with black smokers) usually in areas of active volcanism.

5   Hydrothermal systems associated with hot springs may form high-grade gold-bearing veins and breccias in feeder zones well below ground level, and low-grade disseminated gold deposits in more extensive replacement and near-surface alteration zones.

6   Hydrothermal systems associated with sea-floor volcanism form submarine massive sulphide deposits, known as Cyprus-type when formed in oceanic settings, and Kuroko-type when formed in volcanic arc settings. On a much larger scale, so-called primitive-type deposits, developed in Precambrian times, are of greater importance individually on the world scene.

MINING ACTIVITIES AND EXPLORATION FOR ORE DEPOSITS

5

The Earth's crust contains a wide variety of metalliferous deposits as a result of the concentration of elements by natural geological processes (as described in Chapters 2, 3 and 4). Such deposits can only be resources if they have the potential to be exploited for profit and transformed into useful products. This brings us to consider in this chapter the nature of mining activities and how mineral deposits are found. In the following chapter our attention turns to the economics of mining, what form mining might take, and how ore is processed and transformed into metal. In the final chapter, we look at the environmental and sustainability issues that are associated with exploiting metal resources.

5.1 Mining activities

Today, nearly all mining for metals is undertaken by organized industry, though there remain, especially in poorer parts of the world, individuals who mine with little mechanization and without the backing or support of organized management.

Small-scale or artisanal mining requires little more than basic mining know-how, primitive tools, possibly explosives, and some equipment for separating out ore minerals — so little financial investment is necessary. Labour may be by individuals or a cooperative workforce, who may pay a high price in terms of health and safety by taking part in largely unregulated mining activities (e.g. Figure 5.1). Such operations have more in common with pre-20th-century mining in Europe than with large-scale mining today.

Large-scale mining is a very different proposition. It is conducted mainly by large multinational companies with operations in many countries. Some companies specialize in a single commodity, such as gold, while others, such as Rio Tinto, Anglo American and BHP Billiton, produce a wide range of commodities. The modern counterpart of the old-time prospector is the *exploration company*. Such companies use the latest technology to explore for minerals, but tend to be small and dependent on capital raised on the venture stock exchanges in Australia, Canada and London (see also Section 5.2). Some of their successes can be spectacular, such as the recent Voisey's Bay discovery (see Box 5.1).

Large-scale exploitation of mineral deposits involves a series of activities as shown in Figure 5.2 and outlined below.

1   *Regional targeting* — the selection of a suitable region in which to start exploration, involving desk studies based on historical knowledge of deposits and/or geological indicators. It follows the decision to explore, which is based on economic circumstances and the projected demand for a metal.

Figure 5.1   A cooperative mining venture in Serra Pelada, Brazil. Miners flocked to Serra Pelada in the 1980s following the discovery of gold, where they excavated a deep hole, mainly by hand. Mining continues, but the deposit is largely worked out.

2 *Exploration* — the systematic search for metalliferous deposits by a variety of geological, geophysical and geochemical methods, starting at a regional scale and becoming progressively more localized.

3 *Evaluation and initial feasibility studies* — the determination of metal grade and its distribution at a specific location, so that decisions can then be made as to whether or not to exploit the deposit and, if it shows promise, how to exploit it.

4 *Detailed feasibility studies* — the production of a development plan to satisfy the investment needed to set up the mining infrastructure and ore processing plant. As well as support from investors, approvals are required from governments as well as the local population. An environmental impact statement is necessary to satisfy the regulatory authorities that the site will not have an unacceptable impact either during or after operations.

5 *Mine development* — the construction of the operational infrastructure necessary to gain access to the ore, as well as to process and to ship it. This often involves power and water supplies, accommodation for the workforce, ore-processing plant, and road or rail links for shipment of ore and concentrates. Accessing the ore may involve excavating the overburden to create an open pit, or sinking shafts and tunnelling underground (Chapter 6).

6 *Mine production* — the removal and processing of ore; sometimes the on-site extraction of metals (Chapter 6).

7 *Mine closure* — the ending of mining and the restoration of the surrounding area, as well as minimizing any future impact of the mine on the area (Chapter 7).

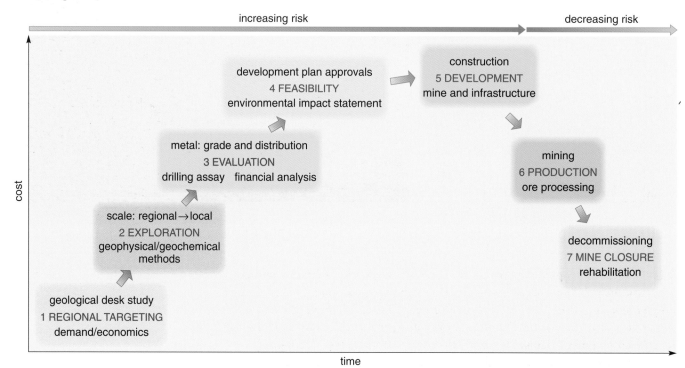

Figure 5.2 The sequence of activities and the escalation of cost during exploration, evaluation and development and then reduction with production and closure of a metal mining venture. The stages do not overlap as much as this schematic would suggest.

Box 5.1 Voisey's Bay nickel mine — overview

The Voisey's Bay operation in Labrador, Canada is a major new nickel mine, which shipped its first concentrates at the end of 2005 (Figure 5.3). The project has had a long and complex history, typical of many major new mines (as detailed later, in Box 5.2). The deposit is one of the most significant mineral discoveries in Canada in the last 30 years and contains nickel and copper sulphides — both disseminated and as discrete pods hosted in an olivine–plagioclase-rich igneous rock forming a dyke-like intrusion (Figure 5.5a).

The resources announced in 2005 were 100 Mt of ore at 1.94% Ni, 1.01% Cu and 0.11% Co, including reserves of 30 Mt at 2.85% Ni, 1.68% Cu and 0.14% Co.

In the case of Voisey's Bay, the reserves can be mined in an open pit, whereas the resources include deposits that would have to be mined underground, the feasibility of which had not been proven in 2006.

The estimated investment at Voisey's Bay for the initial mine and processing plant by Inco, the operators, is C$710 million (~£305 million). However, a key issue is where to process the ore. Inco aim to spend C$85 million (~£37 million) investigating the feasibility of processing the ore to produce nickel metal in both Newfoundland and Labrador. A full-scale nickel extraction plant is likely to cost a further C$670 million (~£290 million).

⬤ What is the essential difference between resources and reserves?

⬤ Reserves contain grades of metal that can be extracted profitably and legally under prevailing conditions; resources include lower-grade mineralization that is potentially exploitable given realistic changes in methods of extraction, metal prices or legal conditions.

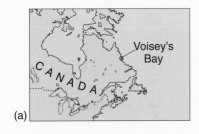

(a)

(b)

Figure 5.3   (a) Location of Voisey's Bay; (b) clearing of the area in preparation for mining in 2001.

It is important to appreciate that every stage of a mining programme requires high-risk financial investment, with no income until production is under way and no guarantee of success. Therefore, at each stage up to full mine production, *financial evaluation* and *risk analysis* are necessary to justify the increasing investment required. Decisions whether or not to continue with the mining activities must take into account the cost implications of likely geological problems, the economic and political vagaries of world markets and the price that the product is likely to command in the future. Many projects under development have to be written off when their viability cannot be demonstrated. To be an attractive investment, the mine must not only be productive enough for the income to cover operating costs and repay the capital outlay, it must also provide a better return on the capital than a 'safe' investment, such as in a bank deposit account.

The stages outlined in Figure 5.2, from the initial decision to explore to development and production, take varying lengths of time. Indeed, the *lead time* for a mining project (the time from discovery to production) is generally 3–20 years, depending on the size, complexity and location of the operation. Profits from existing, successful operations often have to support the cost of developing new projects that might be terminated before the production stage is reached.

If development costs escalate or it takes a long time for production to start, it will be more difficult to achieve a financial return comparable with that of a less-risky investment. To appreciate this point, take a look at the hypothetical financial model in Figure 5.4a, which compares the net cumulative return (profit) from a major mining venture with the compounded return on capital 'safely' invested. A breakdown of annual income and expenditure is given in Figure 5.4b. In the early years, the venture makes a loss because injection of capital is necessary (especially during mine development) and interest is payable on loans. In this example, the mine starts to make an operating profit in year 11; only then can loans be repaid.

- Examine Figure 5.4a and decide when the venture will break even — that is, when cumulative costs are balanced by cumulative income.

- The breakeven point occurs about 13.5 years after the project started (about 4–5 years after mine production started).

- How long after the major capital investment in years 8 and 9 does it take for the mine to bring in a return exceeding that of 'safely' invested capital?

- The curves in Figure 5.4a intersect about 18.5 years after the project started, and thereafter the mine outperforms the 'safe' investment. This occurs about 10 years after the main injection of capital (Figure 5.4b).

You may remember from Section 1.2 that, usually, only a small proportion of an ore is useful, so the cost of shipping metal, even if impure, is much less than the cost of shipping an equivalent amount of ore or ore concentrates. Therefore metals obtained from low-grade ores, such as copper and gold, are commonly extracted at or near the mine site. Rich ores and ore concentrates (such as aluminium and iron ore) are often transported in bulk to smelters located in areas where energy costs are low. However, the costs of metal extraction (smelting) are generally high owing to the complexity of the plant, the large amounts of energy required and the need to protect the environment.

The added value from ore processing and metal extraction can be appreciated by comparing the prices of ore and metal. In the case of aluminium, the 2004 price of bauxite ore (containing 25% Al) was about US\$30 t^{-1} whereas the price of aluminium metal was about US\$1800 t^{-1}. Ore prices vary according to the grade of the ore and the impurities it contains, whereas metal prices depend on the purity achieved — because additional refining increases costs.

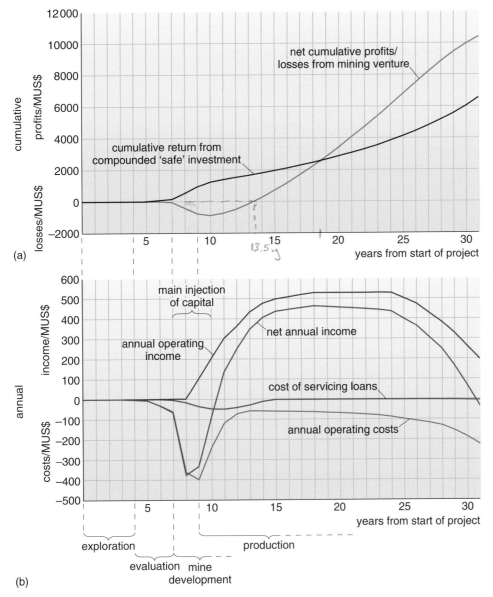

MUS$ = million US$

Figure 5.4   Profit–loss curves for a hypothetical major mining venture with a productive life of about 20 years.
(a) Net cumulative profits and losses derived from net annual mining income and expenditure compared with the return from equivalent capital safely invested (based on compound interest of 5%; calculations include 5% compound interest on operating profits, once achieved).
(b) Annual income and expenditure for the mining venture — net annual income and losses are derived from the annual operating income less development and operating costs and the cost of servicing loans at 5% per annum. *Note*: exploration costs are invisible compared to development costs.

Question 5.1

A considerable period of time elapses from the initial discovery of an ore deposit to production of ore. What are the main reasons for this?

5.2   Background to exploration and targeting

Both the exploration for and the evaluation of ore deposits depend on geological knowledge, but both are costly activities and are therefore controlled by economic considerations. Two types of company explore for mineral deposits — the mining company, which already produces minerals, and the exploration company, which is usually financed on one of the more speculative stock exchanges, such as the Alternative Investment Market (AIM) in London. The mining company aims to maintain its share value by enhancing its portfolio of properties, expanding or diversifying its mining activities and replacing resources depleted by its own mining operations.

As most mines have a working life of only 15–30 years, and many mines much less, large companies must continually acquire new ore deposits for tomorrow's mines. The exploration (or *junior*) company aims to discover a new deposit and either sell it to a large company or raise funds and begin mining on its own account. The sale of Voisey's Bay to Inco (see Box 5.2) is one example. Exploration budgets range from a few tens of thousands of dollars to the many tens of millions of dollars invested annually by large multinational companies with extensive exploration programmes. The most effective programmes are often those which have a handful of experienced geologists and do not become too large.

Box 5.2   Voisey's Bay nickel mine, Labrador — development

The Voisey's Bay project (Box 5.1) has had a long and complex history that is typical of many major new mines. The deposit was discovered by two prospectors, Al Chislett and Chris Verbiski, from a small exploration company, Archean Resources, working under contract to another larger exploration company, Diamond Fields Resources. The discovery was unexpected as they were looking for diamonds — that part of Labrador was generally considered to have little potential for new nickel deposits, although gabbroic rocks were known to exist in the area.

Northern Labrador is very remote, with few roads, so they used a helicopter for transport and took routine stream sediment samples for analysis and to check likely targets. Both prospectors were experienced in looking for base metal deposits and were used to recognizing distinctive weathered outcrops or gossans, which are normally bright red or yellow in colour. Although they had sampled hundreds of gossans in Labrador during the summer of 1993, they recognized one gossan, unlike others developed from weathered pyrite, which was rich in chalcopyrite. It was also large, being 500 m long by 40–80 m wide, with samples containing about 2% copper. Realizing the potential of the area, Archean Resources raised C$15 575 to stake their claim to the surrounding area with the Newfoundland Department of Mines. Under the terms of their contract, Archean Resources were obliged to offer Diamond Fields the right to buy any claims that they discovered. Although the main interest of Diamond Fields was in diamond exploration, the company eventually decided to finance a drilling programme costing C$200 000. They were also encouraged by multi-element analyses, which indicated the presence of nickel and cobalt as well as copper, and by geophysical surveys (see, for example, Sections 5.5.1 and 5.6),

which revealed magnetic and electromagnetic (EM) anomalies in the area.

Although the first drill hole was disappointing, the second hole, drilled in October 1994, intersected 33 m of sulphide mineralization grading approximately 2% nickel. The next four drill holes were less encouraging, but drill hole 7, which tested the EM anomaly, cut through more than 100 m of sulphide mineralization grading more than 4% nickel. At this stage the company realized it had a major discovery.

Further drilling defined the mineralization as a shallow ovoid (egg-shaped) pod, known as the Ovoid Zone (Figure 5.5a and b), which was 400 m long by 300 m wide, located 20 m below the overburden. Further helicopter and ground-based EM work and drilling defined a further two major anomalous zones. Drilling on one of these (the Eastern Deeps Zone), located approximately 1 km to the east of the Ovoid Zone, returned a 32 m thickness of sulphides assaying 1.5% Ni and 0.67% Cu. This confirmed that the potential of the area covered by the claim was not confined to the Ovoid Zone.

The discovery of a potentially large nickel deposit had not escaped the attention of the major Canadian nickel mining companies, Inco and Falconbridge, who produce nickel mainly from deep mines in the Sudbury area of Ontario. Production from those areas was becoming costly and both companies were anxious to obtain less-expensive sources of ore. A large Vancouver-based mining company, Teck Corp, initially bought a 10% stake in Diamond Fields and, in June 1995, Inco bought 25% of the Voisey's Bay prospect for C$525 million as well as providing a further C$25 million for a feasibility study. However, Falconbridge was still interested in buying the Voisey's Bay deposit and entered into a bidding war that led to Inco buying Diamond Fields for C$4.3 billion in 1996.

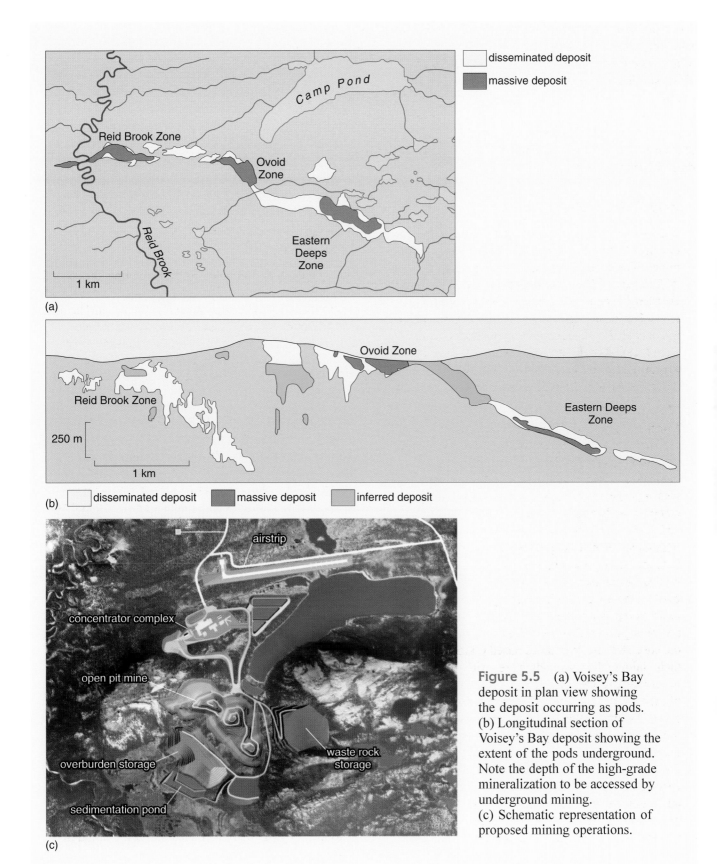

Figure 5.5 (a) Voisey's Bay deposit in plan view showing the deposit occurring as pods. (b) Longitudinal section of Voisey's Bay deposit showing the extent of the pods underground. Note the depth of the high-grade mineralization to be accessed by underground mining. (c) Schematic representation of proposed mining operations.

Having bought the deposit, Inco were keen to bring it into production, but encountered two major problems. Firstly, the native Innu and Inuit population of the area, although few in number, claimed the land and felt they had not been consulted about mining. Secondly, the Labrador/Newfoundland provincial government was keen that as much as possible of the proceeds from producing nickel should stay in the province.

The problem of Innu and Inuit rights was part of a more general issue in northern Canada during the 1990s. Previously, their presence was largely ignored and the land considered empty of ore deposits by mineral exploration companies. The native inhabitants of the Voisey's Bay area were far from happy with developments: they were worried about the impact on wildlife and their own general way of life. Protests began during Diamond Fields' drilling operations, but intensified when Inco wanted to build an airstrip. The Innu and Inuit took their case to the Supreme Court of Newfoundland, which upheld their concerns until the issue had been thoroughly discussed. After much negotiation, an 'impacts and benefits' agreement was signed, under which the indigenous peoples were compensated and given preference for employment opportunities at the mine.

The issue of where to process the ore was difficult to resolve. Inco operates smelters in Canada at Sudbury, Ontario, and at Thompson, Manitoba, and would have preferred to ship the ore there (several thousand kilometres away by sea and land). However, on the insistence of the Labrador Government that as much of the end product as possible should be produced in Labrador and Newfoundland, Inco considered building a smelter in Newfoundland. Most nickel smelters emit considerable amounts of sulphur dioxide (an air pollutant) into the atmosphere and this was a major consideration. To avoid this, Inco suggested an alternative method of ore processing in which nickel is extracted by acid leaching (Section 6.2), a hydrometallurgical approach that involves no sulphur dioxide emissions. However, this procedure had only been demonstrated on a laboratory scale and it was not known whether or not it could be scaled up to a commercial plant. Inco agreed that if the hydrometallurgical scheme were not successful then the ore would not be smelted at other Inco plants, but sent to Newfoundland for refining in a new refinery.

The disagreements took six years to resolve and resulted in a major financial loss to Inco. Once the agreement was in place in 2002, Inco proceeded with a conventional mine plan and the building of a test hydrometallurgical plant in Newfoundland. Construction was scheduled to take three years. The mine was designed as a fly-in, fly-out operation in which staff would work at the mine site for 50% of their time. The initial mine is an open pit based on the Ovoid Zone deposit. The timeline for development of the Voisey's Bay site is summarized in Figure 5.6. An underground mining feasibility study will be conducted in parallel with initial open pit mining. The ore will be concentrated on site and shipped to Newfoundland for refining.

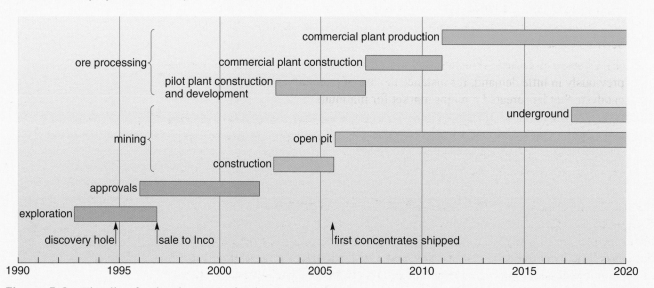

Figure 5.6 Timeline for development of Voisey's Bay mine site.

Why do mining companies need to explore?

An examination of resources lifetimes (specifically reserves lifetimes in Section 1.4) showed that, for most metals, resources are sufficient for many years at current rates of production. So, why is exploration necessary today?

There are several reasons:

- The lead time between the discovery of a deposit and the start of mining can be 10 years — and sometimes much longer (see the timeline for Voisey's Bay, Figure 5.6). So it is important to explore for resources many years in advance of prospective mine closures.

- Few ore deposits are located where they are required (i.e. at the point of demand), so there is often a need to identify alternative, more accessible resources in case it is difficult to maintain existing supplies because of international conflict, political or economic changes.

- The economics of mining a newly discovered (larger or higher grade) deposit might be more favourable than continuing to work an existing one.

Other, less obvious, reasons for exploration include protecting a company's long-term interests by keeping likely mine prospects away from competitors, and the fact that money spent on exploration can be written off against taxation.

It can take a long time to produce a return on the investment in exploration (Section 1.1). In the meantime all sorts of changes both in technology and in demand for the ore can make the venture no longer profitable. Nonetheless, new exploration programmes must be launched for continuity of supply.

Q 12 b

What changes in circumstances would encourage a mining company to expand its exploration programme for a particular metal?

Any of the following might encourage exploration.

(i) Existing supplies of an ore become restrictive, typically because of economic or political changes, for example the major increase in demand for iron ore and copper in the early 2000s due to China's rapid industrialization. The prices of both these commodities have risen and, consequently, exploration efforts have been increased.

(ii) Changes in industrial technology can create new uses for metals that were previously in little demand, for instance the use of platinum in car exhaust catalysts that has created a major market for platinum.

(iii) Improvements in mining technology result in previously uneconomic deposits becoming worth targeting for further exploration. For example, the development of large-scale heap leaching (Section 6.2) that has allowed gold to be extracted economically from very low-grade deposits, and even from earlier mine wastes.

Conversely, in a poor economic climate exploration programmes are cut back, discontinued or simply not begun. The low metal prices of the late 1990s brought about the closure of many metal mines worldwide and, as there were ample reserves, there was little incentive to invest in major new exploration. However, even in times of economic recession, mining companies keep a core team of geologists at work and maintain a low expenditure on exploration. The most profitable time for a mine to start is when metal prices are recovering from a cyclic low in times of economic upturn.

What do they look for?

The first issue to be addressed in setting up an exploration programme is what to look for. Historically, many companies concentrated on particular metals or ores. This had the advantage of building up company expertise in the exploration and marketing of those metals. However, if markets change and new opportunities for other metals open up, it is more difficult for specialist companies to respond quickly. Major mining companies, such as Rio Tinto or Anglo American, tend to explore for a variety of major commodities, whereas smaller companies concentrate on one or two. An exploration strategy needs to fit in with company policy on the range of minerals and other deposits that it mines. It is particularly advantageous when an exploration target turns out to have profitable amounts of more than one metal. In practice, the exploration geologist is likely to be told which metal or type of mineral deposit to look for, and will be required to advise on likely locations to look for specific types of deposit.

Where do they look?

Another issue is to decide whether to explore in a new area or find further deposits in an existing mining area, ensuring that all available ore is worked out before a mine is abandoned.

An exploration programme designed to find new deposits is likely to be a large-scale operation, requiring a high level of understanding of the geological conditions under which such deposits form and how they can be recognized. However, just how much scientific understanding is necessary has long been debated within the industry. Arguably, the highest priority is for the exploration geologist to be well acquainted with the type of deposit targeted and the appropriate exploration techniques, which depend on the form of the deposit and on its physical and chemical properties. The traditional view has been that where one example of a particular deposit was known to exist, there would be more: 'it doesn't matter how they were formed, just go and find another.' However, it is increasingly accepted that understanding the origins of orebodies is important because certain types of deposit are more likely to be found in particular geological settings, or to have formed during particular periods of geological time (see Box 5.3). Similarly, areas least likely to yield positive results are excluded to lessen economic risk. All such information allows exploration programmes to be better focused and more cost-effective.

It is important to appreciate that *geological factors* dictate where to search for deposits of particular metal ores, but *technical, economic and political factors* determine whether or not the size and the grade of a particular deposit is worth mining.

- How would the minimum size of an ore deposit that could be mined profitably in an existing mining area compare with that in an undeveloped area?

- Where an infrastructure, including expensive transport networks and processing plants, already exists, then smaller, less-profitable deposits can be worked economically.

Box 5.3   The age and distribution of ore deposits

Geological processes have created an irregular global distribution of ore deposits. Evidence for this variability is widespread: it includes the platinum and chromium ores in the Bushveld region of South Africa (Section 2.2); the porphyry copper deposits in the volcanic arcs around the Pacific Ocean (Section 2.4); and the BIF deposits in ancient cratonic areas of the continents (Section 3.4). The distribution is irregular because ore deposits are formed under specific geological circumstances that have arisen at different places and at different times in the Earth's history. However, there is a common tendency for similar ore deposits to occur in areas of similar geological development and of a similar age. The old adage, 'If you want to find elephants, go to elephant country' applies. This principle is a valuable exploration guide for economic geologists.

Age dependence of ore deposits

Figure 5.7 demonstrates that certain types of deposit are found in rocks of restricted age range.

The following question will help to familiarize you with examples of deposits that have tended to be formed during certain periods of geological time, the reasons why they formed when they did, and why.

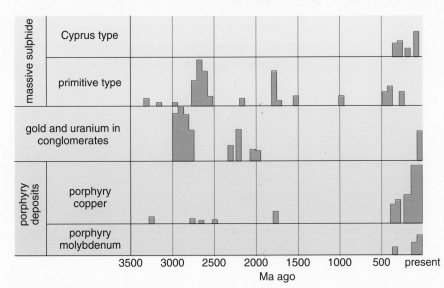

Figure 5.7   The geological ages of various type of ore deposit.

Question 5.2

Match the following series of *observations* (1–4) of age and occurrence of certain ore deposits with the *explanations* (a–d) below.

Observations

1 Banded iron formation deposits of iron ore occur in ancient rocks that are 1900–2500 Ma old.
2 Very few porphyry deposits of copper and molybdenum are older than 400 Ma; most are younger than 200 Ma.
3 Bauxite deposits are generally quite young; rarely are they older than 65 Ma.
4 Placer deposits of uranium are older than 2400 Ma.

Explanations

(a) Deposits formed at the Earth's surface on land are likely to be dispersed and destroyed by weathering and erosion, especially when uplift occurs.

(b) Before the Earth's atmosphere became rich in oxygen, certain metal ions liberated by weathering could have been transported in a reduced state. Precipitation to form sedimentary deposits occurred by oxidation in shallow seas that extended over large areas of early continental crust, which became stable cratons.

(c) These disseminated ore deposits tend to occur within and around the roof zones of granitic plutons. Over long periods of time, granite terranes tend to be uplifted due to their buoyancy and are eroded to great depths at levels where they are largely unmineralized.

(d) Oxygenation of the Earth's atmosphere occurred during the period 1700–2500 Ma ago, and conditions at the Earth's surface became more oxidizing. Particular mineral grains susceptible to breakdown by weathering and oxidation were not preserved at the Earth's surface once this occurred.

Answer   1 b   2 c   3 a   4 d ✓

Distribution of ore deposits

Ore deposits of a similar kind are sometimes grouped within a particular geographic region, often known as a **metallogenic province**. Hydrothermal ores of tin and tungsten (sometimes with copper) are associated with the granites of Cornwall, as well as other granites of similar age elsewhere in Europe. Together, they form a well-defined metallogenic province (Figure 5.8a). Other examples include the iron ore formations in Russia and Ukraine (Figure 3.10).

Another reason for regional localization of ore deposits is **inheritance**, whereby anomalously high concentrations of particular metals occur in certain regions of continental crust or the underlying mantle. Such concentrations can provide sources for mineral deposits to form repeatedly over long periods of time. This arises where a metal anomaly (deviation from background concentration levels) has been established and is reworked by igneous, hydrothermal and sedimentary processes, so that new deposits of the same metal keep appearing in the same region, but at different times. An excellent example is featured in Figure 5.8b, which shows one of the world's major nickel provinces in central Canada, and contains nickel deposits of four different ages. The oldest are associated with belts of ancient metamorphic rocks of basalt and peridotite composition (called 'greenstone belts'); the next are located around zones of faulting (e.g. at Thompson); then come the famous Sudbury deposits (Section 2.2.2), followed by a further set of deposits (at Duluth), both of which are associated with large gabbroic intrusions. The time span between the oldest and youngest of these deposits (Figure 5.8b) is 1500 Ma, which is about one-third of Earth history.

500 km

• Sn–W deposits

(a)

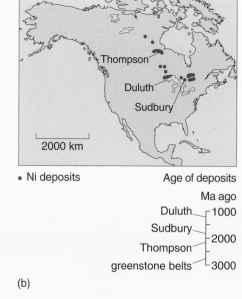

• Ni deposits

Age of deposits

Ma ago

Duluth — 1000
Sudbury — 2000
Thompson
greenstone belts — 3000

2000 km

(b)

Figure 5.8 (a) Distribution of tin–tungsten deposits in Western Europe. (b) Distribution and age of nickel deposits in central Canada.

The decision to set up an exploration programme and justify further investment must take account of many factors, including levels of royalties and taxes, as well as environmental constraints. An assessment of the likely risks is also required. The most obvious risk, and one directly related to the geology, is that, even in a favourable geological setting, a profitable deposit might not be found. In principle, the amount worth investing in exploration can be estimated on the basis of the likelihood of finding a deposit, how big that deposit might be, and the value per tonne of the extractable ore. The outcome of exploration in an established mining area is easier to judge than that in a remote, less well-known region. The chances of making a profitable discovery in an unexplored area and the value of metals that might be present per square kilometre can only be estimated from an assessment of the distribution of ore deposits and production records in a geologically similar, but well-established mining areas.

It is not unusual for companies to undertake major exploration programmes in which the chances of finding a profitable deposit are quite low, with a success rate of perhaps 1 in 200 to 1 in 500. With long lead times, even if exploration is successful and a mine is opened, it might be 10 years or more before an operating profit is made (Figure 1.3), so these are clearly medium- to long-term, high-risk investments.

5.3   Exploration programmes

Until the late 19th century, most ore deposits were discovered by a combination of luck and the experience or 'instinct' of prospectors who had little or no formal training in geology. Indeed, a close look at the records of many major mines reveals that they were found as a result of individuals making direct observations of rocks and soils on the ground. However, most of the more easily discoverable deposits have already been found, and new, hidden deposits are more difficult to find by direct means. To compensate, a great deal more is now known about how and where ore deposits occur. The modern exploration geologist has access to geological maps; to rapidly increasing amounts of ground-imaging data from aircraft and satellites; and to sophisticated geophysical and geochemical techniques for detecting orebodies. Often, favourable areas for exploration can be selected without leaving the office.

Once the metal and the type of mineral deposit to be targeted have been established on the basis of company expertise, market constraints and so on, there are several stages to follow in a typical exploration programme.

1   *Desk studies* (Section 5.4) identify broad areas where deposits are likely to occur. They are based initially on an understanding of the geological settings in which different orebodies form and on information compiled from geological maps, satellite images, and any available exploration studies, national surveys and databases.

2   *Reconnaissance exploration surveys* (Section 5.5) on a regional scale (thousands of square kilometres) are designed to identify the most promising areas for more detailed survey. They might include airborne geophysics, regional field mapping, and geochemical stream sampling. All these activities involve personnel and costly equipment, so this is when exploration costs start to rise, but are still relatively low per square kilometre.

3   *Localized exploration surveys* (Sections 5.6 and 5.7) of promising areas (tens of square kilometres) aim to identify potential orebodies. They involve largely ground-based studies, such as detailed field mapping, ground-based geophysics, and geochemical analysis of soil samples, to identify specific targets worthy of further investigation. Most of these methods are labour- and equipment-intensive and costs per square kilometre are high.

4   *Testing* (Section 5.8) of favourable targets by drilling, trenching, and geophysical logging, followed by *evaluation* in order to define the size of a deposit. These are very costly operations and are practical only over specific and promising targets. Drilling costs are particularly high (around US$10 000–12 000 per 100 metres in 2005).

At every stage of mineral exploration and mine development, costs become greater (Figure 5.2). Risk analysis is necessary at each stage to assess whether the information available justifies progressing to the next stage or whether the risks are too great and the programme should be stopped. Once testing and evaluation is complete, feasibility studies can be undertaken to assess all the factors that would influence the viability and profitability of the operation before development gets the go-ahead.

5.4 Desk studies — regional targeting

The first step in an exploration programme is to select an area for exploration, which could be an area that is geologically similar to existing mining areas. Next, existing information, such as maps, reports and records of earlier mining operations, is collated, and a geological interpretation of the factors controlling mineralization (as described earlier in Chapters 2, 3 and 4) is applied to these data.

Question 5.3

In which of the geological settings (1–3) might you consider searching for each of the types of deposit (a–c)?

Geological setting

1   Relatively undisturbed sedimentary rocks in ancient continental interiors.
2   A large, layered, gabbroic igneous intrusion in ancient continental crust.
3   Ancient oceanic crust with pillow lavas and ocean-floor sediments.

Type of deposit

(a) Massive sulphide deposits of copper, zinc and lead.
(b) Magmatic segregation deposits of chromite.
(c) High-grade haematite deposits in banded ironstone formations.

Ans:— 1c   2b   3a
a3   b2   c1

You saw in Chapters 2 and 3 that certain metals tend to occur in higher concentrations in particular rocks, and that the occurrence of certain rock types can be indicative of specific ore deposits. Thus, the location of appropriate rock types can also help to direct exploration geologists to favourable areas.

Question 5.4

Ore deposits of nickel, tin, uranium and titanium occur in various types of crustal rocks.

(a) Which of these ore deposits would tend to be associated with (i) granitic rocks and (ii) gabbroic rocks?
(b) For which of these metals would you prospect for ore minerals in sand and gravel deposits of modern stream channels?

Refer back to Chapters 2 and 3 to help you with your answers.

Knowledge about mineralizing processes is useful, but it is not possible to predict *exactly* where ore deposits are located. This is why systematic exploration is necessary. For example, volcanic arc settings (associated with modern or extinct subduction zones) are the best places to look for large-scale copper mineralization. Porphyry copper deposits may occur as stockwork vein systems associated with granodioritic rocks where hydrothermal fluids have extensively altered the minerals of the host rock (Chapter 2); but it is not always possible to know why some granodiorites are mineralized, whereas others in similar geological settings are not.

One form of desk study has become increasingly important since the 1970s — that of gathering information obtained from a distance by aircraft and satellites. This is known as **remote sensing**.

Remote sensing

Making maps, whether topographic or geological, once relied solely on ground surveys with theodolites, compasses and measuring chains. Surface mapping is still important, but since the 1930s much mapping has used photographs from aircraft and, more recently, electronically captured images from satellites. The use of high-precision satellite navigation systems has supplanted much of the precise positioning through conventional surveying by an even more precise form of geographical location. The Global Positioning System (GPS), developed for the US military, makes it possible to define locations anywhere on Earth to within 10 m horizontally and 5 m vertically (sometimes even less). Accurate location is important in field surveys and in airborne surveys where large amounts of data are acquired rapidly and height positioning is important. Then, using computer data-handling and drawing procedures, maps of any kind can be produced very quickly, at relatively low cost. Various types of data can also be integrated with spatial mapping on computers using *Geospatial Information Systems* (GIS).

An aerial or satellite photographic image contains much more information than most maps, since it records everything — topography, vegetation, soil cover, rock outcrops, roads and buildings. Box 5.4 illustrates how rapid geological interpretation is possible.

Since the 1960s, many of the limitations of aerial photography have been overcome by using parts of the electromagnetic spectrum that are invisible to the human eye. Information about natural features is carried by infrared radiation as well as by visible light. Surface materials not only *reflect* radiation, they also absorb it (and heat up). On cooling, they *emit* different wavelengths of radiation according to their composition. Thus, information about different kinds of surface material can be obtained by recording the reflected and emitted electromagnetic spectrum radiating from the surface and by measuring the strength of the different wavelengths. By using computers to analyse and combine these measurements, visible false-colour images can be produced that reveal areas with distinctive characteristics. As a result, some rock-forming minerals in soils and rocks (diagnostic of some mineralization processes), as well as different kinds of vegetation, can now be distinguished. Remote sensing can be used for both geological mapping and the detection of particular geological features that might relate to mineral deposits.

Porphyry-type deposits with areas of low-grade mineralization can be detected directly by remote sensing in arid areas because of the weathering of sulphide minerals. Sometimes soils are bleached because soluble iron(II) has been

Box 5.4   Remote sensing interpretation

Figure 5.9a is a Landsat Thematic Mapper satellite image of part of the Bushveld Igneous Complex in South Africa (Section 2.2). The map is a false-colour map created by assigning three spectral bands of the electromagnetic radiation detected at visible and non-visible wavelengths to the colours red, green and blue. Landsat images are a very useful way of examining the geology of an area, especially as some global data are freely available on the internet. Each individual pixel making up the image represents an area of 28.5 m × 28.5 m, so the resolution is fairly coarse. At first sight, the surface appears

extremely complex. This is not surprising as it is a mixture of vegetated areas and rock outcrops set in a rugged, dissected landscape that is shadowed by the Sun. Several geological features control the form of the rock outcrop patterns. Image interpretation relies on the recognition of different combinations of colour, tone, image texture and patterns, and then relates them to geological features.

Figure 5.9b is a geological interpretation of the Landsat image in Figure 5.9a. The dark area trending NW–SE

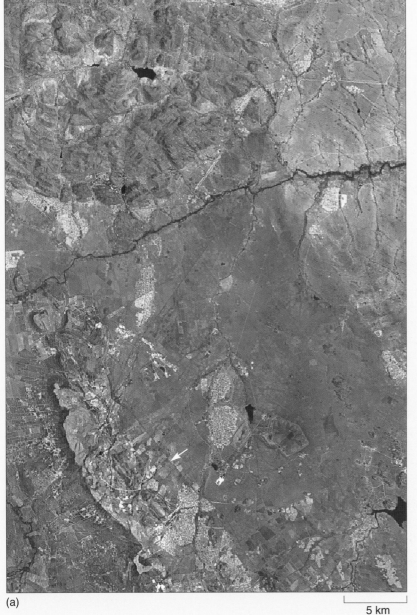

(a)

5 km

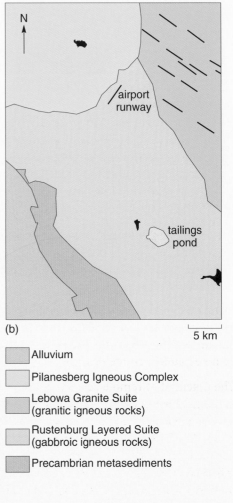

(b)

5 km

Alluvium

Pilanesberg Igneous Complex

Lebowa Granite Suite
(granitic igneous rocks)

Rustenburg Layered Suite
(gabbroic igneous rocks)

Precambrian metasediments

Figure 5.9   (a) Landsat false-colour image of part of the Bushveld Igneous Complex in South Africa. (b) Geological interpretation of image (a).

across the centre of the image is the igneous Rustenburg Layered Suite. Although the rocks are strongly layered, there is no trace of this on the image as the rocks have weathered to a thick, black soil. The layered rocks dip to the northeast; at the base are the Merensky and Upper Group 2 reefs, layers of chromite ore that produce much of the world's platinum supply. The only traces of these horizons are the mining developments, particularly the associated water supplies and tailings ponds that show up as black and purple areas respectively. To the NE, the Rustenburg Layered Suite has an apparently gradational contact with a light-toned area of granitic rocks, the Lebowa Granite Suite.

To the SW of the layered rocks is a narrow area of high relief that also trends NW–SE, and has a very different tone. These are Precambrian sedimentary strata, which have been intruded and metamorphosed by the adjacent igneous rocks. The ridges are formed by quartzites.

The Rustenburg Layered Suite is cut by a large circular feature to the NW. It is clearly intrusive (cross-cutting), but its nature can only be determined from the ground. The feature is the largely granitic Pilanesberg Igneous Complex.

The Lebowa Granite Suite is cut by linear features not shown in the key to Figure 5.9b. They could be faults, or fracture zones, picked out by erosion. In fact, they are basaltic igneous dykes that also intrude the

Pilanesberg Igneous Complex, but their composition could only be known by direct observation of the rocks on the ground or by more sophisticated forms of remote sensing.

- There are other linear features on the image that appear to cut through all the geological units such as the feature arrowed on Figure 5.9a. What do think this feature is?

- It is a railway.

There are a large number of cultural features on the image, including roads, shanty towns and an airport. This airport serves the Sun City entertainment complex, which is situated at the edge of the Pilanesberg Igneous Complex.

You may not have seen all these features easily, but you should have seen some of them. The geological interpretation (Figure 5.9b) was made in about 30 minutes by an experienced photo interpreter, without undergoing any fieldwork. To make the same map by traditional ground-based surveys would have taken at least a week. However, it is still essential to establish 'ground truth', that is, to *prove* the nature of particular types of feature on the image by local ground observation and mapping, but once established, principles can be applied across the whole area.

removed by solution in acidic reducing fluids. At other times a highly coloured capping or gossan of insoluble iron(III) minerals may form, resulting from oxidation of iron-rich sulphides. Both effects result in a visible anomaly that can be detected by remote sensing.

The potential of remote sensing is primarily economic. On average, a geologist in the field using traditional mapping methods would take upwards of 100 days to produce a simple map of an area of 100 square kilometres at a scale of l:100 000. This could cost in the region of US$200 000. Using satellite imagery, the same area could be mapped to the same level of detail in around 10 days at less than one-tenth of the cost, depending on the degree of vegetation cover and rock exposure. Remote sensing is most effective in arid and semi-arid areas, although in humid areas vegetation may show anomalies as a result of mineralization-induced geochemical stress on plants. Moreover, by using information that simply cannot be seen in the field, either because it is invisible or because it is on too large a scale to be grasped from the ground, much more detail can emerge. In addition, the satellite 'sees' the whole area, while the geologist cannot visit every location.

5.5   Regional reconnaissance surveys

In order to follow up desk studies and define a target for detailed study, the exploration geologist must go into the field or commission other forms of surveying over regions identified as being of interest. This is when exploration costs begin to rise substantially (Figure 5.2). Several techniques are suited to regional-scale exploration. In many developed countries, national geological surveys provide regional geophysical and geochemical reconnaissance data that can be considered alongside remotely sensed data and geological maps, making this stage of exploration essentially a continuation of the initial desk study.

5.5.1   Geophysical techniques

Geophysical techniques lend themselves to automated data gathering and, like remote sensing, are applicable to large area surveys. They also give useful results over areas where surface exposures of bedrock are minimal. Magnetic, electromagnetic, radiometric and gravity surveys are rapid and relatively inexpensive per square kilometre especially as measurements can be made from aircraft. Note that some geophysical techniques are best at detecting differences in the physical properties of large volumes of rock, and may be best at detecting particular rock types associated with ore deposits rather than the deposits themselves.

Magnetic surveys measure the Earth's magnetic field, which is locally distorted by the magnetism in rocks caused by the magnetization of magnetically susceptible minerals. Only three reasonably common minerals, normally present in rocks as accessory minerals, are sufficiently magnetized by the Earth's magnetic field to produce a measurable magnetic response. In order of decreasing magnetic strength or *susceptibility*, they are magnetite (Fe_3O_4), ilmenite ($FeTiO_3$), and pyrrhotite (FeS). Consequently, magnetic variations reflect the presence of particularly iron-rich rocks, such as basalt, that typically contain significant amounts of these magnetic minerals.

Electromagnetic surveys are based on a phenomenon known as electromagnetic (EM) induction. This is what happens when two adjacent conductive circuits interact. First, an electrical current flowing in a conductor produces an electromagnetic field, and then the interaction of that EM radiation with another conductor induces an alternating current. As most sulphide and a few oxide ore minerals are good electrical conductors compared with common rocks, it is possible to exploit their capacity for EM induction and to detect them in orebodies — providing the long-wavelength EM radiation can penetrate to the depth of the orebody.

EM surveys involve traversing the search area with two coils: a primary (transmitting) coil and a search (receiving) coil. The search coil is tuned to detect the secondary electromagnetic field created by any conducting geological structure, such as an orebody. The same principle is exploited on a smaller scale in the metal detectors used by treasure hunters and by the military to detect land-mines. The EM method is particularly sensitive to native metals and massive sulphide deposits. Surveys can be conducted from the air or on the ground. The signal from the search coil is recorded electronically and, by flying in a 'grid' of parallel straight lines, builds up a map of EM response.

● Why would airborne magnetic or EM surveys be of little use in the exploration of porphyry ore deposits?

○ Porphyry deposits are low grade and disseminated. Irrespective of the magnetic or electrical properties of the ore minerals they contain, any effects would be diluted by common non-conducting minerals.

Radiometric surveys measure the intensities of gamma rays produced by the radioactive decay of certain uranium, thorium and potassium isotopes. Airborne surveys reveal variations in the concentrations of these elements at the Earth's surface; they can detect local enrichments due to mineralization, but more generally reflect the U, Th and K geochemistry of different rock types. Such surveys can often provide surprisingly detailed and accurate mapping of rock lithologies.

Gravity surveys measure variations in the Earth's gravitational field and, therefore, indicate differences in the density of rocks at or close to the Earth's surface. The results are usually corrected for topography and displayed in image form showing deviations from the gravitational pull that would be expected at the Earth's surface (without density variations) — thus revealing rocks of abnormal density in the upper parts of the crust. An area of high (positive) gravity values indicates relatively high-density rocks; low (negative) gravity values indicate relatively low-density rocks.

5.5.2 Geochemical methods

Rock samples from the field can be analysed geochemically to measure the abundance of just about every element of the Periodic Table that they contain, but geochemical analysis is expensive, requiring laboratories with specialized equipment and skilled operators.

● Would it be desirable to base a regional exploration survey on the geochemical analysis of exposed bedrock?

○ The mineralization might be localized and may not even be exposed, especially if the area is largely covered by soil and vegetation. So, analysis of bedrock samples is unlikely to be helpful without continuous exposure and a high sampling density, which would be extremely expensive.

It would be far better to analyse fewer samples, if each were to represent the mineralization of a large area. How could this form of sampling be possible? The answer is revealed by considering processes that are active at the Earth's surface.

● What happens naturally to rocks (and ore deposits) exposed at the Earth's surface?

○ They are subject to weathering, which breaks up rocks. Some (resistant) minerals may be released, others may be chemically decomposed, to form soils and sediments; and soluble materials may be distributed in surface and ground waters (Section 3.1). The effect is to *disperse* elements more widely, especially those occurring as local concentrations.

The products of weathering are soils, sediments and soluble material in solution. When an orebody is weathered, high concentrations of metals end up in the weathering products and are distributed by surface processes (as described in Box 5.5). This dispersion can provide samples that reflect the bedrock chemistry of a large area and contain a compositional *signature* of any orebody present — which is just what is needed in a geochemical exploration survey.

Box 5.5 Geochemical dispersion

An ore deposit is rather like a needle in a haystack — very small but very anomalous. Most deposits are tiny (only a few hundreds of metres across and very rarely extending for a kilometre or more) compared to the size of the areas in which they are sought. The larger parts of most deposits are probably buried, although at depths much greater than about 1 km they may not be economic anyway. Various geological processes, however, help to reveal ore deposits by dispersing the high concentrations of metallic elements into much larger volumes of rock or surface material. This process is called **geochemical dispersion**, and it produces a dispersed anomaly that is more extensive and easier to find than a localized anomaly due to an orebody itself (Section 5.5.2). Two forms are recognized:

- *primary dispersion*, due to the geological processes associated with the development of an ore deposit itself;

- *secondary dispersion*, occurring as a result of weathering processes and groundwater movement long after an ore deposit has formed.

Secondary dispersion includes the transportation of ore mineral grains or metal ions in surface drainage water, soil, wind-blown sand, and glacial deposits. In addition, plants may absorb certain elements to anomalously high levels, leading to stunted growth or the survival of only metal-tolerant species.

Porphyry-type ore deposits provide good examples of primary geochemical dispersion because the fluids involved in the mineralization process (Section 2.4) penetrate the surrounding rocks for hundreds of metres and give rise to relatively high concentrations of many metals. Figure 5.10 shows anomalous concentrations of metals arranged as concentric zones to form a 'bull's-eye' effect around an orebody. Such dispersed anomalies extend well beyond the actual deposit, thereby enlarging the exploration target. Zones of primary dispersion around a porphyry deposit are usually subjected to secondary dispersion processes that further enlarge the area in which anomalous metal values are detectable.

Some circumstances of secondary dispersion are shown in Figure 5.11. Two important points are worth bearing in mind:

- secondary dispersion can involve solutions or solid particles — and soluble elements in solution usually travel much further than mineral grains;

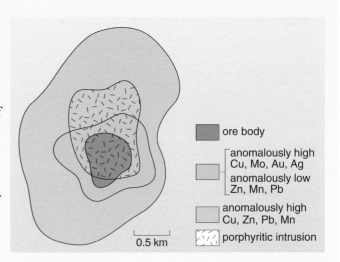

Figure 5.10 Plan of the 'bull's-eye' effect associated with primary dispersed metal anomalies centred on a porphyry orebody.

- water is the most efficient agent of transportation.

A stream or river flowing over a metalliferous deposit (Figure 5.11a) can pick up ore mineral grains and take metal ions into solution and transport them downstream. Anomalous metal concentrations reduce progressively downstream owing to dilution with barren sediment and uncontaminated water entering from tributaries. On entering a lake, grains settle out due to reduction in flow and dissolved metals may be precipitated from solution, but in many cases stream water anomalies persist downstream.

The dispersion pattern in Figure 5.11b is typical of the smearing effect of ice movement preserved in glacial deposits, where there may be 'trails' of mineral grains and mineralized rock fragments leading back to the deposit, sometimes extending for tens or even hundreds of kilometres.

In Figure 5.11c, moisture containing soluble metal ions moves upwards by capillary action to form a 'halo' of anomalous soil chemistry, which may in turn be absorbed by vegetation.

In Figure 5.11d, weathering of the deposit has contributed anomalous levels of metals to the overlying soil. The slope causes the soil to creep slowly downhill, producing a displaced surface anomaly.

In Figure 5.11e, groundwater within permeable rocks flows downslope through a buried mineral deposit and carries away dissolved metals. If it then returns to the surface as a spring or in a swamp, the surrounding vegetation and soil may concentrate the metals from solution and develop geochemical anomalies. With this form of dispersion, geochemical anomalies can also be recognized by analysing water taken from wells downslope of the deposit, as well as from the spring or swamp itself.

The final point to consider here concerns the form of ore deposits and their ease of detection.

Confined and dispersed deposits were discussed in Section 1.3. Which type would be easier to find by geochemical reconnaissance sampling, and why?

The metals in dispersed deposits are widely disseminated over large areas, so elevated levels of metals or other diagnostic elements would be difficult to miss. In contrast, although concentrations of metals in a confined deposit are likely to be extremely high locally, they are also very restricted, and the corresponding geochemical anomaly might be more easily missed. Dispersed deposits, therefore, are more likely to be detected in regional geochemistry surveys because the density of measurements is commonly around 0.5 to 2 samples per square kilometre.

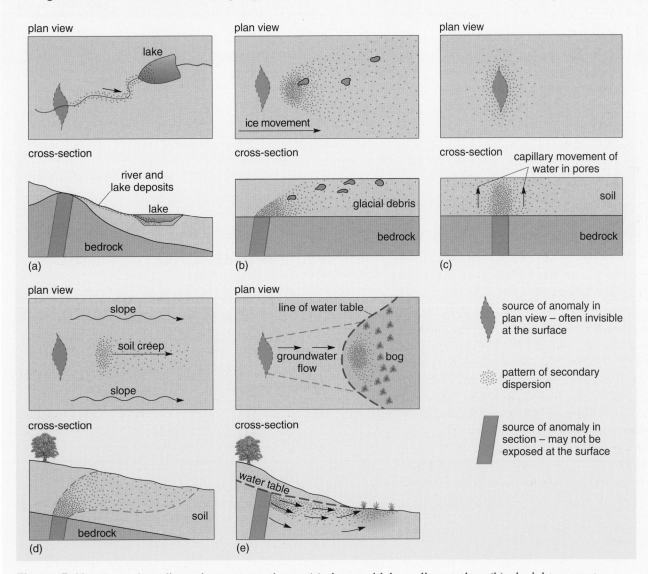

Figure 5.11   Secondary dispersion patterns due to (a) river and lake sedimentation; (b) glacial transport; (c) movement of water in soil; (d) soil creep; (e) groundwater flow.

● In what circumstances would it be more favourable to analyse (i) stream water, and (ii) stream sediment samples?

◑ (i) Stream water analyses are suitable for detecting soluble metal ions that are taken into solution when ore minerals are weathered. Water moves faster and further than sediment, so water samples represent a wider area of dispersal.

(ii) Stream sediment analyses are suitable for detecting ore minerals that are stable (or form stable products on weathering). Sediments move less readily than waters and are better for targeting sources. They also provide important information about the minerals present in a deposit.

5.6 Localized geophysical surveys

Some geophysical techniques used for regional surveys, such as gravity and EM, can be carried out with more precision on the ground as a way of pin-pointing buried rocks with unusual properties. These are essentially *passive* techniques, detecting natural phenomena, whereas others, particularly electrical methods, involve *actively* applying an energy supply to the ground.

5.6.1 Electrical surveys

There are a number of methods of electrical surveying. They either make use of naturally occurring electrical fields within the Earth or require an electrical current to be applied to the ground.

Resistivity surveys detect variations in the electrical conductivity of rocks underground. Conduction of electricity in rocks depends directly on their resistivity (conductivity is the inverse of resistivity). Although electrical resistivity values for common rocks and minerals vary over several orders of magnitude (Figure 5.12), most rock-forming minerals are good insulators because they have high resistivity, as do most rocks. However, many rocks have interconnected pores and cracks that contain water (when below the water table), and water normally contains charged ions, especially if the water is saline, acidic or alkaline, which allows electrical currents to flow by the movement of the charged ions. The resistivity of a body of rock depends, therefore, both on its porosity and on the chemistry of the pore water. As a result, the conductivity of most rocks is essentially that of the water occupying the interstices of an insulating material.

Some mineral deposits conduct electricity better than the surrounding rock because they contain sulphide ore minerals, which generally are better conductors (except for sphalerite) than most rock-forming minerals

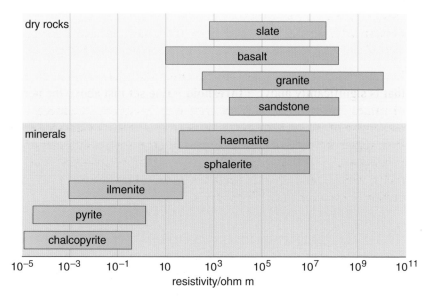

Figure 5.12 Resistivity values for some common rocks and ore minerals.

(Figure 5.12). Resistivity surveys rarely identify ore deposits directly, but can help build up a picture of subsurface geology that helps define a deposit.

Induced polarization (IP) surveys depend on the charge induced in conductive minerals when subjected to a powerful electric field. It measures the ability of some rocks to charge up more readily than others. Passing an electric current at high voltage through the ground induces a polarity in minerals, rather like charging a battery. After the current is switched off, a small current flows in the reverse direction and there is a short time period during which the electrical potential decays (Figure 5.13). This time period is a measure of the *chargeability* of the rocks, and hence the amount of conductive minerals, mainly sulphides, in the ground. Chargeability depends only on the presence of conductive grains — they do not have to be in electrical continuity — so IP works well for detecting many kinds of sulphide deposit, whether the orebody is massive (continuous) or disseminated (dispersed) — as is the case with porphyry deposits. Although IP surveys are more expensive than many other ground-based geophysical techniques, they are widely used in the search for sulphide ores.

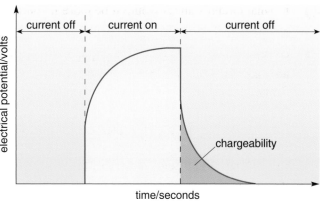

Figure 5.13 Electrical potential plotted against time to show the effect of induced polarization when a high voltage is applied to the ground. The green area is a measure of the chargeability of the rock.

5.7 Localized geochemical methods

Whereas geophysical techniques can locate rocks with particular characteristics, including potential ore deposits, proving a deposit requires direct sampling and mineralogical or geochemical analysis. Rocks, soils, water and vegetation in the vicinity of an ore deposit commonly become enriched in ore metals or associated elements as a result of a variety of surface processes (Section 5.5.2). Geochemical exploration is the systematic search for unusual or anomalous concentrations of elements in these surface materials, with the aim of locating any ore deposits nearby or beneath the surface.

In exploration terms, a **geochemical anomaly** is a concentration of an element that is significantly above a **threshold value** set just above the normal range of values for an area, which are known as **background concentrations**. The magnitude of an anomaly and the background value for any element varies from region to region and according to whether rock, soil, water or vegetation is being analysed. Metals are often present at trace abundances in common rocks, which means that they must be detected and measured at parts per million or even parts per billion levels.

Activity 5.1

Figure 5.14a presents the results of a copper analysis on 100 soil samples taken at evenly spaced intervals across a 900 m × 900 m grid. The purpose of this exercise is to identify areas of anomalously high copper concentrations that might be worth following up in the next stage of an exploration programme.

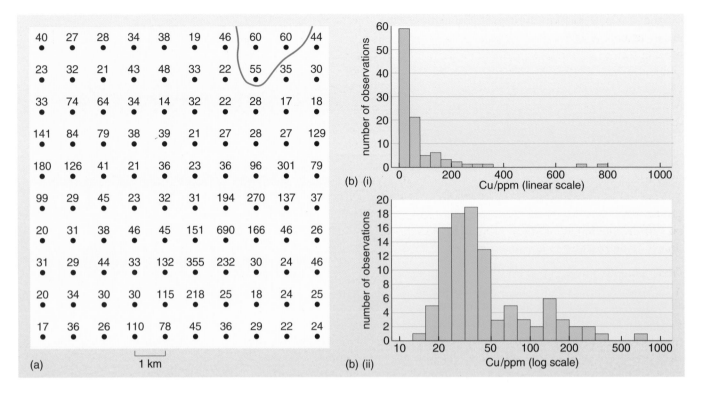

In a geochemical survey, the distribution of elemental data is often analysed using a histogram of the sampled concentrations. Histograms are simply bar charts where the height of a column represents the number of measurements that occupy a particular part of the concentration range. A linear division of the concentration axis tends to compress background and lower anomalous concentration data, making it difficult to define a threshold (Figure 5.14b(i)). A solution is to first convert the data using a logarithmic function. From the histogram of logarithmic values (Figure 5.14b(ii)), it is easier to pick a natural break in the data as a threshold and use this to suggest which areas have anomalous levels of copper.

Figure 5.14 (a) Copper concentrations (ppm) in soil in a gridded geochemical reconnaissance survey for use with Activity 5.1. (b) Histograms of copper values: (i) linear scale; (ii) logarithmic scale.

Identify concentrations in Figure 5.14b(ii) at which you could justify setting a threshold.

Possible thresholds chosen could be around 50 ppm or 200 ppm. The lower threshold is the most obvious, eliminating the bulk of the normal values, i.e. background concentrations (<50 ppm). The higher threshold recognizes only the highest concentrations as anomalous.

(a) To examine the consequences of both options, outline on Figure 5.14a the areas where copper concentrations in soil exceed: (i) 50 ppm (*note*: one area has already been done for you) and (ii) 200 ppm.

(b) Your plans for further exploration might differ according to the level of threshold chosen. What effect would the choice of threshold have on the area identified for follow-up studies?

(c) What are the implications, in terms of cost and targeting of mineralization, of choosing the higher threshold?

Where possible, concentrations of metals that are the objects of exploration are measured directly, as in the case of copper in Figure 5.14. However, some elements, such as gold, can be difficult to sample and measure at very low concentrations. Thus, it is common practice to analyse rocks or sediments for closely associated elements, known as **pathfinder elements**. Arsenic (As), bismuth (Bi), mercury (Hg) and antimony (Sb) are frequently used as pathfinder elements for gold.

5.7.1   Drainage surveys

In drainage surveys, the geochemical composition of water or stream sediment at a particular point reflects the composition of rocks, soils, sediments and groundwater of the *upstream* catchment area draining through that point. The size of the catchment area represented by a drainage sample tends to increase downstream because increasing numbers of tributaries enter the channel.

Geochemical dispersion affects both stream water and stream sediments, and a geochemical survey may sample either or both. These surveys provide an effective means of indirectly sampling soils and bedrock from a large area. Drainage waters and sediments are easy to sample with minimal equipment, most areas are crossed by numerous drainage channels and stream beds are likely to sample bedrock. In densely vegetated areas (e.g. tropical rain forest), they may be the only easy means of access. Sampling a stream nearer its source has a lower probability of detecting a geochemical anomaly than downstream. Once an anomaly is found it can be traced upstream.

● Why would the magnitude of both stream sediment and water geochemical anomalies tend to decrease downstream as more tributaries join the stream being sampled?

○ The more tributaries carrying background levels of metals that join the stream, the more dilute any stream sediment or water anomaly becomes.

However, any anomalous metal contents in solution depend on both the solubility of the metal ions released on weathering and on the chemistry (including pH) of the water. Changes in water chemistry can cause dissolved ions to be precipitated onto the stream bed. This prevents an anomaly from spreading further downstream, and may even produce false anomalies. Thus, drainage water surveys are not as reliable as drainage sediment surveys. Although water may transport soluble elements over greater distances than it could sediments, the metal contents of solutions are harder to interpret than minerals in sediments.

The distances to which processes involved in geochemical dispersion are able to transport various elements is an important consideration when deciding which elements to look for and how to interpret data from both water and sediment samples. The aims of a geochemical survey are to detect a geochemical anomaly and (assuming the anomaly relates to secondary dispersion) to trace the source of the anomaly. An important aspect of any anomaly is its **persistence** (that is, how far from its source it can be detected).

● The persistence of a geochemical anomaly depends on several factors. What factors do you think might be important in determining the persistence of geochemical anomalies in (i) sediment and (ii) water?

◔ (i) In sediment samples (containing mineral grains), persistence depends on the density of the key minerals (i.e. how easily they are deposited), on their hardness (how easily they can be broken into fine grains and carried in suspension) and on their chemical stability (how easily they break down to new minerals and/or soluble products).

(ii) In water samples, persistence depends on how the prevailing water conditions change to affect the solubility of metal ions and the stability of ionic metal complexes.

Question 5.5

Comment on whether the persistence of a stream *sediment* anomaly is likely to be high or low in the case of these examples:
(a) a low-density, easily broken mineral;
(b) a high-density, hard mineral;
(c) a low-density, chemically unstable mineral.

Minerals or elements that exhibit different levels of persistence can provide both reconnaissance and more localized information. An element with high persistence that is detectable over a wide area indicates the presence of mineralization within a catchment area whereas an element with low persistence records an anomaly from a relatively small area, which helps to pinpoint the source of the anomaly. In practice, if sampling of the main drainage from a catchment area looks promising, samples are taken progressively upstream at the inflow of each tributary and the search is directed along promising tributaries until a point is reached where anomalous levels give way to background values. This *cut-off point* (Figure 5.15 and Question 5.6) marks the source of the anomaly.

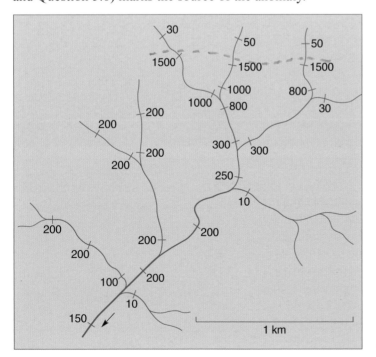

Figure 5.15 A drainage system showing copper concentrations (in ppm) in the stream sediments.

Question 5.6

Examine Figure 5.15 and trace the anomalous levels of copper upstream to identify the cut-off points. Show where you might expect to find a copper orebody. What form would it have?

5.7.2   Soil surveys

A basic assumption in soil geochemical surveys is that soil is derived more or less directly from underlying bedrock.

● How localized will a soil geochemical anomaly be compared with a stream sediment anomaly?

◐ Free-flowing water in streams can transport mineral grains for great distances, creating extensive anomalies. In soils, an anomaly would be more restricted in extent and located closer to the orebody.

In practice, however, soils are complex. Forms of dispersion include downslope movement of solid material (Figure 5.11d), and the addition of material transported and precipitated from groundwaters (Figure 5.11c and e). The soil may also be derived from transported sediment such as glacial till, as shown in Figure 5.11b, where a 'trail' of mineralized material leads back to its source. Moreover, all soils have a layered structure, and the form of layering depends on climatic and chemical factors. Some layers can be 'leached' of their soluble elements (Section 3.3.1) and might appear barren even if situated close to an orebody. Other layers, such as those associated with residual tropical soils, may concentrate elements well above their levels in underlying rocks, so giving misleading anomalies.

The first stage in a soil survey is to determine the source of the locally derived soils and to select a soil layer that is most representative of bedrock geochemistry. Owing to the complexity of soils, soil surveys are more appropriate when following up reconnaissance surveys. They are usually organized on a regular, closely spaced grid and often accompany ground-based geophysical surveys. In densely forested areas, plants can also be sampled to detect their take-up of metal ions from soil.

5.7.3   Rock geochemistry

Obtaining geochemical data for a rock sample usually involves crushing and powdering the sample to homogenize it, followed by laboratory procedures to obtain an elemental analysis. This is both time-consuming and costly, and the data represent only the composition of the rock mass from which the sample was taken. However, rock analysis is an essential part of evaluation when exploration has already identified a promising target.

5.8   Testing and evaluation

Once an exploration program has revealed geochemical and/or geophysical anomalies that point to the presence of a mineral deposit, the next stage is to determine the extent of the deposit. This involves physically intersecting the deposit at and beneath the surface and assessing any mineralization. Drilling is expensive, so surface sampling (including digging pits and trenches to expose bedrock) is undertaken first to determine the best locations at which to drill and test for depth extensions of the mineralization.

- Based on your knowledge of exploration methods, which sampling and evaluation procedures would most likely be used in:

    (i) an arid area of South America with good rock outcrop?

    (ii) an area of central Africa covered by thick soil?

    (iii) an area of northern Canada covered by thick glacial till?

- Depending on the depth of overburden, sampling would involve:

    (i) mapping, sampling and undertaking rock geochemical analysis;

    (ii) digging a trench or pit down, if possible, to the bedrock or undertaking shallow drilling;

    (iii) drilling down to the bedrock or the base of the glacial till — glacial materials are normally too thick for pitting.

Once the nature of the mineralization and the size and shape of the deposit at the surface have been established, drilling can begin. The object of the initial drilling on mineralized outcrops is to intersect the mineralization at shallow depth so as to understand the geological controls on the mineralization and its probable subsurface shape.

- How might the 3-D form and grade of a deposit be determined?

- By geochemical analysis of a 3-D array of samples obtained by drilling.

Drilling, retrieval of drill cuttings or core samples, and assay for their metal contents provide the simplest method of determining the grade of a mineral deposit. Drilling on a grid pattern, with sampling at regular depth intervals, is necessary to generate a 3-D model of the deposit for use in evaluating the distribution of grades and in planning mine development. Figure 1.10 shows simplified models of this kind that are contoured for grade. Because of the high cost of drilling, a few preliminary boreholes may be drilled so that the best orientation and spacing of the detailed sampling grid can be planned. Here, geological knowledge is important.

- What might the drilling strategy be for (i) a dispersed porphyry-type deposit; (ii) a vertically orientated confined massive sulphide deposit only 50 m thick?

- (i) For a dispersed deposit, where the grade varies gradually over a considerable area, widely spaced drill holes would be adequate (Figure 5.16a). These should be drilled vertically to intersect any zone of secondary enrichment (aligned with the water table), rather like the Inspiration Deposit (Section 3.3.2).

    (ii) A close-spaced pattern of drilling would be required to define a confined deposit. Vertical drill holes might well miss a vertically oriented or steeply inclined deposit only 50 m thick. Inclined drilling to intersect the body at different depths would be preferable (Figure 5.16b).

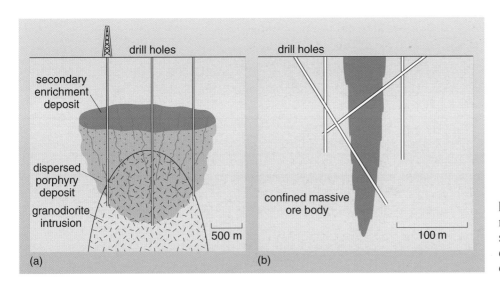

Figure 5.16 Schematic representation of drilling strategies for (a) a dispersed deposit and (b) a vertically oriented confined deposit.

5.9 Feasibility studies

Without evidence that a certain amount of mineralization at a given grade exists and can be mined economically, a mining venture would not be given the go-ahead. All the data obtained from drilling and surface work need to be integrated to decide whether or not a deposit can be mined for profit. Different forms of mining, depending on the form and location of the deposit, have different cost implications (as detailed in Section 6.1.1).

Preliminary investigations of the technical and engineering problems associated with mining and ore processing are important when assessing mining costs. Feasibility studies are carried out to determine, for example, efficient ore processing procedures and the energy requirements needed to derive ore mineral concentrates. Box 5.6 briefly examines the feasibility of mining a gold prospect at Cononish in Scotland.

During evaluation, the costs of setting up the mining infrastructure must also be taken into account. Several questions then arise, such as how accessible is the area? Will a new road, railway or port have to be built? Is there an electricity supply in the area or will power generation be needed? Is there a local water supply or will water have to be piped in? Will the operation need to be self-sufficient or can food and spare parts be obtained locally? Can operations continue throughout the year or does the climate prohibit work during some seasons? What laws govern pollution control during mining and the eventual restoration of the mine area? Are there sites where waste can be dumped cheaply, safely and legally? Who owns the adjoining land and will they hinder development? Is there an indigenous skilled workforce or will a mine township have to be built for immigrant labour? What wages are necessary to attract suitable personnel? The list goes on and on, even to the extent of investigating the best lubricant for vehicles under the prevailing climatic conditions.

The economics of mining are an essential part of evaluation and depend not only on local circumstances but also on metal price and world markets. As metal prices and other factors change with time, the feasibility of mining at prospective sites is periodically reviewed.

Box 5.6 Cononish gold deposit, Scotland

The Cononish gold deposit is one of a very few economically interesting gold discoveries in Britain in recent times. It was found in 1986 by following gold-bearing quartz boulders and small amounts of alluvial gold back to obviously mineralized quartz veins. However, the source of the gold-rich quartz was not easy to determine. It was earlier than the more obvious quartz-hosted lead mineralization, just 3 km to the northeast at Tyndrum, which was worked for lead in the 19th century.

The gold deposit was defined by drainage sampling followed by diamond drilling of 45 holes on a 30 m grid pattern. Based on these drilling results, a resource of 925 000 t at 6.8 g t^{-1} Au and 36.7 g t^{-1} Ag was estimated in 1987. Although the drilling had defined the deposit, because of the highly variable nature of the gold mineralization, underground investigations were required to assess the nature of the vein in detail, as well as the controls of mineralization, and to take samples to study the options for mineral processing. This investigation downgraded the resource to 514 000 t at 9.4 g t^{-1} Au and 52.9 g t^{-1} Ag, allowing for dilution by waste rock during mining. The underground investigation confirmed the grade of gold indicated by drilling and showed that gold could be recovered by collecting sulphides. Detailed underground mapping showed that the quartz vein containing gold is cut by later vein material that is not gold bearing. These later veins make it difficult to follow the gold mineralization when mining the older quartz vein. Such problems, combined with the relatively small size of the deposit, have rendered further development uneconomic for the two companies that undertook feasibility studies of the deposit. An increased gold price, however, could change the economics of any mine.

Figure 5.17 Mine entrance at Cononish, Scotland.

5.10   Summary of Chapter 5

1   Metal resources are exploited on various scales, ranging from small-scale operations involving individuals to large mines run by multinational companies. Large-scale mining operations require major investment, careful planning and financial assessment at each stage of development. There is often a long lead time between discovery of a deposit and production. Mining ventures operate at a loss until production is well under way.

2   Exploration for ore deposits is essential in order to maintain profitable supplies of metals in the longer term. Lead times of 15 or more years may be necessary to allow for exploration, evaluation and development before an exploration target becomes productive.

3   The decision to undertake exploration depends on world markets, supply and demand expectations, and company expertise. Regional targeting is initially based on desk studies involving the analysis and interpretation of available geophysical and remotely sensed data, mining records and geological maps.

4   Modern exploration starts with rapid regional reconnaissance surveys at low cost per unit area, often involving airborne geophysical techniques and sometimes regional geochemical surveys. Localized, often field-based, geophysical and geochemical surveys provide higher resolution (or definition) of targets, but at higher cost. Financing at every stage of exploration, evaluation and development faces a high risk of lost investment; returns are never guaranteed.

5   Geophysical techniques are used to detect bodies of rock with anomalous physical properties. They often record the accompanying rock formations rather than the ore deposits themselves. Gravity and magnetic surveys rely on natural force fields; resistivity, induced polarization (IP) and electromagnetic (EM) surveys rely on applied and induced electrical fields. While geophysical surveys may indicate the presence and form of mineralization targets and associated rock types, geochemical studies are necessary to prove the occurrence and grade of mineralization.

6   Probably the most effective geophysical techniques for locating orebodies are IP, and EM. EM is appropriate only for massive conducting orebodies but has the advantage that it can be undertaken from aircraft and responds to many types of oxide and sulphide orebodies. IP is ground based, but is suitable for detecting both massive and disseminated orebodies as it depends on the chargeability of conductive mineral grains and not on the electrical continuity of the orebody.

IP   Induced polarization
EM   Electromagnetic surveys

7   Geochemical methods aim to reveal anomalous concentrations (that is, deviations from background concentration levels) of mineralizing or pathfinder elements. Surveys generally start on a regional scale with sampling of stream sediments or water, and progress to more localized soil sampling. Direct sampling of bedrock by drilling is necessary to prove mineralization at a likely target.

8   Geochemical sampling depends on the transfer of anomalous compositional characteristics from a mineral deposit to materials that can be sampled, such as sediments, water, vegetation and soils. This process involves geochemical dispersion of these anomalous characteristics: primary dispersion occurs at the time the deposit formed (as in porphyry deposits); secondary dispersion occurs long after mineralization and is due to near-surface groundwater movement and weathering processes.

9   Evaluation of a mineral deposit involves further high-cost drilling to delineate grades of ore and define the extent of the orebody, as well as determining if and how a deposit can be mined profitably. Assessing the cost of setting up the infrastructure to mine and process ore, and the wider political, economic, environmental, and social implications, are all part of evaluation.

MINING AND EXTRACTING METALS

6.1 Mining

Mining is the first stage of metals extraction. It has been carried out on every continent except Antarctica and has been one of the fundamental industries of civilization since the early Bronze Age (about 3000 BC). Modern mines often take the form of shallow, but extensive, pits, where surface deposits are extracted; deep excavations where buried deposits are accessed; and underground shafts and tunnels where even deeper deposits are mined.

- Superficially, mining for metals might seem similar to coal mining (Drury, 2006), but metal mining employs methods far more varied than those used for mining coal — why do you think that is?

- Coal forms from organic debris laid down in fairly regular layers in sedimentary sequences. Metalliferous deposits are formed in many different circumstances — their shapes are varied and they reside within many different kinds of host rock.

Waste disposal is a problem in metal mining and is aggravated by the sheer bulk of the waste that may be produced. Many large metal mines, such as the Bingham Canyon (Figure 2.12), Chuquicamata (Figure 2.17c) and La Escondida (Figure 6.5) copper mines, work deposits where the grade of ore is around 1% copper (sometimes less), so that for every 100 tonnes mined, about 97 tonnes is gangue for which disposal is needed. (Note that it takes about three tonnes of ore mineral concentrate — largely sulphides — to produce about one tonne of copper metal.) The environmental implications of mining low-grade deposits are obvious, but the sheer scale of mine waste from metal mines that produce large tonnages every year is difficult to imagine. For example, at Mount Tom Price — an iron ore mine in Western Australia — 20 million tonnes of ore are excavated each year (Figure 3.13c, Box 3.4). The ore is transported over 300 km to the coast by trains that are 2 km in length, comprising 230 ore wagons each carrying 106 tonnes of ore.

- If the iron ore has a density of 3.5 t m^{-3}, what volume is removed from Mount Tom Price each year?

- The volume of ore removed = $\dfrac{\text{mass}}{\text{density}} = \dfrac{20 \times 10^6 \text{ t}}{3.5 \text{ t m}^{-3}} = 5.7 \times 10^6 \text{ m}^3$

5.7×10^6 m^3 is roughly a 180 metre cube.

Box 6.1 Metal mining in the British Isles

Metal mining has been carried out in various parts of the British Isles for at least 3500 years. Indeed, there was trade in tin between Cornwall and the Mediterranean by the 4th century BC. In prehistoric times, tin was obtained mainly from alluvial deposits in Cornwall; copper and lead were mined from outcropping veins by digging crude pits, sometimes extending to shallow tunnels, as at the Great Orme,

North Wales and iron was mined from outcrops of nodular and bedded deposits in sedimentary rocks. Most early mining was carried out in trenches, open pits and shallow shafts, but gradually, as easily accessible ores were worked out, tunnelling became necessary and by the late 17th century, there were extensive underground mines in many parts of Britain.

Ores of the **base metals** lead, copper and zinc have been mined in many upland areas of England and Wales, as well as in parts of Scotland and Ireland (Figure 6.1). In southwest England, copper, tin, lead and zinc ores were mined from hydrothermal veins associated with large, granitic intrusions. Lead, copper and zinc ores came from veins in the Ordovician and Cambrian sedimentary rocks of north and central Wales, the Lake District, the Isle of Man and the Southern Uplands of Scotland. Mainly lead and zinc with some copper were worked in the Carboniferous limestone of the Mendips, North Wales and the Pennines. In some areas, silver was recovered from the lead ores; gold was mined from quartz veins in central and north Wales.

By the 17th century, northern England had become important for lead mining and Cornwall was important for tin mining. The technological advances and demands for metals during the Industrial Revolution led to the emergence of an important copper mining and smelting industry, together with iron production from the coalfields. In the mid-18th century, copper mining became more important than tin mining in Cornwall and dominated world supplies, but, before the end of that century, the Parys Mountain Mine in Anglesey was producing cheaper copper ore and Cornwall's prosperity declined. But then, as the deposits of Anglesey became more difficult and costly to mine, copper prices increased and copper mining in Cornwall thrived again during much of the 19th century. With its major competitors in central Europe weakened by wars and difficulties in working their mines, the British mining industry dominated world markets in the 18th and early 19th centuries.

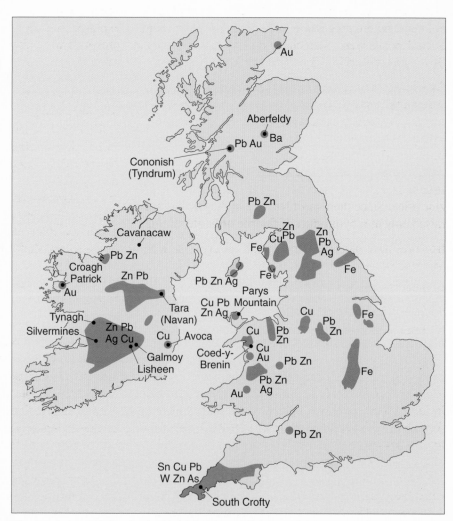

Figure 6.1 Mining in the British Isles. Mining and former mining areas are shaded. Sites of significant metal mining since 1960 and prospective sites are named.

The importance of mining in mid-19th century Britain is illustrated by statistics for 1862, when British metal mines employed over 80 000 people and produced metal worth at the time an estimated £13.5 million (when the annual wage for most people was no more than £50). Metal mining influenced the development and prosperity of industry in mining areas, especially Cornwall. As well as people employed in the extraction and processing of ore, there were many jobs in allied industries — especially engineering, transportation and finance. Indeed, from the 1820s, mining equipment and mining engineers were exported all over the world. Towards the end of the 19th century, world production of ores gradually moved to larger, lower-grade orebodies as mechanization enabled economies of scale to impact on ore processing, transportation and mining. Such deposits were often cheaper to work than mines in Britain because of bulk handling and lower wages.

By the eve of the First World War, much of Britain's base metal mining industry was over. Some mines were saved by switching production to fluorite (used in iron smelting) or barite (used for drilling mud); these had been gangue minerals, hitherto discarded. Others switched to producing zinc ores, but these mines usually lasted only a few more years because of the low zinc price. Since then, most lead ore in the UK has been raised only as a by-product of fluorite or barite mining.

Iron ores have been obtained from a variety of sources in Britain, including:

- nodules in clays of the Weald;
- 'Black Band' ores in most Carboniferous coalfields;
- bedded ironstones in the Jurassic rocks of Cleveland, Lincolnshire and Northamptonshire;
- haematite replacement deposits in Carboniferous limestone along the Cumbrian coast.

In the 18th century, most of the ironstone was worked from the coalfields, but Cleveland iron ores accounted for 30–40% of the total obtained between 1860 and 1910. The Jurassic ores of Lincolnshire and Northamptonshire became important in the 20th century when they were worked in highly mechanized opencast mines. Annual iron ore output reached a peak of nearly 20 million tonnes during the Second World War. This was mainly due to the expansion of mining in Northamptonshire, which continued to be dominant until iron ore mining declined in the 1970s. By the early 1990s it had all but ceased. Ironstone mining in Cleveland ended in 1964, but had been in decline since 1920. The decline of British steelmaking in the 1980s, combined with low steel prices, has also caused the closure of most fluorite mines.

Although tin mining continued through the 20th century and flourished after 1945, the collapse in 1985 of the agreement between producers (a *cartel*) that had controlled the world price of tin resulted in falling tin prices in the mid-1980s and the high-cost Cornish tin mines closed in the next 5–10 years. The South Crofty Mine in Camborne was last to close (in 1998), but (in 2005) attempts are being made to re-open it, aided by an increase in the price of tin (especially in early 2004).

Most, if not all prospective areas in the UK have been explored. Between the 1960s and the 1990s, several new prospects were discovered, and re-evaluation of known mineral occurrences, resulted in some new mining (see Figure 6.1). One notable discovery was the Coed-y-Brenin copper deposit in the Snowdonia National Park. Its discovery led to a UK government enquiry, the outcome of which recommended that no new mining, including the Coed-y-Brenin copper deposit, was to be permitted within National Parks in England and Wales. Gold mining in nearby mid-Wales shifts in and out of production as the price of gold fluctuates, but it operates only on a very small scale. There was new exploration for copper and zinc in the 1980s at the Parys Mountain Mine in Anglesey, where a deep shaft was sunk. Further drilling was carried out in 2005. There has also been prospecting for gold near the Tyndrum mines in Scotland (see Box 5.6) and in Northern Ireland, where gold mining began at Cavanacaw in 1999.

In contrast to the situation in the UK, base metal mining continues in Ireland at the Tara mine near Navan, as well as at the Lisheen and Galmoy mines. Prior to 1961 it was thought that Ireland possessed few significant mineral deposits, although there were well-known historical mining sites at Silvermines and Avoca. Two highway engineers noticed similarities between the terrain of the famous mining camps in the Superior Province of Canada and the poorly exposed bog-covered Central Plain of Ireland. Advice from the Director of the Geological Survey of Ireland took them to the area around Tynagh where copper-stained, red sandstone boulders occur locally in the glacial till. Soil analyses revealed extraordinary concentrations of lead and zinc with significant copper and silver values; a few years later the first mine was opened at Tynagh.

This started a mineral rush to the area and many Canadian companies engaged in systematic exploration of central Ireland using modern geophysical and geochemical methods. By 1972 a number of deposits had been found, including the major Tara deposit, which was probably the largest zinc deposit in Europe. Further exploration led to the discovery of the Lisheen and Galmoy zinc deposits in the 1980s. The potential for other types of deposits in Ireland has also been examined. Several gold prospects were discovered in the west of Ireland, notably at Croagh Patrick, where environmental opposition stopped further development and the exploration permit was cancelled by the Irish Ministry of the Environment.

6.1.1 Economics and mining strategy

The decision whether to mine a deposit at the surface, below ground, or not at all is based on economics. When such decisions are made, a project has not yet earned any money. There is also no guarantee that a mine will be a commercial proposition even after exploration, evaluation and development (see Box 5.6, the Cononish gold deposit). By the time a mine is operating, 10 years or more might have passed, and tens or even hundreds of millions of dollars might have been spent. The design of a mine and associated ore processing facilities need to provide a rapid return for investors (Section 5.1) and, at the same time, continuity of operation and flexibility of production are important to accommodate changing metal prices and demand. In deciding how an ore deposit will be worked, the potential value of the product must be compared with the estimated cost of mining it.

Unit cost

The full cost of transforming *one tonne of ore* in the ground into a saleable commodity is termed the **unit cost** (C_{unit}). In a much-simplified analysis, the unit cost is made up as follows:

C_{ore} = the cost of excavating and transporting one tonne of ore (including ore minerals and gangue).

C_{waste} = the cost of excavating, transporting and disposing of the waste rock (e.g. overburden and waste from access shafts and tunnels) removed in order to obtain one tonne of ore.

C_{proc} = the cost of processing one tonne of ore into a saleable product.

C_{fixed} = the fixed costs in setting up a mine and repaying capital investment plus interest, per tonne of ore extracted per year.

So, the unit cost can be expressed as:

$$C_{unit} = C_{ore} + C_{waste} + C_{proc} + C_{fixed} \qquad (6.1)$$

C_{ore}, C_{waste} and C_{proc} are mine operating costs, made up of wages, consumables (for example explosives, reagents and fuel), maintenance of equipment and spare parts. These *variable costs* depend on the amount of ore being mined. They include the costs of separating ore minerals from waste, disposal of the waste, transportation of concentrates and production of the saleable metal or mineral. C_{ore} and C_{proc} depend on the type of ore, the type of mining operation and the amount of ore produced — economies of scale generally operate. C_{waste} is determined by the form and grade of the deposit and the type of mining operation.

The *fixed costs* are those of setting up a mining operation. They include the costs of long-lived equipment and infrastructure, land, access roads, insurance, environmental restoration, and possibly an environmental 'bond' (Chapter 7); these are overheads and are incurred whether or not the mine enters production. Fixed costs also include the interest paid on borrowed funds and are expressed as cost per tonne of ore extracted per year. C_{fixed}, therefore, depends on the expected lifetime of the mine and its expected annual output (thus higher production reduces fixed cost per tonne). It is important to appreciate that, while the overall fixed cost may not vary, the contribution of fixed cost to unit cost changes during the lifetime of a mine.

● What might cause the contribution of fixed costs to the unit cost to vary dramatically?

○ If, for some reason, anticipated output decreases, then fixed costs per tonne of ore, and hence the contribution of fixed costs to unit cost, will increase. On the other hand, if productivity rises, fixed costs per tonne of ore, and the contribution of fixed costs to unit cost, will decrease.

Underground and surface mining face different problems, consequently there are two main economic differences between surface and underground mining.

1 Underground mining requires extensive permanent constructions and long-lived equipment, including access shafts, underground tracks, ventilation and drainage. Therefore, for underground mining, the fixed costs per tonne of ore, C_{fixed}, are significantly higher than for surface mining, especially as amounts of ore mined underground per year are often less than in surface mines. At the surface, access is generally part of ore excavation, and drainage, if necessary, is relatively inexpensive.

2 The cost of removing rock (both C_{ore} and C_{waste}) is much higher in underground mines than in surface mines.

Unit value

The value of one tonne of ore, its **unit value**, is much simpler to estimate than the unit cost. The variables are the metal content (% or ppm) or grade of the ore, the level of recovery (see Section 6.2.2) and the market price of the product. Thus:

$$\text{unit value} = \text{grade} \times \text{recovery} \times \text{price of product} \tag{6.2}$$

● If, for example, the grade of an ore were 2% copper, metal recovery were 80% and the copper price were US\$2000 t^{-1}, what would be its unit value?

○ The unit value in this case is $\dfrac{2}{100} \times \dfrac{80}{100} \times \text{US\$2000 } t^{-1} = \text{US\$32 } t^{-1}$ ✓

The value of some ore may be reduced if its composition or state lead to increased smelting or refining costs.

Mining cut-off

For any mine, there is a breakeven point where unit cost equals unit value. This point separates working at a profit from working at a loss, and can be expressed in terms of the lowest grade of ore that can be mined at a profit, the *breakeven cut-off grade* (Section 1.3).

● You may recall from Section 1.3 that the cut-off grade is defined in economic terms. What economic factors does it depend on?

○ Cut-off grade depends both on world economic conditions as reflected in the market price, and on local economic factors, such as the presence of valuable by-products, costs of environmental protection, royalties, smelting and refining costs.

Cut-off grade also depends on the local geology — the size, form and occurrence of the deposit, which in turn influence the design of the mining operation and the relationship between fixed and variable costs. Deeper mining incurs greater unit costs and, to be viable, demands a higher cut-off grade. For instance, nickel ores can be mined economically at lower grades from surface residual deposits (Section 3.3.1) than from underground magmatic segregation deposits (Section 2.2.2).

Operating strategies

The profitability of a mine clearly depends on the difference between the unit value and the unit cost. Managers strive to keep their unit costs as low as possible, but they have relatively little control over the long-term fixed costs, as these depend on the size of the operation and its form (surface or underground) mining. There is a financial incentive to develop a mine and its infrastructure as quickly as possible, even if this reduces early profits (Section 5.1). Managers have more control over short-term costs (C_{ore}, C_{waste} and C_{proc}). Mining only the higher-grade ore can provide a quicker return on the initial investment, which is a tempting strategy and very profitable in the short term, but removal of only high-grade ore may be detrimental in the long-term.

Orebodies are very variable in terms of shape, accessibility and ore grade, yet management must strive for smooth and consistent production patterns. Any equipment used for extraction or processing, has a set of *optimum* operating conditions. It would be uneconomic if the throughput rates were too great, preventing maintenance and adversely affecting reliability. On the other hand, if the throughput rates were too low, expensive machinery would stand idle. Possible solutions include:

- several mines feeding a centralized processing plant, so that variations in production are smoothed out;
- the accumulation of stockpiles and the blending of material of different grades to maintain a consistent feed.

Stockpiling is common to all mining operations, but it is particularly useful when mining dispersed deposits where there are large quantities of the resource at grades close to cut-off grade (Figure 1.11). Creation of stockpiles when metal prices are high can safeguard profitability when prices fall as, effectively, the excavation cost would be covered while the price was high. Thus, stockpiling of high-grade reserves can maintain long-term viability.

Another way to achieve financial stability is to agree a price for the product with customers in advance. This demands confidence that the price will not change significantly, at least in the short term. Thus, the products from a mine are rarely, if ever, sold at the daily *spot price* for a metal but are sold on the *futures market* where the price is fixed several months, perhaps even a year, ahead of supply.

Unlike low-grade dispersed deposits, high-grade confined deposits, where grades are well above cut-off (sometimes called 'bonanza' deposits), can be mined continuously and profitably even when costs and prices fluctuate dramatically. However, confined deposits come in all shapes and sizes, and can occur at any depth. Consequently, unit costs for each can be very different, and cut-off grades can vary from deposit to deposit.

6.1.2 Surface or underground mining?

It has been noted already that surface mines are cheaper than underground mines in terms of both fixed and variable costs. They are also easier to operate, especially to accommodate unforeseen geological circumstances, but they often cover large areas and can have a greater environmental impact. Although there are various factors to consider, such as the availability of a skilled workforce and environmental legislation, the choice between surface and underground mining usually depends on geology and economics — in particular, the form, grade, location and depth of the deposit and the level of unit cost to work it, taking into account environmental factors. With lower unit costs, surface working is generally favoured because it tends to be more profitable.

A horizontal ore deposit at the surface, such as bauxite, bedded iron ore or heavy mineral sand, is easiest and cheapest to mine (Figure 6.2a). When it is covered by a layer of barren rock, or rock waste, known as **overburden**, costs rise because this waste has to be removed (Figure 6.2b). Many flat-lying sedimentary rocks — limestone and shale for cement, brick clays, and coal — are mined in this way. The limit of mining depends on the relative cost of removing waste compared with the value of the product and is reflected in the *overburden ratio* (Argles, 2005; Drury, 2006). Usually, this ratio simply compares the thickness of the overburden with the thickness of the deposit. Depending on ore grade, and unit value, an overburden ratio of between 2:1 and 8:1 can be tolerated for many metal deposits, but this concept is more often used for bulk minerals and coal mining than it is for ore deposits. To evaluate the economics of surface mining for many ore deposits requires a rather more rigorous assessment, known as the **stripping ratio**.

Stripping ratio

The stripping ratio is the ratio of the *mass of rock waste* that must be removed to the *mass of ore* that can be extracted. This is a better estimate of the link between the cost of waste removal and the potential income from extracting the ore. It helps explain why many deep surface mines such as the Bingham Canyon Mine (Figure 2.12) have the form of an inverted, truncated cone, known as an open pit. Mining involves the removal of more waste than that which is directly overlying the ore, because even very strong rocks will collapse if vertical faces are cut into them. To ensure the stability of open pit walls, a series of **benches** are cut with an overall angle reaching 60° or more to the horizontal in high-strength rocks (Figure 6.2c), and decreasing in weaker rocks to as little as 25° in poorly consolidated sands.

Figure 6.2 Some different forms of ore deposit: (a) surface layer; (b) shallow layer beneath overburden; (c) deeper layer, accessed by benches.

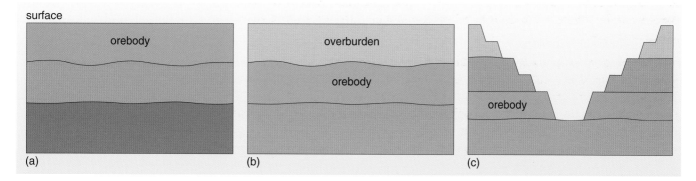

Although the unit cost of underground mining is generally higher than that of shallow surface mining at equivalent depths, the variable costs of underground mining do not increase with depth as markedly as they would for surface mining. Figure 6.3 shows, in a general way, how the unit costs of surface working and of underground working vary with depth.

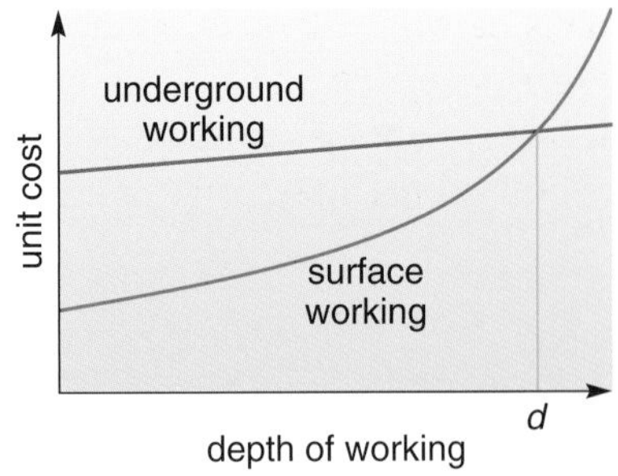

🔵 What is the significance of the depth marked 'd' on Figure 6.3?

⚪ At depth 'd', the unit cost of surface working and of underground mining are equal. At depths greater than 'd' underground mining is more cost-effective than surface mining.

Because the unit cost of underground mining is high, only ores with a high unit value are economic to be mined in this way. Ores with a low unit value are usually mined only in surface operations, and the depth to which those mines are viable is determined mainly by the value of the ore and the thickness of the overburden. Generally, less waste needs to be removed underground compared to an open pit, and in underground mining some of the waste, including tailings, can be used to backfill mined-out areas.

Figure 6.3 Schematic variation in unit cost with depth of working of surface and underground mining.

Question 6.1

Consider Figure 6.4, which shows three different forms of confined deposit.

(a) Assess which of the three deposits could best be worked at the surface and which would be more appropriate to be worked underground. In each case consider the implications for waste.

(b) With unit costs increasing from Figure 6.4a to b, and from b to c, how would you expect cut-off grades to vary?

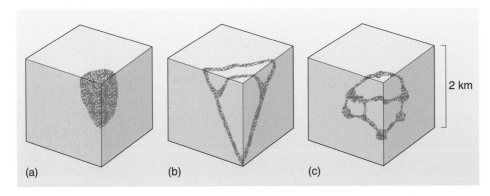

(a)   (b)   (c)

2 km

Figure 6.4 Idealized representations of different forms of confined deposit arranged in order of increasing unit cost: (a) a massive deposit; (b) a simple vein deposit; (c) irregular vein deposits with large ore pockets.

6.1.3   Surface mining

Constraints on space for surface workings are less significant than mining underground, although the form of the deposit and planning constraints (especially in more heavily populated or environmentally sensitive areas) may impose restrictions. Surface mining of a large deposit benefits from economies of scale because large-capacity earth-moving and processing equipment can be used with correspondingly higher productivity. This reduces the unit cost, allowing low-grade deposits to be worked economically at high tonnages (Section 1.3). In many cases, the larger the deposit, the more profitable it is likely to be, especially when mining can be entirely within ore (thus minimizing waste). However, the need for stable pit walls may require large volumes of waste to be removed to access deeper ores (Figure 6.2c).

Surface mines are of three main designs, depending primarily on the form and occurrence of the ore deposit.

1 **Open pit** (or bench) mines are deep holes in the ground that are often shaped like an inverted cone. They are the most common form of surface mining for metals. They are appropriate for deposits that occur near the surface and extend to considerable depth, including large-scale dispersed deposits (e.g. Bingham Canyon, Figure 2.12) and steeply dipping confined deposits.

2 **Opencast** (or strip) mines involve the excavation of shallow, elongate pits, cutting into a rockface and backfilling the rear of the excavation, as often happens in surface coal mines (Drury, 2006). They are appropriate only where the orebody is at shallow depth and laterally extensive (e.g. Figure 3.6).

3 **Dredging** is suited to mining deposits in unconsolidated sediments that are waterlogged or underwater (e.g. Figure 3.3) on land or at the coast. It can also be used in shallow marine environments, whereas in deeper, offshore locations crawler units (submersible collectors) and air-lift mining (suction pipes) are employed, especially for diamond mining.

⬤ From your knowledge of the form and occurrence of ore deposits (Chapters 2, 3, and 4), give an example of a type of ore deposit that could be mined using each of these three types of surface mine design.

⬤ Open pit mines are suitable for exploiting most equidimensional deposits, such as porphyries, and inclined tabular deposits, such as massive sulphides (Sections 2.4 and 4.2.2).

Opencast or strip mines are suitable only for horizontally extensive ore deposits that are close to the surface, such as bauxite and bedded iron ore deposits (Sections 3.3.1 and 3.4.1).

Dredging can be used for alluvial or beach placer deposits (Section 3.2).

As most surface metal mines are open pits, we'll look at this type in more detail.

Open pit (or bench) mining

The development of an open pit mine is quite simple. Overburden is stripped from the area of the pit and downward excavation is accompanied by sideways enlargement as the floor is deepened. The flanks of the working form a series of benches (see Figure 6.2c). These benches:

● improve stability of the pit walls;

● act as traps for debris dislodged from higher levels;

● provide haulage access to the working floor.

The height of each bench (5–20 m) and the angle of the faces depend partly on the need for stability (and hence on the mechanical properties of the rock), partly on the reach of excavating equipment, and partly on the maximum gradient for access by haulage vehicles. In the early days of bench mining — for example at

Bingham Canyon — locomotives requiring low track gradients were used. These have been superseded by high-capacity trucks that can operate on higher gradients. In most cases, open pit excavations extend below the water table and the water must be pumped out to prevent flooding.

● Figure 6.5b is a satellite image of one of the largest open pit mines in the world at La Escondida, Chile. Where are the main spoil heaps in the picture?

○ The spoil heaps are the flat-topped, regular-shaped mounds that surround the open pit and extend over many square kilometres. Because this area is relatively uninhabited, the spoil heaps are located where it is most convenient for the mine engineers.

(a)

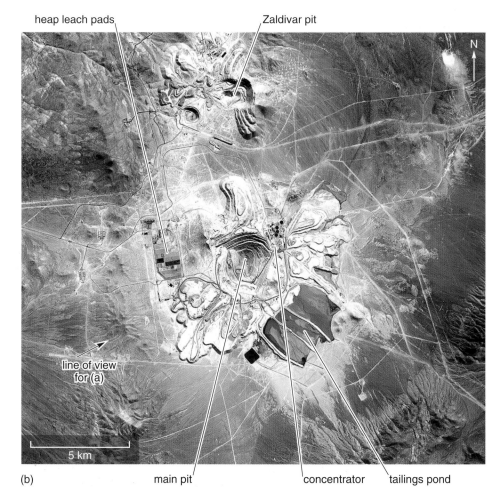

heap leach pads   Zaldivar pit

line of view for (a)

5 km

(b)   main pit   concentrator   tailings pond

Figure 6.5 (a) Oblique and (b) satellite views of one of the largest open pits in the world at La Escondida, Chile. (a) shows the concentrator and some waste storage mounds behind the open pit.

Open pit mining involves three main excavation activities.

1   *Drilling and blasting* loosens rock, whether it is overburden or ore. Vertical holes are drilled in patterns and charges are inserted. The aim is to yield broken rock that can easily be loaded onto trucks and is of suitable size to be fed into the crushing plant without further breakage. Drill core and bench samples can be analysed, so that the distribution of ore and waste can continually be mapped — a process known as *grade control*. This information is used to decide which portions of the material blasted should be taken to the mill for processing, stockpiled, or taken to spoil heaps.

⬤   What are the three main environmental hazards from blasting?

◯   Dust, noise and shock waves.

Figure 6.6   The removal of broken rock from an open pit.

2   *Stripping* involves removal of loose ore and waste from working faces and loading it onto haulage vehicles (Figure 6.6). It is important that the sizes of shovels and haulage vehicles are matched (about three shovel-loads should fill a truck) to ensure an efficient stripping process.

3   *Haulage* of ore and waste from pit to processing plant and spoil heaps, respectively, is the most costly part of operations. Economies of scale minimize costs, with today's vehicles having capacities of up to 300 tonnes. Their size and number are tailored to rates of extraction to ensure continuous stripping and loading. Haul roads have a maximum gradient of about 10% to allow the ascent of fully laden trucks. The weight of the huge vehicles and their loads necessitate continuous maintenance of roadways involving bulldozers, graders and water sprayers (to bind the surface and reduce dust).

6.1.4   Underground mining

Underground mining is much less flexible than surface mining. Sinking shafts and tunnelling are slow processes, and space must be made for the equipment used, thus limiting its size. So, gaining access to the ore generally takes longer, and, once mining is underway, it is difficult to deviate from initial plans. The maximum output from any underground working face is usually much lower than for surface mining, and, to achieve a high output, several working faces are needed rather than the single large working floor commonly encountered in opencast or open pit mining. It is, therefore, vitally important that the mine development plan is scheduled well in advance of actual operations. Consequently, the time elapsing from planning to first income is generally much longer for underground mines than for surface mines.

One of the striking features of many of today's underground mines is the sheer scale of operations. These are not the mines of narrow tunnels with little room to stand upright that characterized early metal mines in Britain. Instead, there are 40-tonne haulage trucks, front-end loaders, mechanized drilling rigs and excavators (Figure 6.7). Before extraction of ore can begin, means of access for workers and equipment, outlets for ore and drainage water, and ventilation must be engineered. There are two access options — either vertical shafts or low-angled declines.

Declines are roads that allow heavy wheeled equipment to enter and leave the mine under their own power. However, to achieve the low gradients necessary for haulage equipment can mean extensive and complex, often spiral, tunnelling (Figure 6.8), particularly in deep mines, so, for technical reasons, they do not go down as far as vertical shafts. For example, declines in some mines go down to 600 m, whereas vertical shafts go down to over 2000 m at Sudbury and over 3000 m in South Africa.

Figure 6.7 Underground mining with wheeled equipment: (a) drilling shot holes; (b) transporting ore.

● If access is by vertical shafts, how can large pieces of equipment be taken down to the deeper levels of the mine?

○ Quite simply, in parts. All large equipment must be taken below ground in kit form and then reassembled in place.

Mine design

In designing an underground mine there are a number of considerations, all influenced by the geology, such as how to:

- reach the ore;
- minimize the extraction of waste;
- maximize the use of gravity for transport and breakage of ore;
- ensure the safety of workers and the excavation itself.

● How can the extraction of waste be minimized?

○ By ensuring that the excavation is as far as possible within the ore deposit.

● How might gravity be used to assist breakage of the ore?

○ Ore from working faces can be dropped down steep shafts (ore-passes) to assist breakage before being picked up at lower haulage levels and transported to the surface (Figure 6.8). A mining technique known as block caving, which undermines the ore allowing it to cave in, smashing itself in the process, is sometimes used for mining large equidimensional deposits, such as porphyry coppers.

Mine designs depend on the depth, form, and mechanical properties of the deposit and its host rocks. Engineering requirements depend on whether the rock (host

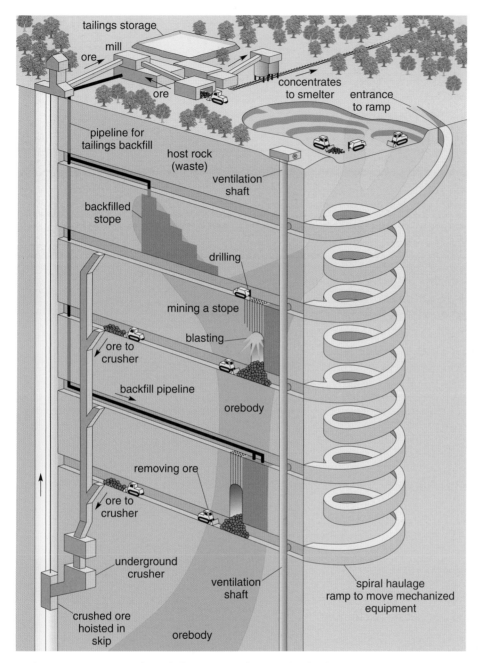

Figure 6.8 Schematic section through an underground mine associated with an open pit. Access to the mine underground is via a spiral decline and a shaft. The orebody is accessed via levels.

and ore) can support the mining excavations and whether gravity can be exploited in the design. The critical geological factors are:

1 The overall *shape of the deposit*, which affects the size of excavations and determines the kind of support necessary, for example a broad deposit needs more roof support than a narrow one. Upright tabular or vertical deposits (as in Figure 6.8), therefore, require a different basic mine design from horizontally oriented or more equidimensional ones.

2 The *dip of the deposit*, which governs the inclination of excavations and the degree to which gravity can be exploited.

3 The *strength of the ore*, which determines the amount of support required for unworked ore and whether or not the ore itself can be used to support the roof and walls.

4   The *strength of the host rock*, which determines the stability of the roofs and walls of the excavation.

Ore deposits come in a huge variety of shapes and sizes and both the ore and the enclosing country rock vary a great deal in their strength. (Rock strength is also affected by the degree of water saturation and fracturing.) So, unlike surface mines for which there are three basic designs (Section 6.1.3), every underground mine is unique, but they fall broadly into two main types, depending on the form of the deposit.

1   Horizontally extensive deposits, such as tabular orebodies with dips less than 10°, are worked by either *room-and-pillar* (also called *pillar-and-stall*) or *longwall* methods as used widely in coal mining (Drury, 2006, and Box 6.2). The method chosen depends on the rock strength and thickness of the orebody. Room-and-pillar operations require strong host rocks and strong ore. Where either is weak, organized roof collapse is allowed by longwall mining.

2   Vertically extensive deposits, such as pipe-shaped, conical and equidimensional deposits, steeply dipping tabular orebodies and vein-like hydrothermal or pegmatite deposits, are worked from horizontal tunnels known as *levels*, with semi-permanent walls (Figure 6.8). Excavation of ore from the roofs and floors of levels is known as **stoping** and the regions mined are known as *stopes*. Where the host rock is strong, the walls need little support, but where it is weak, support is essential. A strong ore requires minimal roof support and can be left temporarily in place to support weak walls; a weak ore needs either support or the use of a mining method where human and machine access to the excavation is minimized.

Question 6.2

Answer the following about the mining operation illustrated in Figure 6.8.

(a) Describe the form of the orebody.

(b) Where and how is the ore being mined?

(c) How is the ore processed underground?

(d) How is the ore transported from the point of blasting until it leaves the site?

(e) What use has the waste from mineral processing?

Box 6.2   Deep-level gold mining

The conglomerate-hosted gold deposits of the Witwatersrand area in South Africa have provided about one-third of the gold ever known to have been mined. The ores have been followed from the surface to depths of almost 4000 m, much the deepest mines in the world. Such depths are a formidable challenge as a safe working environment must be provided while still making a return on the capital investment.

Figure 6.9a is a cross-section showing the geology of the Driefontein mines, where the Tau-Tona mine and the adjacent Mponeng mine are currently the deepest in the world. The conglomerates are mostly less than 1 m thick, so mining concentrates on extracting as much mineralization as possible without dilution by barren rock. They form extensive, shallow-dipping layers, so the mining technique used until recently was longwall mining, in a manner shown in Figure 6.9b. Drilling is largely carried out manually using jackhammers (Figure 6.10). The ore is then blasted and fed into rail trucks before being transported to the shaft.

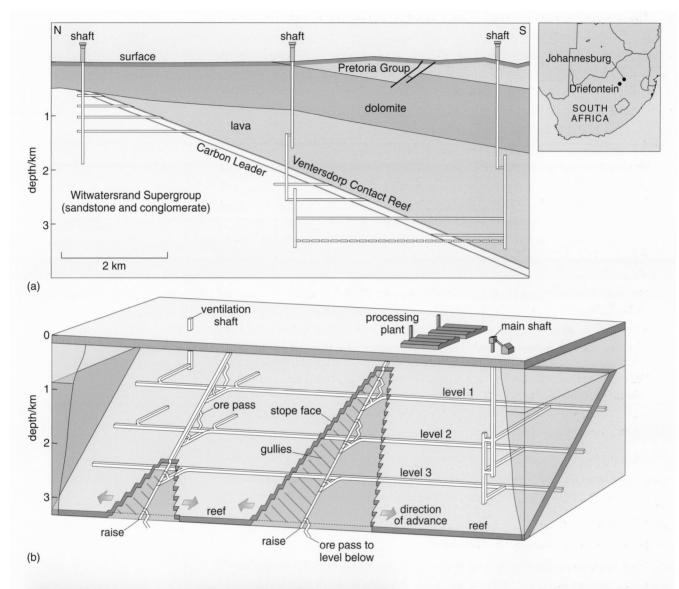

(a)

(b)

Figure 6.9 (a) A geological section through the Driefontein mines adjacent to Tau-Tona. Note access is by more than one shaft as the depth limit for a single shaft was, until recently, approximately 2000 m. The dolomitic limestones are water bearing and must be pumped dry before mining starts. (b) Schematic diagram to show how the thin (<1 m) shallow-dipping gold-bearing conglomerates are normally mined. The ore is blasted and fed down the central gully before being moved along levels to the shaft for transporting to the surface.

Figure 6.10 Manual drilling operations in Tau-Tona mine.

● What do you think the major problems of mining to such a great depth might be?

○ The major issues are:

High rock temperatures. These reach 55 °C, therefore refrigeration is required to maintain a bearable working environment. Cold water is routinely sprayed onto mine workings and used to power equipment.

Maintaining rock stability under very high pressure. The quartzites and conglomerates are very brittle and the mine workings can burst explosively, causing severe injury or death.

The time taken for workers to travel to their working areas. This may be over an hour; in deep areas, two or even three shafts are used at different levels.

The long time required to sink deep shafts. This may take ten years or more for a 3000 m deep shaft at a cost approaching US$1 billion.

Flooding by groundwater. Water is potentially a major problem at Tau-Tona, where the conglomerates are overlain by dolomite aquifers. The area mined must be pumped out before mining.

In the past, the South African gold mining industry relied on manual labour to extract gold, but the major political changes since 1994 have led to greater mechanization in new mines with fewer, but more skilled and better-paid workers. Drilling in the mechanized mines is undertaken with rubber-wheeled vehicles; the ore is then blasted and removed into dump trucks. Mechanization requires openings at least 2 m high for vehicle access, so in general mechanization is economic only where the ores are thick. To prevent the roof falling in, only part of the area is extracted at first. The open spaces left by mining are then filled with crushed waste rock before the remaining pillars can be extracted.

6.2   Ore processing

Most metal mining operations not only involve extraction of ore from the ground, but also ore processing — the physical separation and concentration of ore minerals in preparation for subsequent extraction of metals. A number of stages are involved, as outlined in Figure 6.11. The first is **liberation**, which involves breaking up the ore into fragments to *release* ore minerals from the gangue and from each other. The second is the physical *separation* of liberated fragments of ore minerals from fragments of gangue and other ore minerals, to derive an **ore mineral concentrate**. An alternative to physical separation, and widely used for low-grade gold and copper ores, is to leach the ore with chemicals.

Ores extracted by mining and ready for processing have roughly the same overall grade as when they were in the ground. Low-grade ores, especially from dispersed deposits, may contain over 99% gangue; even high-grade ores usually contain more gangue than ore minerals.

● Is the value of raw, untreated metal ores likely to be high or low, and what does this suggest about where the ores should be processed?

○ The value of untreated metal ores, especially low-grade ores, is low, often even lower than road-building aggregates, so it is uneconomic to transport them very far: they have a high place value (Sheldon, 2005). Consequently, mined ore is often processed close to the mine to remove worthless gangue and produce an ore mineral concentrate.

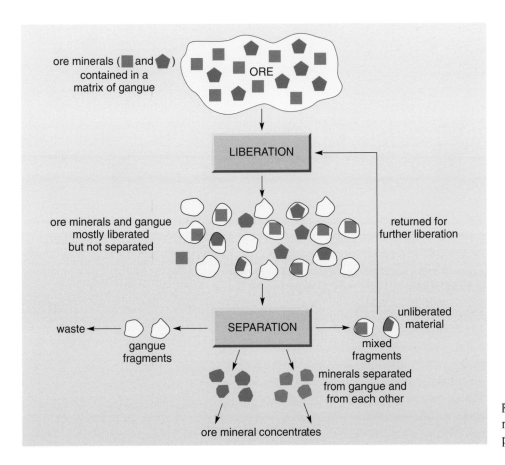

ore minerals (■ and ⬟) contained in a matrix of gangue

ORE

LIBERATION

ore minerals and gangue mostly liberated but not separated

returned for further liberation

SEPARATION

waste ◄

gangue fragments

mixed fragments

unliberated material

minerals separated from gangue and from each other

ore mineral concentrates

Figure 6.11 Schematic representation of the stages of physical ore processing.

Power and water are essential for ore processing. It is clearly an advantage for the processing plant to be sited where these facilities are readily available, although power and water can be more transportable than ore. An ore mineral concentrate has much greater value per tonne than unprocessed ore, and is a saleable commodity; it can be transported efficiently (i.e. has a low place value) and is ready for metal extraction, usually by smelting (Section 6.3).

No two ore deposits contain exactly the same mineral assemblages, and the proportions, textures and grain sizes of ore minerals vary, even across the same orebody. To achieve optimum efficiency and profitability in mineral processing, procedures are tailored to each orebody. Methods of liberation and separation never work perfectly, so rejected material is often recycled and processed again (Figure 6.11). Ore mineral *recovery* is never 100% (Box 6.3), although separation processes are becoming ever more efficient. Indeed, many old mine **tailings**, the material rejected during mineral processing and regarded as waste, can now be profitably reprocessed, thus helping to conserve remaining ore deposits.

6.2.1 Mineral liberation

Ore minerals and gangue are generally intergrown, so before they can be separated they have to be liberated from one another. The easiest way of releasing minerals is to break up the ore into smaller and smaller pieces by crushing using crude mechanical methods. After repeated fragmentation to reduce particle size, some ore mineral fragments are liberated, but many still

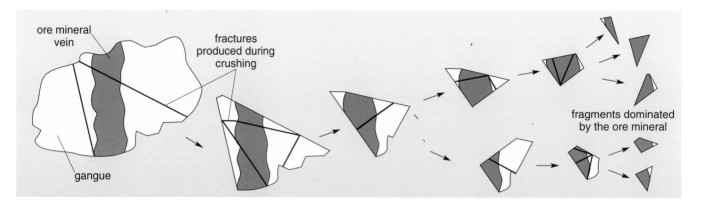

contain varying proportions of gangue and ore minerals (Figure 6.12). Unlike weathering, artificial fracturing during the crushing process cannot exploit weaknesses in the rock as effectively as natural processes; fracturing tends to occur randomly through mineral grains rather than along grain boundaries.

For effective liberation, crushed fragments must be ground, or milled, to sizes smaller than the ore mineral grains. Liberation of fine-grained ore minerals, therefore, demands grinding the rock into very small fragments. However, excessive **milling** is inefficient, it wastes energy and increases processing costs because it breaks up grains already liberated and produces too many **fines**. Fines are a problem because physical methods of mineral separation do not work well on very fine-grained material, so fines become waste.

Figure 6.12 The effect of random fracturing on fragments of ore containing ore minerals and gangue. It takes repeated fracturing and reduction of grain size to produce fragments mainly composed of ore minerals. For efficient liberation, grains must generally be crushed smaller than the size of the ore minerals.

6.2.2 Mineral separation

Even after crushing and grinding to liberate the ore minerals, the concentration of metals in a liberated ore remains the same as in the original mill feed. The next stage is to separate the required ore minerals from the gangue as cheaply and efficiently as possible. Separation usually involves sorting liberated ore mineral grains into groups by exploiting their physical or chemical properties. Separation of the ore minerals from gangue and from each other is often difficult. The success of separation is described in terms of **recovery**, which is the proportion of contained metal or ore mineral in the concentrate produced, relative to that in the ore. As indicated in Box 6.3, complete recovery, like complete liberation, is never achieved.

What physical properties could form the basis of mineral separation techniques?

Density is perhaps the most obvious, as illustrated by its role in forming placer deposits: many ore minerals (often oxides or sulphides) are denser than the gangue minerals (often silicates or carbonates). Other properties with a potential for use in separation include grain shape and colour (handpicking of diamonds) and electromagnetic properties (the ability to be magnetized or to retain an electrical charge). There is a considerable advantage in using techniques or combinations of techniques that lend themselves to automation.

Figure 6.14 summarizes the particle size ranges appropriate for several physical methods of separation. You will see that wet or dry treatments may be involved. Dry processes usually use less energy because there is no water to be pumped

Box 6.3   Recovery from ores

In producing an ore mineral concentrate, ideally all ore mineral grains would be separated from the gangue (achieving 100% recovery) thus maximizing efficiency and conserving raw materials. The concentrate produced would be free of impurities (i.e. 100% ore mineral or metal) so as to minimize transport costs and provide an optimum feed for smelting.

However, to achieve complete liberation of ore mineral grains would require extremely fine grinding (Figure 6.12), and too many fines makes separation inefficient and wastage high. Repeated recycling and reprocessing of waste to minimize losses would also be inefficient and consume large amounts of energy. Even if ore is ground as fine as is economic and practical, there will always be mixed grains. The more mixed grains that are rejected, the lower the recovery, therefore achieving 100% recovery or 100% purity is neither an economic nor a practical proposition.

The relationship between recovery and grade of concentrate is illustrated in Figure 6.13, which is a typical grade–recovery curve. This shows that the higher the grade of concentrate demanded, the lower the percentage of metal recovery (owing to loss through rejection of mixed grains). This relationship varies depending on the nature of the ore and the efficiency of the separation process. As a rough

guide, obtaining a concentrate of 90% purity might entail the loss of 20–30% of the ore mineral, whereas perhaps only 10% might be lost (90% recovery) in producing a 70% concentrate.

Clearly, a balance has to be achieved in maximizing recovery, obtaining a high quality concentrate and, at the same time, minimizing processing costs. Optimum recovery depends not only on the initial form of the ore and the purity required by the smelting process, but also on a range of economic factors, including processing costs, transport costs and metal price.

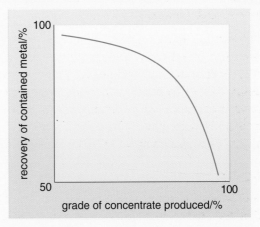

Figure 6.13 Typical grade–recovery curve for concentrates produced by ore processing.

around and the concentrates recovered do not have to be dried, which uses a lot of energy. However, wet processes often separate minerals more efficiently, especially at finer grain sizes. The choice of a wet or dry process depends on grain size, mineral properties and the separation procedure to be used. If crude separation can be achieved efficiently with large grains, separation can take place after crushing and before grinding. This saves energy, but is suitable only for ores that contain large masses of ore minerals.

Figure 6.14 Ranges of particle size appropriate for some mineral separation processes.

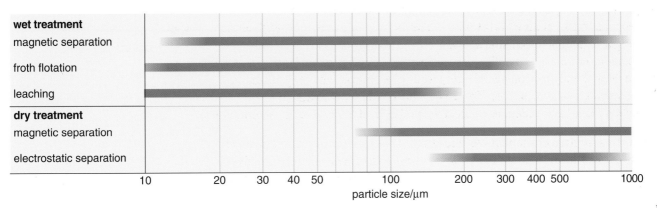

Electrostatic and magnetic separation

If a mineral can be magnetized or if it can accept an electrical charge, its behaviour, when passed through a magnetic or an electrical field, will differ from that of a mineral that is not easily magnetized or electrostatically charged. Magnetic separation can work on wet or dry materials, but the electrostatic method works only on dry material (Figure 6.14). Very similar designs are employed in the two kinds of separator (Figure 6.15).

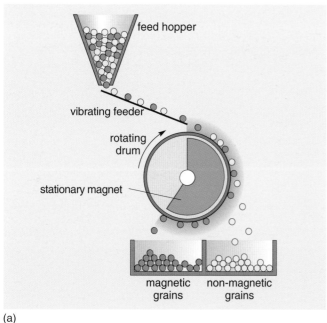

(a)

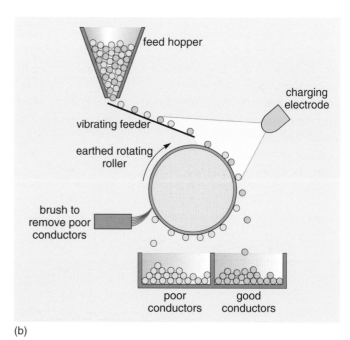

(b)

In *magnetic separation*, a stream of grains, ideally a layer only one grain thick, is fed through a strong magnetic field. The magnetic grains are attracted by the field and collected separately from the non-magnetic grains (Figure 6.15a).

Electrostatic separation is based on the attraction of electrically charged particles to neutral surfaces, where opposite charges are induced locally. This is rather like picking up small pieces of paper using a charged plastic comb — just combing dry hair usually provides sufficient charge. Mineral grains are charged by an electrode as they are fed onto an earthed rotating metal roller (Figure 6.15b). They stick to the roller as long as they hold their electrical charge. Some grains lose their charge quickly and fall from the roller. Others retain their charges and stick to the rotating roller for longer. These grains follow a different trajectory as they fall and are collected separately.

Figure 6.15 Schematic forms of: (a) magnetic separator; (b) electrostatic separator.

⬤ Which minerals would hold an electrostatic charge — good or poor conductors?

◗ Poor conductors retain their charge better than good conductors. Good conductors allow their charge to flow away easily.

Electrostatic separation is often used to recover naturally liberated conducting minerals such as iron–titanium oxides from unconsolidated beach placer deposits. It works best for grains between 0.2 mm and 1 mm in diameter.

Froth flotation

A rather unexpected form of separation process had its origins in a domestic setting. Washing the grimy and greasy clothes of lead miners produced very dark soapsuds: they were covered with tiny grains of galena. This was rather surprising because galena is a dense mineral and would be expected to sink in water rather than float. In fact, a coating of grease was responsible for the galena grains becoming attached to the bubbles. The phenomenon is the basis of **froth flotation**, a mineral separation process used extensively since the early 20th century.

Froth flotation relies on the preferential attachment of particular mineral grains to air bubbles, so that they are carried to the surface of a frothing liquid, while other mineral grains remain submerged in the liquid. Only grains that *repel* water, behaving rather like the non-wetted greasy surface of an oily cloth, become attached to the bubbles. With the addition of suitable chemicals, usually organic compounds, mineral grains may be selectively coated with a thin film that reduces their wettability (as did the grease from the miners' clothes). These non-wetted mineral grains become attached to bubbles when the mixture is aerated, whereas wetted grains remain in the water.

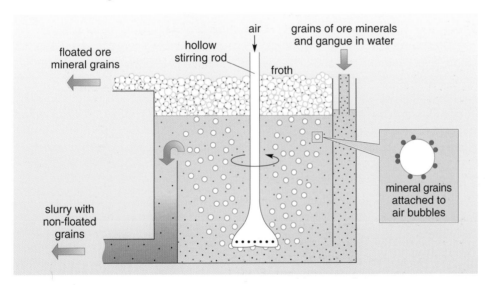

Figure 6.16 Schematic form of froth flotation cell. Mineral grains selectively coated by a non-wetting chemical reagent attach themselves to bubbles and float.

Many of the active chemicals used in froth flotation have been found by trial and error. They allow, for example, the separation of sulphides from non-sulphides, and different sulphide minerals from each other. The maximum size of a particle that can be 'floated' depends on its density. Sulphide minerals with a density of about 5 t m^{-3} can be floated — but only if the grains are between 5 µm and 200 µm in diameter. Figure 6.16 shows the basic design of a single flotation cell. Cells are commonly grouped in a circuit to separate a number of different minerals. The slurry of fine-grained minerals, gangue minerals, chemical reagents and water is fed into the bottom of the flotation cell and stirred by a large paddle as air is introduced. Most systems employ two stages: a roughing stage to obtain most of the target mineral and a cleaning stage to reject further gangue and improve the grade of the concentrate.

Froth flotation can be used to separate fine ore mineral grains from almost any low-grade dispersed deposit, but is widely used for the separation of fine-grained metal sulphides. Froth flotation made possible the processing of low-grade porphyry copper ores and helped to make disseminated deposits, such as those at Bingham Canyon, economic to mine (Section 2.4).

Leaching

The leaching of ore with chemical solutions is a form of ore processing that allows direct metal extraction. It depends on the creation of conditions in which ore minerals can take part in chemical reactions that release the metals they contain into solution. It has several advantages, the most important being that complete liberation is unnecessary as the grains need only to be partly exposed to enter into chemical reaction. Very low-grade ores can be treated, sometimes *in situ*, but more often in what would otherwise be waste heaps, as discussed in Box 6.4.

Box 6.4 *In situ* and heap leaching

The leaching of ores, either *in situ* or after mining, depends on the metal being soluble in a chemical solution (preferably an environmentally acceptable one). The use of *in situ* extraction is well established for mining the industrial minerals potash and rock salt. In this case, the solution used is water-based and either one or a series of wells are used. The major use of *in situ* mining for metals is, at present, for the extraction of uranium. It is used where uranium deposits occur within poorly cemented sandstone lenses. The uranium can be extracted from the mineralized rock by the controlled injection of weak solutions of either acid or alkali, depending on the pH of the rock. It is then extracted from the solution (Drury, 2006). The major problem with this type of mining is controlling and predicting the flow of solutions within the deposit, as well as minimizing any impact on groundwater used for agriculture or human consumption.

Leaching of crudely processed ores can be a relatively inexpensive method of recovering metals and has revolutionized the recovery of gold from low-grade ores. Conventional gold milling requires the expenditure of large amounts of energy to grind ores and to expose fine-grained gold grains for dissolution by cyanide solution, as detailed in Equation 6.3.

$$8NaCN + 4Au + O_2 + 2H_2O =$$

sodium cyanide   gold

$$4[Au(CN)_2]^- + 8Na^+ + 4OH^- \qquad (6.3)$$

gold cyanyl complex

Many near-surface gold ores are, however, already highly altered (oxidized), making them friable, and gold can be extracted by simply piling coarsely crushed or permeable ores into heaps and spraying them with cyanide. This process is known as **heap leaching**, and is illustrated in Figure 6.17. The gold-rich solutions are then collected and passed through activated carbon (burnt coconut shells can be used) onto which the gold is adsorbed.

Figure 6.17 Heap leach gold operation at the Freda Rebecca mine, Zimbabwe. The coarsely crushed rock on the leach pad is in the middle. Cyanide solution is sprinkled onto the tip and then piped back to the plant in the foreground.

● What problems do you think might be associated with heap leaching of gold ore?

◐ Potential problems include:

- the gold minerals need to be accessible to the solution and not completely enclosed by other minerals;

- the heap must be permeable to allow the solution to percolate through it; excessive clay, for example, would impede percolation;

- animals and humans must be protected from exposure to the highly toxic cyanide solution. The heaps are placed on a series of natural or synthetic liners that prevent the solution leaking into the underlying rock;

- the recovery rates for heap leaching are much lower (60–70%) than for conventional milling (85–95%). It also takes several months for the solutions to have leached most of the gold.

Heap leaching involving acids and natural bacteria, such as *Acidithiobacillus ferrooxidans*, is also used to extract copper and nickel from oxidized sulphide ores and laterites. Leaching (a *hydrometallurgical* process) is becoming an increasingly popular alternative to smelting as it avoids the release of sulphur dioxide (SO_2) into the atmosphere. As an example, Inco is building a pilot plant to develop hydrometallurgical processing of nickel sulphide concentrates from the Voisey's Bay operation (Box 5.2).

6.3 Metals extraction

Extracting metals from ore minerals that have been mined, liberated and concentrated can take several forms. Traditional smelting involves the roasting of ore minerals (such as iron ore), together with other substances, such as carbon (in the form of charcoal, coal or methane), which chemically reduce the ore minerals to their contained metal. After traditional smelting, metal products often require **refining** to improve their purity. Another way of extracting some metals from their ore minerals is by *electrolysis*, which involves passing an electric current through a conducting liquid, either of a molten ore mineral (in the case of bauxite), or of a solution produced by leaching (containing copper, for example).

The procedure used for smelting depends on the chemistry of the ore mineral, especially whether it is an oxide or a sulphide, and the ease with which bonds can be broken to liberate the metal. Some metals, such as copper and nickel, tend to form sulphide ore minerals, but oxides are more suitable for smelting, so sulphides are usually converted first to oxides by roasting in air. Oxides of highly electronegative metals (Section 1.2), such as copper and mercury, can be decomposed simply by heating. Oxides of rather less electronegative metals, lead and zinc for example, do not decompose directly, but can be reduced by carbon in a similar way to the smelting of iron ore.

Ore mineral concentrates contain impurities, especially silicate minerals. To remove these, a *flux*, commonly limestone, is added during smelting. The flux combines with impurities and gangue minerals to form a silicate melt called *slag* (see Equation 6.4). The slag is lighter than the molten metal, so it floats and can be tapped off.

$$CaCO_3 + SiO_2 = CaSiO_3 + CO_2 \qquad (6.4)$$

limestone   silica   slag   carbon
                (silicate)   dioxide

Carbon chemically reduces oxide ore minerals and releases carbon dioxide, as illustrated by the reduction of haematite in Equation 6.5.

$$2Fe_2O_3 + 3C = 4Fe + 3CO_2 \qquad (6.5)$$

haematite carbon iron carbon
dioxide

Carbon dioxide is not a poisonous pollutant, but it is a serious long-term contributor to the *greenhouse effect* and implicated in global warming (Drury, 2006). The release of sulphur dioxide when sulphide ore minerals are roasted is serious in the short term as sulphur dioxide is a major pollutant, a respiratory irritant and a cause of acid rain (Drury, 2006). One environmental consequence of its release is the destruction of plant habitats, especially forests on soils that cannot neutralize the enhanced acidity (Sections 3.4.3 and 4.3.3).

Before electrolytic methods became available, carbon reduction was the main form of smelting. But for some metals with even lower electronegativity (such as titanium and aluminium) that are very strongly bound in their oxides, a more powerful form of reduction was required. This usually involved the reaction of one of the salts of the metal, often a chloride, with a more highly reactive metal, such as sodium (Equation 6.6).

$$AlCl_3 + 3Na = Al + 3NaCl \qquad (6.6)$$

aluminium sodium aluminium sodium
chloride   metal   metal   chloride

In the 19th century, aluminium was produced in this way and was available only in small quantities. Hence it was highly priced and regarded, rather like silver and gold, as a precious metal. Titanium is still produced in a similar way, which accounts for its high price (Table 1.2).

With the availability of electricity in the late 19th century, a new process was discovered by which aluminium could be extracted by dissolving alumina (Al_2O_3) from bauxite ore in a molten mixture of cryolite (Na_3AlF_6) and fluorite (CaF_2) — both natural minerals — and then passing an electric current through the melt. Molten aluminium collects at the cathode while the anode burns away as oxygen is liberated from the melt. However, not until the mid-20th century was the process scaled-up to produce aluminium in sufficient quantities to reduce its price and allow its widespread use.

Today, extraction of metals involves a variety of procedures and sometimes takes place close to mine sites to minimize transport costs provided there are high enough tonnages for the operation to be economic. At many sites, a range of processing and refining activities are carried out, including the leaching of low-grade ore followed by electrolytic recovery of metals such as copper, nickel or zinc.

Question 6.3

Pyrite is commonly found in sulphide deposits. Why is it less suitable as an iron ore mineral than haematite?

6.4   Summary of Chapter 6

1   Mining may be carried out at the surface or underground, depending on the location and form of the deposit and on the economics of mining, which can be described in terms of unit cost and unit value per tonne of ore. Unit cost includes the variable costs of extracting ore, processing ore and handling waste, and the fixed costs of permanent constructions and provision of infrastructure. Unit value depends on the grade of ore mined, the level of metal recovery and the metal price.

2   With increasing depth of surface mining, stripping ratios become greater because the proportion of waste increases. This is because benches must be cut in barren rock to provide access and to maintain stability of the pit sides. Consequently, costs rise and it becomes more economic to move to underground mining. The unit cost of mining underground is generally high; it is only economic to mine ores with a high unit value in this way.

3   Open pit mining is the most commonly used method for mining surface ore deposits, but it requires surface storage of waste. Opencast mining can be used only for laterally extensive near-surface deposits and involves backfilling excavations with waste. Dredging can be used where a deposit is unconsolidated and either waterlogged or underwater.

4   Underground mine design depends on the strength and structure of the host rock as well as the form of the deposit. Underground mining has the advantage of being out of sight and the workings can be backfilled with waste.

5   Ore processing generally involves crushing and milling to liberate ore minerals and a combination of processes to separate them from gangue and produce an ore mineral concentrate suitable for the extraction of metal.

6   Liberation demands milling of ore to a size fine enough to release ore minerals yet coarse enough for separation to be efficient. A practical and economic balance has to be struck between the grade of concentrate produced, the ore mineral or metal recovery and costs of crushing, milling and separation.

7   Separation exploits physical properties of ore minerals, for example magnetization and electrical conductivity. Separation by froth flotation and leaching are appropriate for low-grade deposits. Leaching may eliminate the need for fine grinding, and may even be carried out *in situ*.

8   Metals are extracted from ore mineral concentrates by various methods. Smelting traditionally involves roasting ore, often with a flux and a reducing agent, to produce molten metal that separates from molten slag containing the gangue and impurities. Electrolysis may be used both to extract metals (for example, copper) from leachate solutions as well as to refine metals (for example, zinc) to a high degree of purity.

ENVIRONMENTAL IMPACTS OF METALS EXTRACTION AND SUSTAINABLE MINING

It is necessary to mine ore deposits to provide primary supplies of metals for today's world, yet mining, by its very nature, disrupts the natural environment. Mining involves much more than just digging large holes in the ground: the ore generally has to be crushed; ore mineral concentrates have to be produced; the metals have to be extracted; and the end product shipped before use. All these operations not only take up land, with visual (aesthetic) and ecological consequences, they also have associated wastes and emissions.

The satellite image of the Escondida mining operation (Figure 6.5b) gives a graphic representation of the extent of modern mining operations, showing the huge open pit, mounds of waste, a vast tailings pond, roadways and buildings. However, Escondida is located high in the Andes in a sparsely inhabited part of the Atacama Desert, where visual and ecological impacts have not been major issues.

Environmental consequences are not confined to the vicinity of a mine site. The dispersal of wastes through pollution of drainage systems — not just by solid or particulate wastes, but by chemicals in solution — and through pollution of the atmosphere by gaseous emissions, can be extensive, especially if released in a catastrophic incident. There are also social considerations: it is mainly local people that suffer the environmental consequences of mining, and for mining programmes to be acceptable today without opposition from pressure groups and public discontent, the local benefits of mining must be seen to outweigh the disadvantages.

The environmental impacts of mining were relatively small until the Industrial Revolution, when the scale of mining and ore processing began to increase. Even then, the environmental effects were largely ignored unless they had a severe impact on the mining operations themselves. Yet, much earlier, in the 16th century, the German scientist and physician, Agricola, in his extensive mining survey *De Re Metallica*, had reported concerns about the effects of mining:

> … the strongest argument of the detractors is that the fields are devastated by mining operations … when the ores are washed, the water which has been used poisons the brooks and streams … the inhabitants of these regions, on account of the devastation of their fields, woods, groves, brooks and rivers, find great difficulty in procuring the necessaries of life. … Thus it is said, it is clear to all that there is greater detriment from mining than the value of the metals which the mining produces.
>
> (Agricola, 1556)

Such sentiments still find favour with some campaigning groups today. Indeed, the impacts of mining became more severe with the increasing scale of operations during the 20th century, and it was commonplace for mine closures to leave hazardous legacies. This was partly due to mines becoming unprofitable when near to closure, when funds are not readily available to make good any consequences. However, in the last quarter of the 20th century there was an increasing realization of the severity of such problems, and the concerns of pressure groups, governments and even the industry itself have led to a change in attitude to environmental issues by many mining companies. As will be shown in the final part of this chapter, there are now requirements in most parts of the world for environmental management systems to be implemented during mining and for mine sites to be cleaned up on closure. Many companies now subscribe to the view that it is best practice and financially beneficial to plan for closure and to minimize environmental impacts during operation.

The first part of this chapter examines the potential for various environmental and socio-economic impacts to result from activities associated with metals mining. It also indicates how such impacts, or the risks of impacts, might be reduced — or mitigated. The second part reveals how the mining industry is moving towards what might be considered a contradiction: that is, sustainable mining.

7.1 The impacts of mining

The physical impacts of a mining activity are often the most obvious because of their visibility, whereas the chemical impacts may be more damaging, especially to living organisms. The socio-economic consequences of mining can also be significant, particularly in developing countries.

7.1.1 Land 'take', visual and ecological impacts

The visual intrusion of mining activities and the extent of land taken up by mining vary with the type, location and scale of mining. Many open pit metal mines are exceedingly large excavations that are very conspicuous from the air, yet can be almost invisible from the ground. The Bingham Canyon copper mine (Figure 2.12), Utah, is said to be the largest artificial hole on Earth; it is approximately 2.5 km across, about 1 km deep, and only 20 km away from Salt Lake City, but this gigantic hole is visible only from above or from close range. Open pits in raised topography can be highly visible, but their impact may be minimized by leaving the surrounding hillsides intact and excavating the area behind using 'keyhole' access via a narrow chasm or even a tunnel. Some underground mines, however, may be little more than holes, a few metres in diameter, in a hillside, or marked only by steel structures no bigger than a grain elevator.

In addition to the land taken for the mine itself (e.g. Figure 3.13c), even more land is required for mineral processing plant, the storage of waste in settling lagoons and waste tips, stockpiles and loading facilities (Figure 7.1). Every mine site also requires an infrastructure of roads and power lines, perhaps a rail link, and usually a water supply. Such constructions can easily be more extensive and conspicuous than the mine itself. All of these developments and activities destroy the existing landscape and habitats. In remote areas such impacts may not cause concern, but if the area is recognized as having scenic or heritage value, it may well have national park or wilderness area status and special controls on mining will apply. Habitat destruction generally attracts far less attention in developing countries such as the Congo or Zambia.

Figure 7.1 Visual impact of mining: ore handling and processing plant, stockpiles awaiting shipment, and waste tips.

Open pit mining, especially for low-grade ore, produces huge amounts of waste rock that may take up more land and have a much larger visual impact than the mine itself. Waste originates not only from ore processing, but also from the removal of overburden to create a pit shaped for optimum production and safety (Section 6.1). However, the amount of waste produced generally occupies a larger volume than that of the hole from which it was extracted.

●   Bearing in mind the nature of mining, why does this increase in volume occur?

○   Rocks are fragmented by blasting and crushing, so the volume of excavated rock is not only that of the rock itself but also includes the spaces between the fragments.

So, even if a mine was completely filled with its waste, there would be an excess. Waste is usually stored in large heaps near to the mine to minimize transport costs, but such tips can have a major visual impact on the landscape and may pose a hazard through mechanical failure or the erosion of the poorly consolidated waste by surface run-off. Landscaping and planting of waste rock and tailings heaps can reduce their visibility, improve stability and minimize erosion.

When mining is underground, the worked-out parts of a mine can be backfilled with waste (e.g. Figure 6.8), which helps to solve the disposal problem. In open pit mines, filling with waste may only become an option when the mine is worked out. In remote areas, it may seem to matter little if the pit is left open, perhaps to fill with water, but in other areas a large pit may be of value as a landfill site. Backfilling of pits and underground workings is expensive, but is increasingly a regulatory requirement, and more acceptable when built into the cost of the whole mining operation.

The impact of mining on the land surface can be reduced significantly where **remediation** (i.e. steps designed to alleviate environmental problems) is carried out, or where rehabilitation during mining is possible. **Rehabilitation** can simply be returning a site to its former state (which is also called *restoration*) or it can involve the creation of an alternative but environmentally acceptable state, such as might be achieved by flooding a pit to make an amenity or a nature reserve. In opencast (or strip) mines (Section 6.1.3), the area from which the ore has been removed is continually backfilled with overburden and waste from the area about to be mined, then covered with stockpiled topsoil, so as to rehabilitate the area and return it to its former state.

●   What kinds of ore deposits can be mined in this way?

○   Deposits that can be mined extensively, but only at shallow depth — for example, bauxite deposits (Figure 3.6) and some bedded iron ores.

Mining heavy minerals by dredging from 'black' sands covered by vegetated sand dunes is another example where simultaneous rehabilitation can be employed (Section 3.2, Figure 3.3). Overburden and waste is used to build up and reshape the land in worked-out areas prior to replanting to provide soil stability until indigenous plants recolonize. In some instances, rare or endangered plants and wildlife may have to be relocated before mining starts.

It is now standard practice when a mine is decommissioned for mine structures to be made safe and mine plant demolished. A striking example is shown in Figure 7.2, which shows rehabilitation at the former site of a uranium mine and ore processing facility at Elliot Lake, Canada. Tailings in the storage areas to the top right of Figure 7.2a were in part disposed of in the mine and in part redistributed and flooded to reduce oxidation (see Section 7.1.4).

However, there remain legacies of dereliction at many old abandoned mine sites. Although many of these sites are blots on the landscape, others can be important for industrial archaeology and may even be developed as tourist attractions. It would be hard to imagine the tin and copper mining area of Cornwall, England without its engine houses, which are now an established part of the landscape and a reflection of its mining heritage.

7.1.2 Mining subsidence

Underground mining may appear to be invisible in comparison to surface mining, but there is a potential for it to cause instability in overlying rocks and environmental damage resulting from either continuous or discontinuous subsidence.

Continuous subsidence is usually predictable, less disastrous and more or less limited to the lifetime of a mine. This type of subsidence occurs when thin, shallow-dipping or horizontal ore bodies are removed and the roof allowed to collapse, as in longwall coal mining (Drury, 2006) and in the underground mining of evaporite deposits, such as halite and gypsum.

Discontinuous subsidence is less predictable and often gives rise to rapid surface displacements over restricted areas. This type of ground failure can occur in a variety of circumstances. For example, in old deserted mine workings the pillars or timbers used for support eventually decay and collapse. Unsupported, a mine cavity may propagate towards the surface as blocks repeatedly cave-in from the roof. The 'block caving' mining method is designed to draw ore from above in a similar way. If the overlying waste rock also caves in, this could, in turn, eventually cause subsidence at the surface. The uncontrolled upward migration of an unsupported mining cavity through weak overlying rock is known as *chimney caving*. Such chimneys have been known to extend upwards for many hundreds of metres. Modern-day mine planning and engineering controls aim to ensure that such problems do not arise.

A particularly disastrous case of subsidence through chimney caving occurred at the Mufulira mine, a large copper mine in the Zambian Copperbelt. On

(a)

(b)

Figure 7.2 (a) The Denison mine site at Elliot Lake, Canada, with extensive milling plant and tailings storage areas, in 1993, shortly after closure. (b) The same site in 1998 after rehabilitation: mining plant has been removed, the shafts have been sealed and the tailings storage areas have been flooded.

25 September 1970, a cave-in propagated upwards about 500 m and broke surface under the mine tailings pond. Approximately 450 000 m³ of water-saturated mud (tailings) poured down the chimney and flooded part of the mine. Eighty-nine miners were killed and a large section of the mine was rendered inaccessible.

The damage potential for catastrophic, though localized, subsidence in populated areas overlying mine workings is obvious. Such problems occasionally arise in old mining areas, as in southwest England (Box 7.1), due to the presence of unrecorded workings. Backfilling of underground mines with waste is one solution to subsidence, but it is costly unless carried out as part of the mining operation. Another solution, where mining is in strong, competent rocks, is to plug or cap the shafts with concrete.

Box 7.1   Mining subsidence in Cornwall, England

Prior to 1876, UK mines were not required to keep accurate survey plans, and mining sometimes continued upwards (by stoping, Section 6.1.4) almost to 'grass root' level. In addition, the shafts, when abandoned, were often capped by timbers and covered with soil. Where no mining records exist, or where shafts were inaccurately marked on old maps, modern housing developments, schools and roads have sometimes been built over them. These shafts may only come to light years later when the timbers disintegrate and the surface fill collapses down the mineshaft. Subsidence can occur rapidly and without warning, causing catastrophic damage to property and death or injury to the inhabitants. The potential for disaster is shown in Figure 7.3. This form of collapse results either from deterioration of the shaft cappings, especially by periodic drying out of saturated timbers due to fluctuating groundwater levels, or from the erosion of shaft fill by the inflow of water.

- Bearing in mind the methods used for ore deposit exploration (Section 5), what kind of survey could detect mine workings in old mining areas?

- Surveys that 'see' underground and look for continuity of rock formations, i.e. geophysical surveys and drilling (Sections 5.5.1 and 5.8).

Geophysical surveys are cheaper to carry out than drilling, but drilling will be necessary for confirmation when a 'target' is found. Ground penetrating radar is particularly useful for detecting discontinuities

underground. Once found, the action taken may simply be to avoid the unsafe area, fill the shaft, or cap it securely with a plug or a concrete raft that is much bigger than the hole.

Figure 7.3   Unexpected subsidence from long-abandoned mine workings near Gunnislake, Cornwall, England.

7.1.3 Acid mine drainage

A major impact of many metal mines is **acid mine drainage** (AMD): the formation of acidic water (pH 1–3) due to the oxidation and breakdown of sulphide minerals, particularly pyrite (Drury, 2006; Smith, 2005). At nearly neutral pH, oxidation of pyrite and other sulphides by groundwater proceeds slowly (Equation 7.1). The hydrogen ions produced reduce the pH of the solution, creating conditions in which oxidation is assisted by natural bacterial action (Section 3.3.2) and iron(II) is soluble. Although the soluble Fe^{2+} ions produced may be transported in the acidic solution, oxidation often occurs, precipitating insoluble hydrated iron(III) oxides (Equation 7.2).

$$2FeS_2(s) + 7O_2 + 2H_2O = 2Fe^{2+}(aq) + 4SO_4^{2-}(aq) + 4H^+ \quad\quad (7.1)$$
pyrite   oxygenated water   soluble ions

$$4Fe^{2+}(aq) + O_2 + 10H_2O = 4Fe(OH)_3(s) + 8H^+ \quad\quad (7.2)$$
iron(II) ions   oxygenated   hydrated
           water   iron(III) oxide

Formation of acidic waters occurs naturally where near-surface (unmined) sulphide deposits have been oxidized and leached by percolating surface waters to form colourful iron(III) oxide cappings that are often called *gossans* (see secondary enrichment deposits, Section 3.3.2). These acidic solutions are sometimes known by the more general term *acid rock drainage*.

Through mining, the exposure of sulphide minerals to weathering and to oxygenated groundwaters is increased, thus accelerating this natural process. The decomposition of sulphides (Equation 7.1) not only acidifies the water, but also contaminates it with dissolved ions, including those of toxic elements such as As, Cd and Hg. In addition, mining waste also contains sulphides (often mainly pyrite), which are finely ground during ore processing (Section 6.2.2) and then either discarded into tailings dams (see Section 7.1.4) or heaped onto waste tips where they are oxidized and leached by mildly acidic rainwater to form AMD seepage or runoff. Figure 7.4 shows heavily contaminated acidic waters in Manitoba, Canada, derived from mine tailings rich in pyrite with minor chalcopyrite and sphalerite that have undergone oxidation for more than 50 years.

Although all mineral deposits that contain iron sulphides have a potential to form AMD, a number of other factors are important. The rate of the oxidation is controlled by temperature; the ease by which oxygenated water can access sulphide grains; the rate of bacterial growth; and the chemical nature of the host rock. Limestone, for example, neutralizes rapidly any acidity generated by sulphide oxidation.

 How is acidity neutralized in limestone rocks? What chemical reaction could remove the hydrogen ions produced by sulphide oxidation?

Figure 7.4 The shoreline of Woods Lake, Sherridon, Manitoba, which has been receiving AMD for over 50 years. The wine-red waters are highly acidic, pH 2.3, and contain elevated concentrations of metals.

Hydrogen ions (H^+) react with the limestone ($CaCO_3$) as follows (see also Box 3.1):

$$CaCO_3(s) + H^+ = Ca^{2+}(aq) + HCO_3^- \qquad (7.3)$$

This *removal* of H^+ ions increases the pH, thus neutralizing the solution, but a consequence is increased salinity with high levels of SO_4^{2-} (see Equation 7.1), which can be costly to eradicate.

The high acidity of AMD poses major problems for aquatic organisms, causing their distress and even death. At the same time, the oxidation of iron(II) in solution leads to the precipitation of red–brown hydrated iron(III) oxide, which forms slimes that coat surfaces in and around drainage channels (Figure 7.5) that stop fish and other organisms feeding and breeding. However, the names of the rivers in some major mining areas — the Rio Tinto in southern Spain and the Red River in Cornwall — suggest that this effect is not a new phenomenon and may have occurred naturally prior to mining.

Figure 7.5 The Carnon River in Cornwall with overbank areas contaminated by rusty-coloured hydrated iron(III) oxide.

The pollutants in minewaters largely depend on the chemistry of the mineral deposit, the availability of water, and its chemistry (i.e. its pH and oxidation state). The level of hazard depends on the toxicity of the pollutants. For example, cadmium may be only a minor component of sphalerite in some zinc deposits, but if released during oxidation of the sphalerite, it could be hazardous, whereas the zinc is less harmful. An acidic oxidizing solution may carry a range of metals, including toxic metals, especially at pH <5, when cations such as Cu^{2+} and Zn^{2+} are soluble. Elements from associated minerals (e.g. arsenic from arsenopyrite, FeAsS) also form soluble complexes, such as the arsenate anion, AsO_4^{3-}. Such ions are then transported in solution until, perhaps, a change of pH or oxidation conditions, or the interaction with other ions, causes their precipitation. Alternatively, they may be adsorbed onto grains of sediment: the arsenate ion being attracted to surfaces that carry a positive charge, particularly those coated by hydrated iron(III) oxides. Arsenic is then transported in the iron-rich coating on these composite sedimentary grains.

When an active mine is pumped to provide access to working faces, the water that has percolated through the mineralized rock, where oxidation reactions can take place, is likely to be contaminated by AMD and to contain soluble metal ions. However, these reactions are generally slow, and while meteoric water is being flushed through, the AMD is diluted. In an abandoned mine, however, where no such flushing occurs, concentrations of metals and acidity can build up. Also, many secondary ore minerals, formed on exposure to moist conditions, are more susceptible to dissolution than primary minerals, and on flooding, release even more metals into solution. Therefore, levels of toxic metals and acidity from an abandoned mine may well exceed those from an active mine. In addition, the pumping of an active mine is likely to be controlled and procedures set in place for the decontamination of discharges, whereas at an abandoned mine there might be no such systems in place for treatment, and discharges would more likely be irregular and unpredictable, depending on groundwater levels and rainfall. Probably the most serious and the best-publicized case of AMD affecting metal mines in the UK is that reviewed in Box 7.2.

Box 7.2   AMD at Wheal Jane Mine in Cornwall

In the early 1990s the Wheal Jane tin–copper mine in Cornwall (Figure 7.6a), which had been worked underground on a large scale for some 20 years, was closed down and allowed to flood. Environmental concerns had not been a priority when the mine opened in 1970, or when planning permission was obtained to continue operations a decade later. Following closure, it was left to the National Rivers Authority (NRA; now the Environment Agency) to monitor water quality. They recognized that the measures taken by the last operating company were inadequate and implemented interim treatment measures: the main drainage adit was plugged and water was pumped into the tailings pond for treatment with lime to precipitate metals and to reduce the acidity before being released into the Carnon River. However, in January 1992, when water levels in the mine were high, pumping was stopped because the weather turned stormy and the tailings pond was approaching full capacity. With the build-up of pressure, the plug burst and many millions of litres (1 Ml = 10^3 m^3) of metal-rich AMD escaped into the Carnon River and flowed into the Carrick Roads estuary.

Cadmium levels in the Carnon River rose dramatically following this incident (Figure 7.7). Previously, the average background level of cadmium had been 6 µg l^{-1}, which was well above the NRA's quality standard for cadmium of 1 µg l^{-1} (1 µg l^{-1} = 1 ppb).

● According to Figure 7.7, what level did the cadmium concentration in the river reach after the 'burst' incident? How does that compare with the background level of cadmium in the Carnon River?

◐ It reached at least 600 µg l^{-1} Cd, which is more than a hundred times the background level.

The company that abandoned Wheal Jane was under no legal obligation to carry out corrective measures because the original mining activities pre-dated planning requirements. Therefore, the NRA, with its responsibility for water quality, had to take control. After pumping was resumed and the capacity for treatment increased, it took about 3 months to remedy the situation (Figure 7.7).

Prior to the exceptional discharge of January 1992, there had been little aquatic life in the Carnon River

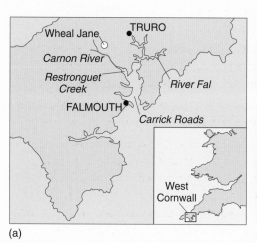

(a)   (b)

Figure 7.6   (a) The location of the Wheal Jane Mine; (b) aerial view of the tailings dam with the mine beyond.

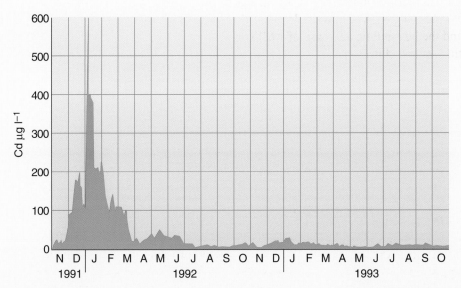

Figure 7.7 Cadmium concentrations in the Carnon River between November 1991 and October 1993.

because of the high background levels of metals; even in the tidal waters of Restronguet Creek only a few metal-tolerant species thrived. Shortly after the metal-rich discharge, surveys revealed only minimal impact on the biological community, but in the mid-1990s, the deposition of contaminants from minewaters was still evident in the Carnon River (Figure 7.5). It is difficult to evaluate the consequences of the 1992 contamination. Although bird deaths in the area (particularly swans in the winter of 1993) were blamed on the spillage, shellfish in the Carrick Roads estuary were unaffected.

In the mid 1990s, pilot schemes were set up at Wheal Jane to develop and study long-term solutions for AMD. The work was carried out by the Environment Agency at a cost of £3.4 million to set up and almost £1 million each year to run. The minewater was pumped to prevent another build-up of pressure and sudden discharge, and treated by either an active or a passive treatment scheme.

The *active* scheme treats most of the minewater flow. The AMD is mixed with lime slurry, raising the pH to 9.5, and aerated to bring about chemical neutralization and oxidization. The precipitated solids settle and are transferred to the tailings pond. The clarified water is reused or discharged to the Carnon River. In a 22-month period, 12.3 Mm³ of AMD was treated, removing some 3200 t of metals at a removal efficiency of 99%.

The *passive* scheme involves splitting the flow through three separate experimental wetland **bioremediation** systems that differ only according to which of the following pre-treatments is employed:

1 lime dosing, which raises the pH to 5 (the limit in oxic conditions without causing excessive precipitation of metal oxides);

2 an anoxic limestone drain, which raises the pH to 6 by limestone dissolution with minimal oxidation (and precipitation) of iron;

3 no modification, which leaves the pH at <4.

The pre-treatment stage modifies the pH of the water before it passes through the main extraction stages of each bioremediation system. These are:

- a series of aerobic reed beds designed to remove iron and arsenic;

- an anaerobic cell to encourage bacterial reduction of sulphate and the removal of zinc, copper, cadmium and remaining iron as sulphides;

- aerobic rock filters to promote algal growth, remove manganese and act as a 'polishing stage'.

The passive scheme has been operating for several years and has proved effective at removing toxic metals such as cadmium, copper and arsenic. Some experimental results are listed in Table 7.1. Although a passive bioremediation system has limitations in terms of throughput, once established it requires little maintenance or intervention, and in this case, it has a planned life of some 30 years.

Table 7.1   Metal contents of minewaters measured at various points in the three experimental bioremediation systems (Whitehead et al., 2005).

concentrations (mg l^{-1}):	Lime dosing (pH ~5)			Anoxic limestone drain (pH ~6)			No pre-treatment (pH <4)		
	Fe	As	Zn	Fe	As	Zn	Fe	As	Zn
initially	143.6	2.7	82.0	143.6	2.7	82.0	143.6	2.7	82.0
after pre-treatment	136.0	1.6	80.8	112.0	0.3	60.2	n/a	n/a	n/a
after aerobic cells	41.8	0.0	80.8	25.3	0.0	48.4	35.3	0.0	84.6
after anaerobic cells	43.8	0.0	34.5	17.6	0.0	1.0	52.3	0.0	47.1
after anaerobic rock filters	13.2	0.0	45.6	2.2	0.0	4.9	12.7	0.0	51.3

n/a = not applicable

Question 7.1

(a) Given the background of the Wheal Jane discharges, what lessons might be learnt that could help to avoid such problems following mine closure in future?

(b) With reference to Table 7.1, which of the passive bioremediation systems, as defined by its pre-treatment, is the most successful? Which stage of treatment is usually the most effective?

Once developed, AMD is difficult and costly to control with lime neutralization and/or bioremediation (Box 7.2). Prevention and mitigation — by reducing access of oxygenated water and bacterial activity — are better solutions. With regard to waste, this demands isolation, such as by sealing or encapsulation. Options include: covering the waste with water so as to restrict water migration and contact with oxygen; reducing permeability by mixing waste with inert fines to reduce water migration and oxygen penetration; and use of bactericidal agents to reduce bacterial activity. Maximizing the removal of sulphides from wastes (e.g. by flotation) and their separate disposal is another option. In pits and mines, backfilling with inert waste and flooding may reduce access of oxygen, but flooding is effective only where groundwater is static and unable to migrate — unlike the circumstances at Wheal Jane.

7.1.4   Tailings

Processing ore, particularly low-grade, disseminated ore, produces large quantities of fine-grained waste, or tailings, the handling of which presents major problems for the mining industry. The waste from the wet separation of ore minerals forms a slurry of finely ground rock that still contains ore minerals (as the separation process is never 100% efficient, Box 6.3), and is contaminated by processing chemicals that cannot be reclaimed.

● What are likely to be the main environmental problems of tailings disposal?

○ They are:

   ● the sheer volume of material, which requires large areas for storage;

   ● the production of AMD due to the presence of fine-grained sulphide minerals, especially pyrite, that are susceptible to decomposition in wet oxidizing conditions;

- toxicity due to heavy metals released from decomposing ore minerals and to chemical reagents used for ore processing.

Historically, tailings were often dumped into the nearest watercourse, but the environmental problems associated with large volumes of acid-generating sediment have led to this practice mostly being discontinued. However, this method is still used for waste disposal at a few major mines, such as the Grasberg mine in Indonesia and the Ok Tedi mine in Papua New Guinea, where the rainfall is high and the nearby terrain is steep and unstable. Today, most tailings are deposited in containment areas, which often cover large areas (several square kilometres, e.g. Figure 6.5b), where the solids settle out and the water is either recycled to the ore processing plant for re-use or allowed to evaporate. An embankment provides containment, and the whole structure is often referred to as a **tailings dam** (see Figure 7.6b). Some forms of containment immerse the tailings beneath more than a metre of water (as, for example, at the Lisheen sulphide mine in Ireland) to restrict access of oxygen, thus inhibiting the oxidation of fine sulphides that would generate AMD (Section 7.1.3).

Tailings dams are usually engineered with an impermeable clay liner to avoid seepage (Figure 7.8). The embankment is built up in stages to accommodate increasing amounts of tailings. Some structures are built (Figure 7.8a) so that the crest of the embankment migrates towards the interior of the impoundment (the upstream method), but this design has often been unstable and its use largely discontinued because, when saturated, the fine tailings that form the foundation of

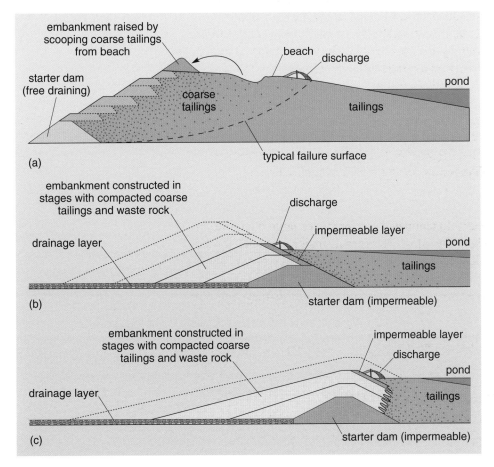

Figure 7.8 Tailings dam embankment design: (a) the upstream method (with failure surface); (b) the downstream method; (c) the centreline method.

the extended embankment are liable to shear and cause dam failure. The design in which the crest migrates outwards (the downstream method) requires much more material to build the embankment, and takes up more space (Figure 7.8b), but is more stable, as is the similar, centreline version (Figure 7.8c).

Spillage or overtopping of the containment must be prevented, as it can cause erosion of the embankment and lead to major leakage. This occurred at Baia Mare, Romania, in January 2000, when heavy rain and snow caused the cyanide-contaminated waters of a gold mine tailings pond to spill over and to reach major rivers. Huge numbers of fish were killed: either by the cyanide, which did not break down in the icy conditions as quickly as expected, or by bleach used by some local authorities to neutralize the cyanide. Elevated levels of cyanide were still detectable four weeks later in waters flowing out through the Danube delta, some 2000 km downstream.

The failure of a tailings containment through a structural defect can lead to the catastrophic release of contaminated water and large quantities of potentially acid-generating sludge with a complement of toxic metals. Thus, tailings dams require careful engineering, maintenance and constant monitoring as failures can result in severe environmental impacts on low-lying areas nearby. The Los Frailes incident in Spain in 1998, though without loss of human life, involved economic and ecological damage to large areas (see Box 7.3). Tailings containments are built up over many years and maintaining engineering quality control can be a problem, particularly when mining operations change hands. A particularly serious example of tailings dam failure occurred at Merriespruit, South Africa, in the spring of 1994, when water laden with tailings from a gold mine flowed into a small town after a rainstorm, killing 17 people. The mining company and their consulting engineers were forced to pay out large sums (R20 million, which was about US$5 million in 1995–96) in compensation. Clearly, it is in a company's best interests to manage its operations well.

Box 7.3 Los Frailes tailings dam failure

Overnight on 25 April 1998, an embankment retaining a 2 km^2 tailings impoundment failed at the Los Frailes mine near Seville, Spain (Figure 7.9a). In the space of a few hours, 1.5 Mm^3 of tailings solids and 5.5 Mm^3 of acidic tailings water, with pH 2–4 and elevated levels of Cu, Pb, Zn and Fe, were released. Most of this material flowed into the Rio Agrio and the Rio Guadiarmar, killing fish and other aquatic life, flooding over fifty irrigation wells and affecting 4600 hectares (46 km^2) of flood-plain agricultural and fruit-growing land (Figure 7.9b). Fifty kilometres downstream, it reached the edge of the Doñana National Park, a UN World Heritage Site, where a series of embankments were rapidly built to stop the advance and hold the floodwater in the Entremuros irrigation canal until the water dispersed along its usual path to the east.

The embankment had been constructed of waste rock, with a clay liner, and reached a height of 25 m. The storage facility was originally constructed in the 1980s to service the Aznalcóllar mine, which closed in 1996. The tailings dam continued to be used when the nearby Los Frailes ore body was brought into production in 1997. The failure occurred because the pore pressure of water in the sedimentary rock strata beneath the dam wall was too high, overstressing the rock and causing slippage within a weak layer of rock, allowing the embankment and its foundations to move. Although some reports suggest that there were earlier

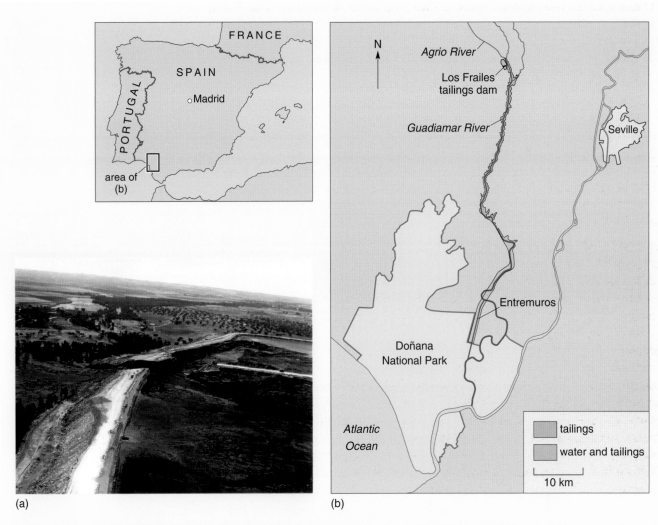

Figure 7.9 (a) The failed Los Frailes tailings dam, showing the 60 m displacement of the embankment, erosion of the tailings deposits behind the breach and mud covering the flood plain below the breach. (b) The area affected by the release of tailings and contaminated water.

signs of instability and leakage, the official report concluded that the failure could not have been foreseen.

The clean-up was handled by the mining company, regional government and environmental agencies, at a cost in excess of US$135 million. Remediation work involved the removal of 4–5 Mm³ of tailings and contaminated soil that were dumped into the mined-out Aznalcóllar pit. The work had to be completed in a 5-month period before the wet season started, and it left a barren landscape devoid of vegetation. A soil-sampling programme was carried out to check that levels of Cu, Zn and

As were acceptable; repeated cleaning was necessary in some places. A diverse community of aquatic organisms had become established in the river only 6 months after the incident, and fish had returned by 1999. Significant long-term effects on the river's ecosystems are unlikely.

The embankment was rebuilt, but the impoundment was taken out of service and covered to reduce infiltration and risk of future failure. After the incident, waste from the Los Frailes mine was dumped in the Aznalcóllar pit until 2001 when the mine closed due to insolvency and liabilities for compensation.

Submarine disposal of tailings offshore is an alternative means of disposal that has been used in recent years, particularly in island locations.

● What advantages might be associated with submarine tailings disposal?

○ It avoids taking up land for tailings storage, especially where space is limited and, at the same time, effectively disposes of tailings under water thus avoiding oxidation and AMD implications.

However, it is has been recognized that disposal in shallow coastal waters is environmentally unsatisfactory: the waste increases water turbidity and smothers organisms, spreads over large areas, and can be washed up on shore. Deep-water disposal to depths where little light penetrates and marine life is sparse is arguably less damaging and favoured by some mining companies, but pipeline failures and the uncontrolled spread of fine sediment over large areas can still cause considerable ecological damage. Also, unless there is a suitable slope to carry material away from the outfall, the slurry bubbles through the accumulating mound of sediment, creating turbulence and mixing with the oxygenated waters above. For example, tailings from Minahasa Raya gold mine in Indonesia are piped 800 m out to sea to a depth of 80 m, but leakages into shallow water due to pipeline fractures have caused serious losses to the fishing industry and have destroyed coral reefs (MMSD, 2002).

The dumping of waste into river systems has long been a cheap and convenient form of tailings disposal and the environmental damage caused is well known. There are only three large mines still using this method of disposal, all in western Pacific islands, where dangers of erosion by high rainfall and the likelihood of seismic events triggering instability pose greater risks: alternative means of disposal such as tailings dams would be susceptible to mass movement and mud flows. The Ok Tedi gold and copper mine in Papua New Guinea is one that disposes of tailings and waste rock into a major river and has created severe ecological problems downstream. These are due to overbank flooding and the deposition of sediment containing mine waste in which oxidation of sulphide grains produces acidity and causes vegetation 'die-back' over large areas of the flood plain. One of the companies involved in the project, BHP Billiton, withdrew in 2002 because it no longer wished to be associated with this method of disposal. However, all around the world, rivers are still used for disposal of mine waste, especially from small-scale operations.

One option for the disposal of tailings from underground mines is mixing with cement and coarser rock waste for use in backfilling the mine workings (e.g. Figure 6.8), thus reducing the incidence of rock failure and subsidence.

7.1.5 Ore processing reagents

Many different chemicals are used in the various procedures for concentrating minerals and extracting metals: froth flotation employs inorganic and organic chemicals, including oils; leaching of metals employs various solvents, including sodium cyanide (Section 6.2.2).

Some chemical reagents are harmless: others are highly toxic. The wastes from these various separating procedures are likely to be contaminated with reagents and may pose risks to the environment. Here, two examples of the potential for contamination during the processing of gold ore are examined: mercury is used in primitive mining operations; cyanide is used by mining companies on an industrial scale.

Mercury extraction of gold

Small-scale artisanal mining (Section 5.1) frequently causes environmental problems because the operators have insufficient capital to invest in clean methods or to maintain environmental safeguards. A prime example is the impact of artisanal gold mining on parts of the Amazon Basin. The miners, who numbered at least 500 000 in the 1980s, use mercury to extract gold from alluvial placer deposits. The sediment is first hosed to wash away light minerals and mud; the remaining gold-bearing sand is then concentrated either by panning or using flowing water in sluice boxes. The concentrate is mixed with mercury, which dissolves the gold to form a dense *amalgam* (a mercury solution) that settles out. The gold is then recovered by roasting the amalgam to vaporize the mercury, which boils at 357 °C, leaving the gold behind.

Workers inhaling mercury vapour often suffer mercury poisoning of the respiratory system, but can recover once their exposure to mercury ceases. Although most of the mercury is condensed and reused, much ends up in soils and rivers, where it is transformed by bacteria into methyl mercury, the complex ion $[CH_3Hg]^+$, a cumulative poison for humans that attacks brain cells and affects brain control functions, thus presenting a much more serious problem. Over 1 kg of mercury is lost (for every 6–8 kg used) in recovering 1 kg of gold, and around 100 t of mercury have been released into the Madeira River of the SW Amazon Basin. Once in the river, mercury enters the food chain as methyl mercury and becomes concentrated in fish, the staple diet of the native Indians. Similar problems of mercury contamination associated with artisanal mining are endemic in the Philippines and Indonesia, and in Tanzania and Zimbabwe. Improved technologies are being developed that would reduce risks to artisanal miners, but changing traditional practices proves difficult.

Cyanide extraction of gold

The revival of gold mining in the western United States (Section 4.2.1) in the last decades of the 20th century has involved low-grade ore deposits and relies on large-scale, mechanized open pit mining and the use of heap leaching (Section 6.2.2).

   What is the chemical basis for heap leaching of gold, and how is it used?

   Sodium cyanide solution dissolves gold by forming the soluble gold cyanyl complex ion, $[Au(CN)_2]^-$ (Equation 6.3). The ore needs only to be coarsely crushed to allow the solution access to the fine gold grains. Crushed ore is piled onto an impermeable membrane and sprayed with sodium cyanide solution. The gold-laden cyanide solution is collected and the gold extracted by adsorption onto carbon (Box 6.4).

Worldwide, almost 90% of mined gold is now extracted with cyanide solution. Environmental problems arise due to the toxicity of cyanide compounds, which can be lethal to humans and other organisms, especially aquatic life. Fortunately, cyanide in solution is rapidly oxidized by exposure to sunlight. To minimize losses, cyanide solutions are contained by lining the leach pads with an impermeable membrane (e.g. Figure 6.17), enabling as much as 90% of used leach solutions to be recycled. Warnings prevent humans from taking water from collection ponds, but migratory birds are unable to distinguish them from ordinary waterholes. The problem of bird deaths has been largely solved by mechanical bird-scarers and the use of nets and polystyrene balls to cover smaller ponds. The US Environmental Protection Agency has imposed severe fines to ensure precautions are taken to prevent bird deaths. One company was fined US$25 000 each time a duck was found dead on its property. With no economic alternative to the use of cyanide for extracting low-grade gold, the mining industry has developed a comprehensive Code of Practice to manage cyanide and minimize the risks for workers, communities and the environment.

A greater problem can be leakages of wastes containing cyanide, particularly cyanide-bearing solutions from tailings ponds, as already noted for the Baia Mare spill in Romania (Section 7.1.4). Such contamination of watercourses has acute impacts on aquatic organisms (e.g. deaths of fish) and can destroy fisheries and livelihoods. Although the contamination is usually a short-term effect, recovery of populations can take many years. Another danger is the uncontrolled use of cyanide by artisanal miners (Figure 7.10), with the consequent detrimental effects on the health of miners and the contamination of watercourses.

Figure 7.10 A cyanide pond in close proximity to an artisanal miner's hut in the Philippines.

7.1.6 Emissions from smelting

Obtaining metals from ore minerals involves chemical processes (sometimes very aggressive ones) generally known as smelting (Section 6.3). Smelting poses major problems as metal oxide dust, volatized metal particulates and sulphur oxide gases are released into the atmosphere, along with chimneystack emissions. Through direct fallout, often assisted by rainfall, these pollutants can accumulate in soil, surface water and groundwater. Pollutants are not confined to the metals sought: volatile elements released from smelting fluxes and ore mineral impurities may also be toxic. For example, many electrolytic aluminium smelters have polluted the surrounding areas with fluorine released from the fluxes used to dissolve the aluminium ore (Section 6.3). However, the consequences of fallout from smelters are due mainly to toxic metals and acid rain.

Toxic metals

The smelting of lead and zinc poses special problems because of the toxicity of lead (Box 7.4) and the presence of toxic metals such as arsenic, cadmium, mercury and thallium as trace constituents in the ore mineral concentrates. Cadmium is of special concern in zinc smelting as it is commonly present (substituting for small amounts of zinc) in the main zinc ore mineral, sphalerite (Table 1.5). It has been responsible for serious health problems and even deaths in Japan, where high levels of cadmium released into the atmosphere from smelters have contaminated rice-growing soils in surrounding areas. Rice is the staple diet in Japan and cadmium-contaminated rice causes Itai-Itai disease, which destroys human bone structure. Whereas background levels of cadmium in rice plants were less than 0.1 ppm, plants within 0.5 km of one smelter contained 18 ppm, and the soil contained over 30 ppm cadmium.

Although it closed in 2003, the largest lead–zinc smelter in the UK was, for many years, at Avonmouth, near Bristol, and had long produced metal from imported

Box 7.4 Bioavailability — lead

Metals are released in different forms during the mining, processing and smelting of ores. Although small amounts of many metals are essential to the health of humans and other organisms, larger amounts can be toxic, causing health problems and even death. Some metals, such as arsenic, cadmium, mercury and thallium, are toxic even in small quantities. However, the effects of metal pollution on humans and wildlife depend in part on the bioavailability of these toxic metals. **Bioavailability** is the extent to which a metal can be absorbed by organisms, which depends on its chemical form.

The bioavailability of lead has been investigated in detail because lead is a neurotoxin, and has a particularly severe impact on young children, causing impaired intelligence and slowed reaction times. Studies have demonstrated that children take up lead from several sources, mainly by ingestion of dust from hand contact. The amount of lead taken up depends on its bioavailability and thus on its chemical and mineralogical form. The bioavailability of lead to humans depends on the solubility of ingested dust particles during their passage through the gastro-intestinal tract. Lead is taken into the blood by absorption through the wall of the small intestine after dissolution by acidic stomach fluids (pH ~1.4).

The potential for lead poisoning from flaking paint and vehicle exhaust emissions (Sections 1.1.1 and 1.1.2) has been the main concern, and has led to the banning of its use in these applications. Lead also occurs in the contaminated soils of mining and smelting areas. Although galena (lead sulphide) is the main mineral of lead ores, complex lead oxides dominate in the soils of mining areas, occurring with lesser amounts of lead sulphates and phosphates. Although galena is the most soluble of these in the stomach, it is only sparingly so; the complex oxides and phosphates are even less soluble. Sulphides dominate only in areas contaminated by dust from ore loading.

In areas of lead smelting, however, the main lead minerals are simple oxides, which are more readily soluble and much more easily absorbed into the body than lead minerals in mining areas. Consequently, there are dangers in living close to lead–zinc smelters and particular care is necessary in clean-up operations at, and around, former smelting sites. In the past, clean-up operations were often inadequate and left highly contaminated sites.

lead–zinc sulphide ores. The smelting process involved the roasting of ore and the reduction of the oxide sinter with coke to produce metal. Emissions included metallic vapour that condensed, along with lead, zinc and cadmium oxide particulates. In recent times, cadmium has been removed, along with sulphur and mercury oxides, from waste gases, but in the past it was not collected from smelter chimneystack emissions and was released into the atmosphere. Soil surveys conducted around the Avonmouth smelter (Figure 7.11) have revealed lead and cadmium contamination extending almost 5 km from the smelter, and quite heavy contamination within 2 km.

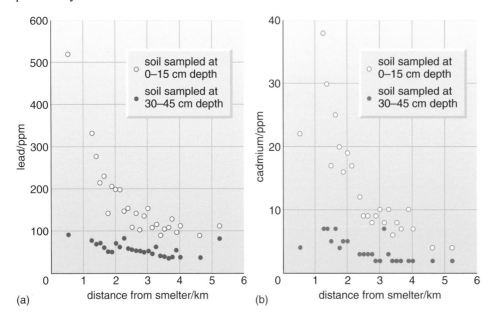

Figure 7.11   Contamination in soils along a traverse downwind for ~5 km from the Avonmouth smelter: (a) concentrations of lead; (b) concentrations of cadmium.

Question 7.2

Examine Figure 7.11, and then answer the following:

(a) Around the Avonmouth smelter, how do the concentrations of lead measured in soil compare with those of cadmium? Would you expect their harmful effects to differ correspondingly?

(b) For what reason are the concentrations of lead and cadmium from well below the surface of the soil less than they are nearer the surface?

Nowadays, smelter stack gases are filtered to remove particulates, and sulphur dioxide is recovered to produce sulphuric acid. In the UK, emissions from smelter stacks must comply with limits set by the Environment Agency. Slag disposal is another problem. Around 90 000 tonnes of slag per year were produced at Avonmouth and, having no market, it had to be stored on site. Slag often contains up to 12% base metal (more than many ore deposits) and during long-term storage may be susceptible to leaching by ground and surface waters. Besides pollution of the surrounding area, lead smelting is potentially hazardous to workers within the plant, and their exposure to lead has to be monitored regularly by blood sampling.

The impact of individual smelters can be more serious than that of individual mines, and they are traditionally sited near to energy supplies, often near to markets. For example, although Europe mines only 10% of the world's lead, it smelts 25% of all the lead mined. Around smelters, soils may be contaminated with metals deposited as particulates, which are likely to be in a bioavailable form (Box 7.4). Clean-up operations are generally expensive. The clean-up costs of the US lead smelting industry have been estimated at 9–12% of net production costs. Burial with 'clean' topsoil is often the cheapest option. A promising technique for cleaning up contaminated sites is described in Box 7.5. In most countries today, however, environmental safeguards are becoming increasingly stringent and regular monitoring is obligatory to ensure smelter emission levels are within regulatory limits.

Acid rain

Emission of sulphur dioxide produced by the oxidation of sulphide minerals during smelting has made major contributions to acid rain in some parts of the world. The two largest nickel smelters — at Sudbury in northern Ontario, Canada, and at Noril'sk in northern Siberia, Russia — are two of the largest single emitters of sulphur dioxide. If vented into the atmosphere, sulphur dioxide is converted into sulphuric acid by reaction with water to form acid rain. At both Sudbury and Noril'sk, the smelters are surrounded by areas of crystalline rocks with a limited covering of soil, which is unable to neutralize the acid rain. Elements that are normally stable, such as aluminium (soluble below pH 4: Figure 3.7), are leached from soils and pollute lakes, killing fish.

Box 7.5   Green mining and land decontamination

Some specialized plant species, known as metallophytes, grow in mineralized areas, tolerating soil conditions that would be hostile to most plants. Some of these are **hyperaccumulator plants**, which take up large quantities of toxic metals. The dried foliage of *Thlaspi caerulescens* (Figure 7.12), a member of the cabbage family, which grows on sites of zinc mineralization in central Europe, can contain up to 30 000 ppm Zn and 10 000 ppm Cd.

Various hyperaccumulator plants can concentrate metals such as zinc, cadmium, lead, nickel, copper, cobalt, manganese and chromium. Hyperaccumulators are capable of extracting appreciable quantities of metals from enriched soils and produce metal-rich ash when the dried foliage is burnt.

- What uses could be made of these specialized hyperaccumulator plants?
- They could remove toxic metals from contaminated soils and their foliage could be harvested to extract the metals.

Thus, hyperaccumulators could provide a 'green' method of cleaning up or remediation of contaminated land around mine sites or smelters, and could even be a basis for 'green mining'. But, to function effectively, large quantities of foliage would have to be produced, and most hyperaccumulator species, such as *T. caerulescens*, tend to have low growth rates, even when fertilizers are applied. Therefore, although hyperaccumulators might seem to have great potential for decontamination, their use may only be practical if they are part of a long-term (15–20 year) programme of remediation.

Figure 7.12   *Thlaspi caerulescens*, a Zn–Cd hyperaccumulator plant.

Efforts to reduce the problem at Sudbury are detailed in Box 7.6. The problem at Noril'sk has not yet been tackled: sulphur dioxide emissions in the early 2000s are thought to be about 2 Mt per year and satellite imagery shows that some 6000 km^2 of forest to the southeast of Noril'sk has been destroyed.

Box 7.6   Acid rain — Sudbury, Ontario

Acid rain, from the smelting of nickel and copper sulphide ores, has had a profound environmental impact on the region around Sudbury. For every tonne of nickel produced from the ore, as much as eight tonnes of sulphur potentially could be released as sulphur dioxide.

Nickel production at Sudbury goes back over 100 years, when open-bed roasting was part of the smelting process. This was extremely damaging environmentally for two reasons: vast quantities of sulphur dioxide pollution were released at ground level, and indigenous pine forest was felled to provide timber as fuel. By the 1920s, smelting was contained in factories and emissions were vented through chimneystacks. In the late 1940s, magnetic separation technology was developed to improve the separation and removal of pyrrhotite, the iron sulphide mineral that contains small amounts of nickel, but which is a major source of SO_2. Further processing steps were introduced in the 1960s to remove more pyrrhotite and cut SO_2 emissions.

In 1972, the 387 m Sudbury 'Superstack' was built (Figure 7.13) to raise the height at which waste gases were discharged and to achieve greater dispersal of those wastes. It significantly improved the air quality and vegetation growth around Sudbury and allowed the rehabilitation of local environments. However, the pollutants discharged had unforeseen impacts elsewhere. Some 60 km downwind of the superstack is the Killarney Provincial Park, where the lakes had been alkaline to neutral, but became acidic due to the acid rain from the Sudbury plume. Recognition of this problem in the 1970s led to intensive monitoring of ecosystems in the area.

Increased effort and investment have been put into ore processing technologies at Sudbury, both to improve productivity and to mitigate environmental impacts. New smelting technologies have reduced SO_2 emissions — SO_2 is now reclaimed to produce marketable sulphuric acid — and the improved separation of pentlandite has further reduced the amount of pyrrhotite fed into the smelter. As a result, SO_2 emissions had dropped to 265 000 t a year by 1994 — only 12% of the 1965 level and a drop of 60% on the 1980 level. By 2002 emissions were down to 243 000 t, with only 1.11 tonne of SO_2 emitted per tonne of metal produced. However, a consequence of more efficient mineral separation is that appreciable quantities of nickel now reside in waste tips awaiting technological advances to extract nickel cleanly from pyrrhotite at a reasonable price.

Reclamation of waste tips and tailings in the Sudbury area has established habitats for wildlife and restored much of the devastated landscape. Rehabilitation involves the use of grasses and clovers, which grow on the toxic acidic soil with the aid of fertilizers and lime, to establish a humus layer for subsequent colonization by indigenous trees.

Figure 7.13   The Sudbury 'Superstack', built to achieve greater dispersal of sulphur dioxide, dwarfs earlier chimneystacks.

Question 7.3

Why does smelting sometimes present a greater environmental threat than mining operations?

7.1.7   Socio-economic consequences

Consequences of mining extend beyond the physical environment. Mining has implications for local people, both those involved in mining and those affected by it, and for whole nations, especially developing ones. There can be economic benefits, however, with improved standards of living as a result of employment or compensation measures. For example, mining has often been responsible for bringing large numbers of people into sparsely inhabited areas. Mount Isa in Queensland, Australia, is a substantial town that would not have existed but for the discovery of rich copper ores in the 1920s. Another example is Noril'sk in Northern Siberia, which, with a population of 180 000, is one of only three large towns north of the Arctic Circle and would not have existed without nickel mining and smelting.

There can also be social disruption through displacement of settlements, loss of livelihoods, and social unrest where peoples may have been treated unfairly, or where residents are subject to attacks or other forms of lawlessness from disaffected or renegade groups. For example, copper mining on the island of Bougainville, part of Papua New Guinea, was the catalyst for a civil war that lasted some ten years and cost an estimated 15 000 lives. The mine, opened in 1972, created severe environmental devastation, largely due to waste disposal, and conflict with landowners. The mine closed, following sabotage, in 1989. The local people saw insufficient benefits or compensation, yet national government gladly received taxes and then sent in troops to deal with the unrest. In 2005, a new government in Bougainville voted to reopen the mine, thus creating new concerns that there might be a recurrence of earlier hostilities.

The economic benefits of mining may be questioned when it causes significant changes to the lives of indigenous people. For example, the 1849 gold rush in California was one of the main factors that encouraged the settlement of the American west coast, and led to the development of rail links and the opening up of the Mid-west. It could be argued that this was progress and an economic benefit, but the Native American population would no doubt have disagreed. In modern-day frontier areas of New Guinea, the hiring of young men for mining has disrupted traditional values of the society by introducing a cash economy and changing traditional ideas of seniority and common ownership. Such situations are not uncommon in developing countries.

The transformation from small-scale traditional mining to modern large-scale mechanized mining methods can also have major social consequences. At Potosi, in Bolivia, thousands of individuals have mined silver, zinc, lead and tin ores in adits and underground mines in a mountain called Cerro Rico (Figure 7.14) for over 450 years. Although working conditions are poor, with earnings equivalent to only US$150 per month and the life expectancy of miners only 35–40 years, around 6000 men work in, and around, the mountain. Interest from mining companies in what could be the largest deposit of silver in the world is a cause of concern locally. With 140 Mt of ore at a grade of 170 ppm silver, the operation could be highly profitable using modern large-scale mining methods and heap leaching. However, this would destroy the 'sacred profile' of the mountain, and miners fear for their livelihoods, along with the disruption of their society and its traditions.

In the past, mines were often established with little consideration for the welfare of local peoples. This situation has changed during the latter part of the 20th century, especially since 1990. Where mining is in remote areas, the indigenous population are now involved as well as national governments in determining whether a mining operation will be approved, and in negotiating the conditions of compensation, employment and environmental protection that are imposed (see Section 7.2). This was the case during the protracted permitting stage for the Voisey's Bay operation (Box 5.2).

A major socio-economic problem is what happens to people (or a nation) when a mine on which there is a high economic dependency ultimately closes and no longer provides income through taxes, employment and associated commerce. One solution would be early economic planning and the establishment of alternative sources of employment and funding streams. If this does not happen and a country is dependent on the income from a mining operation, poverty and unrest may result. There is also a likelihood that low cost, but undesirable, environmentally insensitive practices may be allowed to avoid losing the industry and its economic benefits.

Figure 7.14   The 'sacred profile' of Cerro Rico at Potosi, Bolivia, and the mines where thousands of miners still work in primitive conditions.

One way to minimize social impact is to use fly-in, fly-out workforces, as operates at some remote mines in Australia and Canada, including Voisey's Bay. This may beneficially provide employment for workers who commute from established mining settlements. Although hotel accommodation must be built close to the site, the cost is much less than building an infrastructure for whole families and minimizes the need for roads. However, it provides little direct benefit for local people.

Question 7.4

In what ways might a mining operation in an undeveloped area of a developing country affect local communities?

7.2   Environmental impact assessment and sustainable mining

Against a background where the demand for metals — through global expansion of industry, technological developments, rising populations and increasing standards of living — has increased throughout the 20th century and is likely to continue, the metals industry strives to meet that demand. Mining has spread from established centres in Europe and parts of North and South America to locations worldwide, often in remote, undeveloped areas. Throughout much of this time, the emphasis had been on obtaining metals at minimal cost without regard for the consequences, particularly in remote areas. That attitude has changed during the last decades of the 20th century. With the increased dissemination of information by the media, the impact of news of damage and disasters has strengthened the environmental and social consciousness of society as a whole.

Greater awareness of the potential for environmental problems to arise as a result of mining has led individuals, international organizations, governments and even some mining companies to be critical of the causes of environmental and social impacts of mining and to increase their efforts to protect the environment. The consequent proliferation of regulations and controls at international, national and local levels in many parts of the world demand that:

● an **environmental impact assessment** (EIA) (Box 7.7 overleaf) is carried out before approval is given for a mine to be developed;

● environmental safeguards are implemented and monitoring continues during mining operations;

● mine closures are planned and include rehabilitation of the area.

The extent to which arrangements are in place to administer and enforce such measures varies around the world, but such procedures are becoming standard practice for major mining companies. Greater attention to the consequences of mining has had many positive results, and better planning, mitigation and monitoring may, for example, be partly responsible for the reduction in the numbers of tailings dam failures, which reached a peak in the 1970s (Figure 7.15).

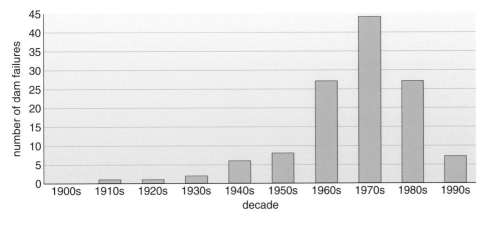

Figure 7.15   Tailings dam failures during the 20th century.

● With reference to Section 7.1.4 and Figure 7.8, what other possible reason might there be for the improvement in the tailings dam failure record?

○ The number of dam failures may have been reduced by improved construction methods, such as the discontinuation of the upstream embankment design with its susceptibility for failure.

Box 7.7 Environmental impact assessment

An EIA has been a requirement for mining approval in many countries since the early 1990s and is also a necessary condition to qualify for project funding. The purpose of an EIA is to identify the potential consequences of a proposed project both to humans and to the natural environment.

The first step involves a full description of the environmental state of a proposed site before any development has occurred. This includes setting a **baseline** for the compositions of soils and waters, i.e. their starting composition, which will reflect any natural enrichments of metals around an ore deposit. This baseline is essential for:

- evaluating the potential impact of a mining project at its various stages of development;
- monitoring the environment when the project is under way;
- returning a site to its former state on closure.

The potential impacts of a mining project must be identified and their environmental and social consequences recognized, along with the means to mitigate those effects and to adopt alternative operating schemes. For example, water quality can be modelled from hydrology and rock properties, so, in the event of untreated AMD being released into a river system, theoretical models can predict the consequences to ecosystems, such as the impact on fish stocks.

An environmental management system (EMS) must be devised, established and implemented effectively to ensure that operations, constructions and wastes are monitored regularly to detect potential hazards that could result in damage or contamination. Mitigation, remediation and rehabilitation procedures must be put in place during mining and after mine closure.

The environmental impacts recognized by an EIA are not confined to ecological and physical disruption, but include socio-economic and cultural issues associated with the use of the land and the installation of infrastructure. It is especially important to ensure harmony with the indigenous population. To promote good social relations, local communities should be consulted at all stages about the consequences of mining. These discussions should address economic benefits, jobs and wealth creation as well as the environmental drawbacks.

A problem with EIAs is the lack of generally accepted technical standards for reporting investigations that gather baseline data. In different parts of the world, and, depending on technical competence and developmental pressures, the decision-making bodies that judge EIAs will apply different standards of assessment.

The responsibility for funding the cost of any clean-up operation has varied from country to country and with the kind of incident. In many countries today, the 'polluter pays' principle is applied, but in cases where the company is bankrupt or the problems result from past mining activities and the company no longer exists, the clean-up usually becomes the responsibility of the national or regional government or their environmental agencies. In the USA, it is the US Environmental Protection Agency that administers the US 'Superfund' programme. This was formerly funded by a levy on the profits of large companies, but the burden is now placed on the US taxpayer. In the UK, the clean-up of abandoned mines is the responsibility of the Environment Agency.

As many mine-owning companies are legally separate from their multinational parents, which are not responsible for the debts of their subsidiaries, many countries have instituted bond schemes for mining projects. Such a scheme requires a company to deposit a sum of money, called a bond, before production starts so as to cover costs of remediation and restoration of the site to its original state. A controversial situation occurred at Summitville, Colorado, in the 1990s, when the company operating a heap leach gold mine filed for bankruptcy because it had not provided sufficient financial surety to cover the cost of mine closure and clean-up. Mine engineers have since dubbed this gold mine 'the worst conceived, worst operated and worst designed mine in the history of mining'. The cost of the ongoing clean-up to the US Environmental Protection Agency has been estimated to be some US$225 million.

It is for reasons such as this that obtaining government approval for new mining projects, i.e. the **permitting** process, has become a requirement in most countries, even developing ones. This process normally includes an assessment of the financial viability of the project as well as an EIA (Box 7.7). Any deviation from the measures approved is likely to result in legal action. Operating procedures may also require approval. The length and complexity of the permitting process has turned many mining companies away from Europe and North America where permitting may take many years, and where consent may not be forthcoming at all for environmentally sensitive areas. Instead, companies have looked to developing countries such as Chile, or to non-industrialized, resource-rich countries that are desperate for revenues such as Papua New Guinea, where the permitting process is much shorter (and less rigorous).

In most parts of the world, government consent to mine has to take into account the views of all stakeholders, including government agencies, non-governmental organizations and local communities. Thus, companies need to demonstrate that their proposals have wider benefits than just their own profitability. In addition, pressures on companies not only arise from the permitting process, and its associated legal constraints and agreements, but through liabilities for high levels of compensation when major problems arise, and from the demands of their own investors and those of financing institutions that the business is not likely to be endangered as a result of social or environmental risks.

Mining projects, particularly in developing regions, require high levels of funding, and financial support is often obtained from organizations such as the International Finance Corporation, which is part of the World Bank Group. To obtain their financial backing, the project has to comply with a range of environmental and social policies and processes established in 2003 and known as the Equator Principles. In particular, these require that the EIA has addressed the following:

- assessment of the baseline environmental and social conditions;
- requirements under host country laws and regulations, applicable international treaties and agreements;
- sustainable development and use of renewable natural resources;
- protection of human health, cultural properties, and biodiversity, including endangered species and sensitive ecosystems;
- socio-economic impacts;
- land acquisition and land use;
- involuntary resettlement;
- impacts on indigenous peoples and communities;
- cumulative impacts of existing projects, the proposed project, and anticipated future projects;

- participation of affected parties in the design, review and implementation of the project;
- consideration of feasible environmentally and socially preferable alternatives;
- efficient production, delivery and use of energy;
- pollution prevention and waste minimization, pollution controls (liquid effluents and air emissions), and solid and chemical waste management.

7.2.1 Sustainability in the mining industry

All these demands and influences have made an impact on many mining companies to the extent that the principles of corporate social responsibility have been actively integrated into their management systems. Corporate social responsibility in the mining industry can be regarded as a means to maximize positive and minimize negative social and environmental consequences of mining, while maintaining profitability. It involves responsibilities to society at large, but more specifically to stakeholders, including employees, consumers, communities, governments and investors, and to the environment. It addresses business practices and ethics as well as the promotion of health and education in communities and stewardship of the environment.

Recently, several major mining companies set up a process that they called the Global Mining Initiative and commissioned the International Institute for Environment and Development to conduct a global consultation to review the industry's social and environmental record and its future role in sustainable development. The results of this Mining, Minerals and Sustainable Development (MMSD) project were published in 2002. The report, entitled 'Breaking New Ground', has its critics: on the one hand, those who believe it reflects too much the views of international pressure groups that oppose mining, and on the other, those who feel that the process had marginalized some interest-groups, that the report itself was not subject to sufficient scrutiny, and that many of the deficiencies and excesses of the mining industry had been ignored. However, it created a debate and identified a range of principles and processes that the industry should adopt in order to address sustainable development.

Sustainable development has been interpreted in many different ways, and the MMSD report has its own version. It considers that the minerals sector should:

> …maximize [its] contribution to the well-being of the current generation in a way that ensures an equitable distribution of its costs and benefits, without reducing the potential for future generations to meet their own needs.
> (MMSD, 2002)

Although this statement is subtly different to that of the Bruntland Report of 1987 (see Sheldon, 2005), it appears to have a similar intent. It highlights an apparent anomaly in the concept of sustainable development when applied to the mining industry. Where *renewable* resources are concerned, the current generation can benefit without disadvantaging future generations; but in the case of *finite* (non-renewable) resources, such as metals, this situation cannot be maintained for ever. It is worth posing the question: 'Is it more sustainable to maintain supplies for the benefit of consumers until resources run out, or to leave resources unused in the ground indefinitely, for some future generation?' The pragmatic approach must be a compromise, which is effectively what the MMSD statement is. However, it is clear from Section 7.1 that the mining and extraction of metals inevitably create unsustainable environmental disruption. It is not surprising, therefore, that the industry's interpretation of sustainable development encompasses:

● economic prosperity of mine operators and their hosts (both countries and communities);

● environmental protection and rehabilitation;

● social benefits to host countries and communities both during and after mining.

Thus economic and social issues are included, not just environmental ones. Whereas it is difficult to avoid negative environmental consequences, arguably they can be balanced by positive economic and social benefits.

To achieve sustainability in mining the MMSD report proposes that the industry develops structures to:

● establish the demands of sustainability;

● develop planning procedures that take on board economic, social and environmental factors;

● create effective environmental management systems (EMS) to operate during and after mining.

Much of this already exists as part of an EIA (Box 7.7). An EMS provides the operational framework for defining baseline conditions; controlling operating systems to minimize impacts; monitoring conditions or contaminants to detect whether hazards exceed specified levels; acting on identified problems; and rehabilitating the site during operation and/or on closure. The aim is for these environmental responsibilities to be integrated into everyday management practices at all levels, from the detailed inspection and monitoring of specific mining operations and processes, to the formulation of environmental and social policy.

In the past, environmental problems might not have been appreciated or, because of costs or greed, were often ignored by mine operators. Today's mining activities are subject to ever more stringent environmental regulation and the whole operation is monitored as part of the EMS. All this has greatly changed the role of many geoscientists in the mining industry. Previously, the main roles involved geologists and mine engineers in determining the most profitable rock to mine and how to mine it, taking into account ore grades and geological problems of extraction. Today, mining geoscientists are also involved in:

● defining baseline levels of metals, especially potential contaminants;

● monitoring conditions that may impact on the health and safety of workers;

● monitoring the effectiveness of systems for the containment and treatment of wastes;

● monitoring environmental conditions and consequences.

◑ What traditional mining activity can be likened to the monitoring of chemical contaminants?

◔ Geochemical exploration, which involves sampling and performing geochemical analyses to determine anomalous levels of chemical constituents. Environmental monitoring demands regular measurement to ensure that levels of contaminants do not exceed regulatory limits.

With appropriate planning and finance, the environmental impacts of mining and smelting can be sharply reduced. Increasingly, environmental costs are being identified at the outset and *internalized*: that is, included as part of the planned operating costs, rather than being left to a later date when there may be a reluctance to fund solutions and risk bankrupting the operation. Most forms of mining now require land restoration or rehabilitation after closure. With planned environmental management, and with mitigation and remediation accompanying mine production, clean-up on closure should be easier.

7.3 Concluding remarks

The metals production and mining industry has often been regarded as dirty and polluting. In the past, with the drive for increased production and profitability, little thought was given to the environmental consequences. With the ever-growing scale of mining operations the potential for environmental impacts became increasingly serious in the 20th century. Environmental concern amongst the public and by governments, especially in the past few decades, has resulted in increased pressure on mining companies to clean-up their practices and new mining developments have been rejected in environmentally sensitive areas. However, the NIMBY (not in my backyard) attitude of banning mining completely from parts of North America and Western Europe is not a sustainable answer; it only exports problems to places where public opinion is not mobilized or where governments and companies put economic gain before the environment.

Increasingly, the principles of sustainable development (Sheldon, 2005) are gaining credibility in the mining industry and are being implemented. A balance between positive and negative economic, social and environmental consequences of metals extraction is sought that satisfies the need to provide raw materials for the present, without compromising the future. In the 1970s, the 'future' in this context would have meant only the 'future *supplies of metals*' — the major concern of the times, when it was thought by some that many metals had relatively short reserves lifetimes until their exhaustion. Today, there is general acceptance that supplies of metals are unlikely to run out in the medium term at least, and the 'future' is seen in a much broader framework — it includes 'future prosperity of all stakeholders and global well-being'.

In much of the mining industry today, avoiding practices that may spread contamination and building in environmental safeguards are principles that are becoming at least as important as maximizing the recovery of metal during extraction. The monitoring, treatment, and management of minewaters is particularly important in controlling pollution. Planning incorporates risk assessment and, where necessary, precautions are set in place to mitigate against the effects of accidents, equipment failures, human error and natural disaster.

Taking action to minimize the environmental impacts of the metals extraction industry is only possible through a comprehensive understanding of the environmental consequences of the industry's activities. The industry's efforts are increasingly focused on human health, education, community well-being and the stewardship of ecosystems. It is claimed that only a well-managed, well-regulated, technologically aware and profitable mining industry can be capable of taking the necessary measures to minimize its own environmental consequences.

Another way to minimize the various impacts of mining (summarized in Figure 7.16) is in consumers' hands, that is to reduce the need for mining by greater re-use and recycling of metals, as discussed in Section 1.4. This is already being done to varying degrees of success, and most effectively for lead, iron and aluminium (Table 1.10). Such activities are important for the longer-term conservation of resources and to help ensure the sustainability of supplies until, perhaps, technology provides alternative materials derived from renewable sources or, perhaps, dematerialization (Sheldon, 2005) reduces demand.

Environmental planning and management systems do not stop environmental impacts from happening, but their implementation should ensure that catastrophic events occur less frequently and the environmental consequences of routine operations are mitigated. In most mining operations, a balance has to be found, and compromises must be made, but there is an increasing likelihood that, despite the increasing scale of operations, and migration of mining development to remote areas, mining companies with a strong corporate social responsibility will be more sympathetic to the environmental and social consequences of their activities.

Figure 7.16 Schematic representation of some of the main environmental impacts of mining, ore processing and smelting; and of manufacturing, using and disposing of metal goods.

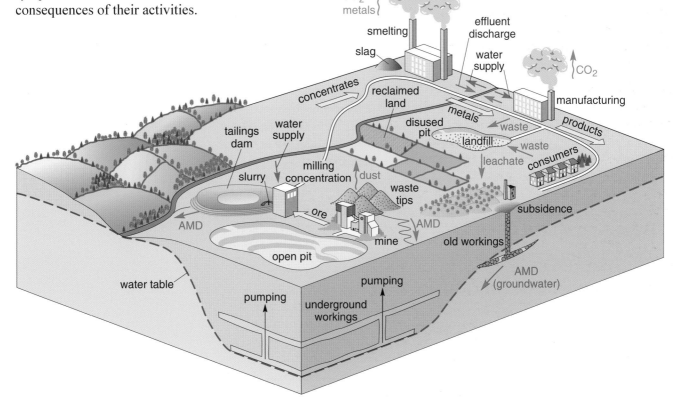

Question 7.5

In what ways do you think the recycling of metals could reduce the environmental impacts associated with the extraction and use of metals as shown in Figure 7.16?

7.4 Summary of Chapter 7

1   Mines, plant, waste tips, tailings ponds, stockpiles and the infrastructure of mines have an obvious visual impact, take up land and destroy the ecology of mine sites.

2   Ground subsidence can result from either planned or unexpected collapse of mine workings, especially after abandonment.

3   Sulphide ores exposed to air and water by mining activities undergo oxidation to produce acid mine drainage. AMD leaches toxic metals from mineralized rocks and waste, and can contaminate surface and groundwaters. It lowers the pH of local streams, rivers and groundwater, often leading to the precipitation of hydrated iron(III) oxides, discolouring stream beds and smothering organisms. AMD may be treated by active or passive methods. Active treatment involves raising the pH and precipitating metal compounds. Passive treatment, involving bioremediation, is less costly, once set up, but has limited capacity compared with active methods.

4   Tailings from ore processing are stored in heaps or tailings dams. They are liable to produce AMD through oxidation of fine-grained sulphides in moist or wet conditions, and may be contaminated with chemicals used in ore processing. After treatment and settling, clarified water is recycled and the solids concentrated in slurry are contained, either by deposition under water to prevent oxidation, or by being left to dry out. Tailings are sometimes dumped in watercourses or into submarine environments, but such practices are environmentally undesirable and have been outlawed in many parts of the world.

5   Some chemical reagents used in ore processing are hazardous to humans and other organisms. For example, mercury used to extract gold contaminates many areas of artisanal mining, entering the food chain as highly toxic methyl mercury; and cyanide, used for industrial-scale extraction of gold, requires strict control as spillages can be deadly, especially to aquatic organisms.

6   Smelters release toxic metals and sulphur dioxide to the atmosphere, thus contributing to local contamination of soils and to acid rain on both a local and regional scale.

7   The toxic effects of metals depend to a large extent on their bioavailability, which depends on the chemical form in which they occur, and how easily a metal in that form can be taken up by living organisms.

8   Social impacts of mining can be considerable, especially in developing countries where a sudden influx of modern mining operations and workers into small, previously isolated, rural communities can cause great disruption. In remote regions, whole towns may be founded on mining. In developing countries, economic dependency on mining can be a serious problem when mining operations cease.

9   Increasingly, mining companies are assessing the environmental impacts and sustainability of their operations. Environmental impact assessments are now a requirement both for the permitting and financing of large projects. Environmental management systems are employed to minimize damage during operations, to monitor the potential hazards and to rehabilitate sites following closure.

LEARNING OUTCOMES

When you have completed this book, you should be able to explain in your own words, and use correctly, all the **bold** terms printed in the text and defined in the Glossary. You should also be able, amongst other things, to do the following:

Chapter 1

1.1 Account for the extent to which metals are used in terms of (i) their properties, which influence demand, and (ii) their availability, which influences supply, and explain how both of these factors affect prices.

1.2 Discuss global trends in levels of metals production and explain why the countries dominating world production have changed during the 20th century.

1.3 Explain the importance of natural concentration processes in forming ore deposits and understand why it is that metals are extracted from ore minerals contained in ore deposits.

1.4 Know which metals the more important ore minerals contain and explain the relationships between ore, ore mineral, grade, cut-off grade, reserves and resources.

1.5 Distinguish between dispersed and confined deposits.

1.6 Discuss the reasons for ore deposits being considered non-renewable and the ways in which metal resources can be conserved.

1.7 Understand the framework of ore deposit formation in terms of Sources of metals, Pathways through which Agents transport them to a site of Deposition, and the Energy that drives the mineralizing system (the mnemonic SPADE).

Chapter 2

2.1 Explain how magmatic concentration processes can form segregation deposits by crystal fractionation and liquid immiscibility, how pegmatite ores and porphyry ore deposits form, and why these deposits tend to be associated with gabbroic, granitic and granodioritic igneous rocks, respectively.

2.2 Describe the form and occurrence of layered chromite and sulphide deposits, pegmatite deposits, and copper and molybdenum porphyry deposits.

Chapter 3

3.1 Explain the involvement of both physical and chemical processes in concentrating elements and ore minerals at the surface of the Earth to form ore deposits.

3.2 Describe the form and occurrence of placer deposits, residual deposits, secondary enrichment deposits and bedded iron deposits.

Chapter 4

4.1 Outline the workings of a hydrothermal system in the context of SPADE.

4.2 Explain the various factors that favour the concentration of elements to form ore deposits in hydrothermal systems.

4.3 Describe the form and occurrence of hydrothermal deposits that are precipitated from those hot aqueous fluids rising towards the land surface and those emerging onto the sea floor.

Chapter 5

5.1 Outline the main stages of operations involved in the exploitation of ore deposits, accounting for escalating costs, investment risks and lead times before mine production commences.

5.2 Describe the progression of activities typically involved in an exploration programme carried out by a mining company.

5.3 Discuss reasons for initiating exploration for ore deposits, and the use of desk studies, including remote sensing, to target suitable areas for exploration.

5.4 Outline the basic principles behind the use of magnetic, electromagnetic, radiometric, gravity and electrical exploration surveys, and appreciate their applicability to different scales of approach and for detecting different kinds of mineral deposits.

5.5 Explain the effects of primary and secondary geochemical dispersion.

5.6 Account for the applicability and limitations of geochemical surveys involving bedrock, soil, drainage water, and drainage sediment sampling.

5.7 Outline procedures used in evaluating the feasibility of working a mineral deposit.

Chapter 6

6.1 Describe the main forms of surface and underground mining, and recognize the various economic, geological and technical factors that control their use and viability.

6.2 Explain the principles of ore processing methods used to liberate and concentrate ore minerals, especially their applicability to different types of ore mineral and different grain sizes.

6.3 Explain the economic and practical significance of metal recovery in ore processing.

6.4 Outline the basic principles of metal extraction by leaching and by smelting of ore mineral concentrates.

Chapter 7

7.1 Describe a range of potential environmental impacts resulting from metal mining; explain their causes, and relate them to the likely scale and duration of impact.

7.2 Outline a variety of procedures for remediation of environmental impacts and rehabilitation of mine sites.

7.3 Outline the socio-economic implications of metals mining.

7.4 Describe how metals mining activities have become subject to increasing regulation and environmental controls, and indicate how modern regulatory processes are designed to minimize the environmental impacts of mining.

7.5 Discuss whether metals mining today may be considered to be a sustainable activity in the context of economic, social and environmental considerations, as well as its exploitation of finite resources.

REFERENCES AND FURTHER SOURCES OF INFORMATION

The information in this book has been obtained from a wide range of sources, too numerous to mention. However, specific reference is made in the text to the following:

Agricola, G. (1556) *De Re Metallica*, translation by Hoover, H.C. and Hoover, L.H. (1950) Dover Publications.

Argles, T. (2005) *Minerals: Bulk Materials for Building and Industry* (Book 2 of S278 *Earth's Physical Resources: Origin, Use and Environmental Impact*), The Open University, Milton Keynes.

Drury, S. (2006) *Energy: Fossil fuels, Nuclear and Renewables* (Book 4 of S278 *Earth's Physical Resources: Origin, Use and Environmental Impact*), The Open University, Milton Keynes.

Mining, Minerals and Sustainable Development (MMSD) (2002) *Breaking New Ground*, Report of the MMSD Project, Earthscan. Available online at http://www.iied.org/mmsd/mmsd_pdfs/finalreport_es.pdf [last accessed July 2006]

Sheldon, P. (2005) *Earth's Physical Resources: An Introduction* (Book 1 of S278 *Earth's Physical Resources: Origin, Use and Environmental Impact*), The Open University, Milton Keynes.

Smith, S. (2005) *Water: The Vital Resource* (Book 3 of S278 *Earth's Physical Resources: Origin, Use and Environmental Impact*), The Open University, Milton Keynes.

United States Geological Survey (2005) *Mineral Commodity Summaries*. Available online: http://minerals.usgs.gov/minerals/.

Whitehead, P. G., Hall, G., Neal, C. and Prior, H. (2005) Chemical behaviour of the Wheal Jane bioremediation system, *Science of the Total Environment*, **338**, pp. 41–51.

The following are appropriate to the general subject areas covered in this book:

Aswathanarayana, U. (2003) *Mineral Resources Management and the Environment*, A.A. Balkema Publishers.

Holland, H. D. and Petersen, U. (1995) *Living Dangerously: The Earth, its Resources and the Environment*, Princeton University Press.

Robb, L. (2004) *Introduction to Ore-forming Processes*, Blackwell Science.

Whateley, M. Evans, A. and Moon, C. (2006) *Introduction to Mineral Exploration*, Blackwell Publishing.

Yakovleva, N. (2005) *Corporate Social Responsibility in the Mining Industries*, Ashgate Publishing.

The topics of this book are covered by a huge number of internet websites, including government departments; mining companies; research institutes; universities; environmental organisations, etc. The following are useful examples (accessed May 2006):

World mineral production statistics are available from the United States Geological Survey (*Mineral Commodity Summaries*): http://minerals.usgs.gov/minerals/ and from the British Geological Survey, along with other surveys of metals in the UK: http://www.bgs.ac.uk/mineralsuk/home.html

When this book was written, metals prices were quoted for 2003 (Table 1.2), but the metals industry is dynamic and metals prices respond to changes in demand. To see how prices have changes since 2003, you can access the long-term prices data at: http://www.kitco.com/charts/ and http://www.kitcometals.com/charts/

For information about mines and mining projects across the world: http://www.mining-technology.com/projects/

For more extensive information about:
mines and metal commodities: http://www.infomine.com/
the mining industry: http://www.natural-resources.org/minerals/aboutf.htm
organisations that promote metals: http://www.gold.org/index.html and
http://www.copper.org/homepage.html

ANSWERS TO QUESTIONS

Question 1.1

(a) The filament of a light bulb needs to reach a high temperature (>1700 °C) to emit light; tungsten has a very high melting temperature (3410 °C), so it does not melt at the required operating temperatures. Tungsten also has fairly poor electrical conductivity, making it a good resistor and able to heat up readily.

(b) Glass thermometers normally contain a liquid that expands and contracts with changing temperature much more than the glass. Mercury is the only metal with a low enough melting temperature (–39 °C) to be a liquid at normal temperatures. Its metallic appearance — that is, its colour, reflectivity and opacity — makes it clearly visible. (Note that alcohol has replaced mercury in most new glass thermometers as it is non-toxic.)

(c) Aircraft construction requires strong materials that are light in weight. Aluminium (density 2.70 t m^{-3}) has a lower density than titanium (4.55 t m^{-3}), but it melts at a much lower temperature (660 °C) than titanium (1660 °C) and is not as strong. Hence titanium is used for high-speed aircraft, where frictional heating causes the aircraft frame to reach high temperatures.

(d) Overhead power cables need to be good conductors of electricity and light in weight so that large spans can be supported. Aluminium is much lighter (by a factor of more than 3) than copper, although copper is the better conductor. Even though an aluminium cable is less conductive than a copper cable of the same thickness, weight for weight it is more conductive. It is also cheaper, weight for weight, than copper. In practice, a steel core is used to increase the strength of aluminium power cables.

Question 1.2

(a) Copper and nickel, the raw materials of cupro-nickel, cost much less than silver (Table 1.2) and the alloy is more durable.

(b) Stainless steel does not rust and is hard enough to keep a sharp edge. Both of these properties are important for the long-term durability of cutting equipment. (Table 1.3)

(c) Solder melts at a lower temperature (203 °C) than either pure tin (232 °C) or pure lead (334 °C). Lead is much cheaper than tin. (Tables 1.2 and 1.3)

(d) Many rocks are very difficult to break, especially crystalline igneous and metamorphic rocks that contain quartz, which is harder than the steel used for knife blades, so a very hard metal is required for crushing. Manganese steel is suitable because it is a very hard alloy (Table 1.3).

Question 1.3

(a) The notional value of iron produced = 6.47 × 10^8 t × 174 US$ t^{-1} = US$1.13 × 10^{11}.

The notional value of gold produced = 2520 t × 1.17 × 10^7 US$ t^{-1} = US$2.95 × 10^{10}.

(b) Notional value of metals (iron + manganese + nickel) used in steels = US$(11.3 + 0.92 + 1.35) × 10^{10} = US$13.6 × 10^{10}.

Notional value of the major metals aluminium + copper + zinc = US$(3.96 + 2.42 + 0.74) × 10^{10} = US$7.12 × 10^{10}.

Thus, the notional value of metals used in steelmaking is almost twice that of the top major metals used in their own right, demonstrating the dominance of iron and steel in the metals markets.

Question 1.4

(a) In 1930, the USA was the leading producer of iron, copper, zinc and lead, and the second greatest producer of gold. In 2000, the USA's place in the producer league tables had dropped to sixth for iron, second for copper, fifth for zinc, and third for lead. It remained the second leading producer of gold.

(b) In 1930, the main iron producers were the USA and European countries that were also important centres of industry; this reflects the high place value of iron ore at the time. In 2000, the main producers were China, Brazil and Australia, where extensive deposits of high-grade iron ores occur. Today, the long-distance transportation of bulk materials is not so much of a problem as formerly and, consequently, the place value of iron ore is lower.

(c) Countries listed in Table 1.5 that have elevated their position among world producers since 1930 are:

- for copper: Chile, Indonesia, Australia and China;
- for zinc: China, Australia, Canada, and Peru;
- for lead: China, Australia and Peru;
- for tin: China, Indonesia, Peru, Brazil and Australia.

Question 1.5

(a) (i) Na^+ and K^+ have the same ionic charge, but different ionic radii, whereas Na^+ and Ca^{2+} have different charges but similar ionic radii.

(ii) Mg^{2+} and Fe^{2+} have the same charges and similar ionic radii; the Fe^{3+} ion has a smaller ionic radius than the Fe^{2+} ion.

(iii) Both Rb^+ and Ba^{2+} have similar radii to K^+, so are more likely to substitute for K^+ than they are for Na^+.

(b) Nickel is more likely to substitute for iron in pyrrhotite than for lead in galena because the size of the Ni^{2+} ion is similar to that of iron(II) (Fe^{2+}) but much smaller than that of lead (Pb^{2+}).

(c) The structure of cassiterite could accommodate Fe^{3+}, Ti^{4+} and Nb^{5+} ions as substituted impurities because their ionic radii (Figure 1.9) are similar and their charges are the same as, or not very different from, Sn^{4+}.

Question 1.6

Concentration factors are:

$$\frac{3}{0.008} = 375 \text{ for zinc;} \quad \frac{1}{0.011} = 91 \text{ for nickel;}$$

$$\frac{0.5}{0.0075} = 67 \text{ for copper;} \quad \frac{0.5}{0.00025} = 2000 \text{ for tin;}$$

$$\text{and } \frac{4 \times 10^{-4}}{3 \times 10^{-7}} = 1333 \text{ for gold.}$$

Question 1.7

Veins are narrow sheets of crystalline rock, which form where minerals are deposited from fluids in constricted planar pathways, such as joints or fractures. Low-porosity, brittle rocks tend to form fractures more readily than soft, porous rocks during tectonic movements. In soft, porous rocks, fluid pathways are likely to be more diffuse, thus forming dispersed deposits rather than hydrothermal veins.

Question 2.1

See the completed columns in Table 2.3. The answers for the concentration factors and rock types are shown in red.

Question 2.2

(a) The missing words are shown below in red.

The ore minerals in both the chromite-rich and PGE-rich layers are dense and form sequences of thin layers over a wide area. They formed by gravity settling and the repeated injection and mixing of magma pulses during crystallization of the intrusion. The chromite layers contain mainly minerals that crystallized from the magma, whereas the Merensky Reef contains sulphide minerals that originally separated as an immiscible melt that scavenged precious metals from the magma.

(b) PGE reserves of 63 000 t are said to represent only 80% of the total PGE. These would be contained in

Table 2.3 Answer to Question 2.1.

Trace metals	Peridotite /ppm	Gabbro /ppm	Diorite /ppm	Granite /ppm	Igneous rock type with greatest abundance	Average minimum exploitable grade/ppm	Minimum concentration factor
chromium, Cr	2 000	200	30	10	peridotite	300 000	150
copper, Cu	20	70	50	10	gabbro	5 000	71
lithium, Li	0.5	10	22	40	granite	20 000	500
nickel, Ni	2 000	130	30	5	peridotite	10 000	5
niobium, Nb	5	15	25	40	granite	1 000	25
platinum, Pt	0.05	0.01	0.005	0.001	peridotite	5	100
tantalum, Ta	0.25	0.75	1.5	2.5	granite	500	200
tin, Sn	0.5	1.5	2	3.5	granite	5 000	1 430
titanium, Ti	5	10 000	5 000	1 000	gabbro	30 000	3
tungsten, W	0.5	1.0	1.5	2.0	granite	5 000	2 500
uranium, U	0.005	1	2	3.5	granite	350	100
vanadium, V	60	400	100	30	gabbro	20 000	50

1500×10^9 t of magma, representing an average (initial) concentration of:

$$63\,000\,\text{t} \times \frac{100}{80} = 78\,750\,\text{t, i.e. } 7.9 \times 10^{10}\,\text{g PGE}$$

$$\text{in } 1500 \times 10^9\,\text{t of magma}$$

$$\text{i.e. } \frac{7.9 \times 10^4\,\text{t}}{1.5 \times 10^{12}\,\text{t}} = 5.3 \times 10^{-8}\,\text{t} = 0.053\,\text{g t}^{-1}$$

To produce an ore grade of 10 g t^{-1}, the concentration factor is $\frac{10}{0.053} = 189$ times.

Question 2.3

The metals that appear in Table 2.2 and Figure 1.9 are: Be, Cs, Li, Ta, Sn, W and U.

Comparing their ionic radii with those of the major metals Na, Ca, K, Fe, Mg and Al in order of increasing ionic charge:

- ionic charge +1: lithium has a far smaller ionic radius than sodium; caesium has a far larger ionic radius than either sodium or potassium;
- ionic charge +2: beryllium has a much smaller ionic radius than iron(II) or magnesium;
- higher ionic charges: tantalum, tin, tungsten and uranium all have ionic charges greater than any of the major elements.

These metals have either ionic charges or ionic radii that differ from the major elements and therefore they are *incompatible* in the structures of common rock-forming minerals.

Question 2.4

In these circumstances, the enrichment of lithium is equivalent to that shown for water in Figure 2.11, which is from 0.2% to 8.0%, an enrichment of 40 times. With an initial concentration of 10 ppm, the final concentration of lithium should be 40×10 ppm = 400 ppm.

Question 2.5

(a) Hinder. Porphyry ore deposits depend on high levels of magmatic water to concentrate and scavenge metals and to fracture rocks when the watery fluid separates from the magma on rising to a high level in the crust.

(b) Hinder. At deep levels in the crust, which are under high pressure, water is more soluble in magma and will not separate. Separation of magmatic water is essential in the formation of a porphyry ore deposit.

(c) Favour. The fluids that form porphyry ore deposits derive most of their Cu and/or Mo from the magma. If the proportions of these elements in the magma are relatively high, it is more likely that the grade of the resulting deposit will be high.

(d) Hinder. If the magma erupts, aqueous fluids will be lost to the atmosphere and not be available to form a porphyry deposit within the crust.

(e) Favour. Crystallization of anhydrous minerals, such as feldspars, increases the concentration of water in the magma.

Question 3.1

Zircon, ilmenite, columbite, cassiterite and gold are most likely to be found in placer deposits.

Zircon, ilmenite, columbite and cassiterite are dense and hard. Although dense, bornite is a sulphide, rather like chalcopyrite, and breaks down in oxidizing waters. Molybdenite and barite are soft and cleave too easily to survive as large grains. Gold is also very soft, but, being a metal, it is malleable, so lumps and flakes bend and distort but do not break up easily. Its very high density and chemical inertness make gold an ideal placer mineral. Panning for gold must be the one form of mineral prospecting that everyone has heard of!

Question 3.2

See Table 3.6. Of the rock compositions listed, granite has the highest proportion of alumina in the insoluble residue. It would appear to be the most likely to form a residual bauxite ore. However, granite also contains quartz, a fairly insoluble mineral, which is not as easily dissolved as silica that is released from decomposing minerals.

Question 3.3

(a) Iron can be produced cheaply because:
- After aluminium, iron is the most abundant metal in crustal rocks (Table 1.4).
- Iron ores are available that consist of iron oxide and carbonate minerals, which are rich in iron and suitable for smelting.
- Iron ore deposits are well distributed around the world, often occurring at the Earth's surface, and are both easily accessible and extensive enough to be worked in bulk with the minimum of effort and processing, which helps keep the price down.

Table 3.6 (completed Table 3.1) Estimation of alumina contents of insoluble weathering products for a range of igneous rock types. *Note*: answers are shown in red.

	Calculation	Peridotite	Gabbro	Diorite	Granite
% Al_2O_3 in rock	A	4.0	14.1	16.0	14.0
% $Fe_2O_3 + TiO_2$ in rock	B	14.1	15.0	9.1	2.9
total % of insoluble oxides (residue)	A + B	18.1	29.1	25.1	16.9
% Al_2O_3 content of insoluble residue	$\dfrac{A \times 100}{A + B}$	22.1	48.5	63.7	82.8

(b) Substitution of iron and steel by lightweight materials could save energy required in transportation and, hence, fuel resources.

Question 4.1

(a) Na, K and Ca. They are between 5 and 70 times more concentrated in the Salton Sea brine than in seawater.

(b) Fe, Mn, Cu, Pb, Zn, Ba, Rb, Li and Ag are enriched in the Salton Sea brine more than 1000 times above their concentration in seawater.

(c) The Salton Sea brine is an extremely saline solution, dominated by Na^+, Ca^{2+}, K^+ and Cl^- ions. It is very rich in trace metals, and is slightly acidic (pH 6).

(d) The Broadlands fluid is only about one-tenth as saline as seawater, but is richer than seawater in some trace metals (Rb, Li). It is also slightly more alkaline than seawater (pH 8.6).

(e) Salton Sea fluids clearly contain much higher concentrations of dissolved salts, which would be liable to precipitate and, like limescale, fur-up the pipework, thereby causing a constant maintenance problem. Hence the more dilute Broadlands fluids would be better suited to supply a geothermal plant.

Question 4.2

Many metals that form *insoluble* sulphides form *soluble* complex ions with the HS^- ion. These ions provide a means of transporting metals and sulphur in the same solution, ultimately to be deposited as sulphides when the complex breaks down, whereas they could *not* be transported together as metal cations and sulphide (S^{2-}) anions.

Question 4.3

Barren quartz and calcite veins are common hydrothermal deposits, especially in metamorphic rocks and limestones, respectively. The silica and calcium in these rocks are available to be taken into solution and are subsequently precipitated from aqueous hydrothermal fluids. Many metals are not abundant in common rocks and several conditions must be met for mineralization to occur: metals must be available to the fluids; the fluids must be available in sufficient quantities; a suitable site of deposition and conditions for precipitation must be developed — and all for a sufficiently long time.

Question 4.4

The reason has much to do with the much larger scale of modern mining, but Precambrian massive sulphide deposits such as at Kidd Creek are, in general, very much larger than Cyprus-type massive sulphide deposits and a much larger quantity of ore is available in a single deposit.

Question 5.1

From initial discovery, it takes time to fully evaluate a deposit, produce a development plan, carry out environmental impact studies, build the infrastructure for processing ore, organize a labour force and gain access to the ore before production can start. Obtaining approvals from government and making financial evaluations at each stage also take time.

Question 5.2

The age and occurrence of the ore deposits are matched with the reasons why they formed when they did as follows:

1–(b) (see Section 3.4.1); 2–(c) (see Sections 2.4 and Figure 5.7); 3–(a) (see Section 3.3.1); 4–(d) (see Section 3.2).

Question 5.3

Deposits (a–c) are likely to be found in geological settings (1–3) as follows:

(a)–3 (Section 4.2.2); (b)–2 (Section 2.2); (c)–1 (Section 3.4.1).

Question 5.4

(a) Tin and uranium deposits are more likely to be associated with granitic rocks (Section 2.3); nickel and titanium deposits are more likely to be associated with gabbroic rocks (Section 2.2).

(b) Nickel forms sulphide minerals, pentlandite (and pyrrhotite), and many sulphide minerals, as already demonstrated for chalcopyrite (Section 3.3.2), decompose on weathering and tend not to form detrital grains. Uraninite may have been a detrital mineral in the Archaean, but uranium is soluble under today's oxidizing weathering conditions (Box 5.3). Only cassiterite (for tin) and rutile/ilmenite (for titanium) are stable under today's weathering conditions and likely to occur in placer deposits (Section 3.2).

Question 5.5

(a) A low-density, easily broken mineral will be dispersed along with the grains of rock-forming minerals. The persistence of the anomaly will be high, but so will its dilution.

(b) A high-density, hard mineral will resist breaking but will be trapped easily in the sediment, therefore the anomaly will have low persistence; the mineral will accumulate locally to form high concentrations.

(c) A chemically unstable mineral will decompose, forming new minerals or ions in solution, to form a water anomaly. Even with a low density, the mineral would have very low persistence but the water anomaly could have a high persistence in the sediment.

Question 5.6

The cut-off points you should have identified in Figure 5.15 and the likely location of the copper orebody are shown in Figure 5.18. The form of the orebody is likely to be linear, i.e. a sheet.

Question 6.1

(a) The massive deposit (Figure 6.4a) is a good candidate for surface mining; much of the excavation could be in ore, so there would be little waste. Simple veins (Figure 6.4b) could be worked initially at the surface, but must be followed underground to avoid mining excessive waste. The simple geometry makes it easy to mine underground within the orebody. Most of the reserves in the irregular vein deposit (Figure 6.4c) are ore pockets that must be mined below ground. It

would be necessary to remove a lot of waste to gain access to the pockets from the surface.

(b) As the order of increasing unit costs is from Figure 6.4a to b, and from b to c, cut-off grades would also increase from a to b to c.

Question 6.2

(a) The orebody appears to be a near-vertical pipe or sheet resembling the form of a branching tongue.

(b) Ore is mined (i) by stripping from an open pit at the surface and (ii) by tunnelling underground and cutting stopes.

(c) Processing underground is limited to crushing of ore, which takes place both underground and in the surface mill depending on the location of the ore.

(d) After blasting, ore is transported by front-loader and tipped into a shaft to assist breakage by gravity fall. Crushed ore is hoisted into a skip and loaded onto a conveyor at the surface. The ore concentrate is then shipped by rail.

(e) Waste is returned to the mine to backfill mined stopes and to help support the overlying rock mass.

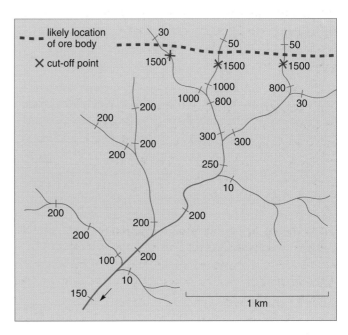

Figure 5.18 A drainage system showing copper concentrations (in ppm) in the stream sediments, exploration cut-off points, and the likely location of the orebody.

Question 6.3

Before pyrite could be smelted it would have to be roasted to drive off the sulphur. The sulphur dioxide would be environmentally damaging and, although emissions can be reduced, the whole process would be unnecessarily costly when abundant sources of haematite ore exist. Haematite ores are richer in iron than pyrite and can be smelted without appreciable pollution.

Question 7.1

(a) The control measures at Wheal Jane were set up only *after* problems arose. Fully funded plans for closure could have put preventative measures in place *before* problems occurred. Control measures obviously have financial implications, and are difficult to implement when a company is failing. It is better for a mine to be made safe during operations, for example by backfilling to limit the access of groundwater to exposed mineralization.

(b) The anoxic limestone drain pre-treatment system is the most effective because it reduces Fe and Zn by the largest amounts. Aerobic cells are the most effective for removing iron; anaerobic cells are the most effective for removing zinc.

Question 7.2

(a) Lead concentrations in the soil are about ten times greater than those of cadmium. That doesn't mean that the lead present is ten times more harmful than the cadmium — the harmfulness of any element also depends on its effect on an organism's metabolism (its toxicity), which varies from element to element. It also depends on the chemical form in which it occurs — its bioavailability. The simple oxides of lead that tend to occur around smelters are also the most soluble (and bioavailable) form of lead (Box 7.4).

(b) Concentrations of both lead and cadmium are higher close to the surface where particulate fall-out accumulates. Migration downward through the soil is slower than accumulation at the surface.

Question 7.3

First, smelting involves heating ore mineral concentrates. If these are sulphide minerals, sulphur oxides and some toxic trace elements are released that would have been held 'safely' in minerals during mining and ore processing operations. The spread of the atmospheric pollutants, like sulphur dioxide and particulates from smelters, may be greater than that of dust and contaminated waters from mining. Secondly, smelters are often close to populated areas, whereas mines tend to be in remote areas. However, it is arguable whether the threats of AMD, cyanide or tailings from a mine cannot be just as serious.

Question 7.4

Mining in an undeveloped area often has severe effects by upsetting the social balance and culture of the indigenous population. This is caused both by the influx of mine personnel and by the employment of local labour, creating a cash economy. The building of an infrastructure (roads, railways, electricity, and power lines) to support mining activities and the workforce (accommodation and services) is likely to stimulate the economy. Such development may be seen as a benefit to local communities, but it almost inevitably leads to destruction of the way of life that previously existed.

Question 7.5

Recycling of metals back through the smelter or through manufacturing would mean:

- less mining and, therefore, less land taken for mining and less disruption of the landscape, communities and ecosystems;
- less mining and ore processing, so less rock waste and tailings for disposal;
- reduced demand for water and reduced contamination of surface and groundwater by AMD;
- less traffic (road, rail, sea) for transporting ore and concentrates;
- reduced energy consumption, use of fuel and CO_2 emissions in mining, ore processing and transportation.

However, there will be energy implications in recycling and the potential for pollution associated with the separation of metals in used products.

COMMENTS ON ACTIVITIES

Activity 1.1

(a) See completed columns in Table 1.12: answers are shown in red.

$$Note: \frac{\text{average grade of copper (\%)} \times \text{size of orebody (Mt)}}{100}$$

$$= \text{ contained copper (Mt)}$$

For example, copper reserves contained in the dispersed deposit for a cut-off grade of 0.6% Cu are 250 Mt × 0.008 = 2 Mt copper.

(b) With increasing size of the orebody in Table 1.7 the average grade decreases, but the reserves of copper increase.

(c) At a cut-off grade of 0.4% Cu, the dispersed orebody would contain 800 Mt of ore at an average grade of 0.5% Cu — that is, 800 Mt × 0.005 = 4 Mt of copper — an amount four times greater than for a cut-off grade of 0.8% Cu. However, it would be necessary to mine 800 Mt of ore — sixteen times as much.

At a cut-off grade of 0.4% Cu, there would be 800 Mt – 4 Mt = 796 Mt of waste, instead of only 50 Mt – 1 Mt = 49 Mt of waste at a cut-off grade of 0.8%. These estimates of waste assume that copper is extracted as the metal. Usually, it is extracted as an ore mineral concentrate and the amounts of waste are slightly less.

(d) See completed columns in Table 1.12: answers are shown in red.

(e) Your completed version of Figure 1.11a should be as shown in Figure 1.16a.

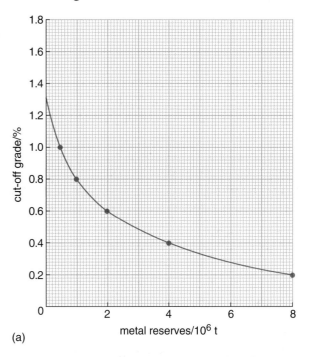

(a)

Figure 1.16   (a) Completed grade–tonnage graph for dispersed deposits featured in Figure 1.11.

Table 1.12   Completed Table 1.7.

(a) Dispersed deposit				(b) Confined deposit			
Cut-off grade /%Cu	Average grade of orebody /%Cu	Size of orebody /Mt	Reserves of copper/Mt	Cut-off grade /%Cu	Average grade of orebody /%Cu	Size of orebody /Mt	Reserves of copper/Mt
1.0	2.5	20	0.5	4.0	5.0	0.04	0.002
0.8	2.0	50	1.0	3.0	3.3	0.3	0.0099
0.6	0.8	250	2.0	2.0	2.5	0.8	0.02
0.4	0.5	800	4.0	1.0	2.2	1.0	0.022
0.2	0.4	2000	8.0	0.5	2.1	1.1	0.023

(f) Your completed version of Figure 1.11b should be as shown in Figure 1.16b.

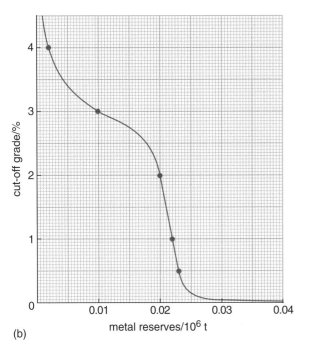

(b)

Figure 1.16   (b) Completed grade–tonnage graph for confined deposits featured in Figure 1.11.

Activity 5.1

(a) Compare your answers with Figure 5.19.

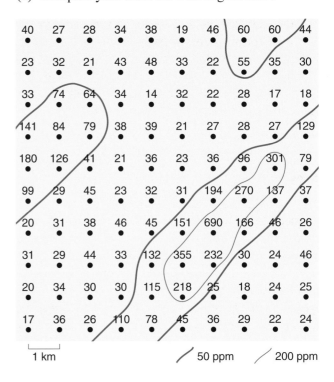

Figure 5.19   Copper concentrations (ppm) in soil in a gridded geochemical reconnaissance survey with regions exceeding thresholds of (i) 50 ppm and (ii) 200 ppm outlined.

(b) Choosing the higher threshold would reduce the area selected for follow-up studies.

(c) Choosing the higher threshold and, therefore, the smaller area would lessen the cost of follow-up work but might result in sites of mineralization being missed.

ACKNOWLEDGEMENTS

Among the many people who helped in various ways during the preparation of this book, the author would particularly like to thank the Block Assessor Dr A. Annels for helpful comments and suggestions, and Dr Charles Moon (Leicester University) who was consultant for Chapters 5 and 6. Thanks to *Metal Bulletin* for access to 2003 prices data for metals, from which the year averages were compiled, as used in Tables 1.2, 1.4 and 1.8.

Grateful acknowledgement is made to the following sources for permission to reproduce material within this product.

Figures

Figures 1.1a, 1.2f, 3.8c and 4.7c Copyright © Tony Waltham Geophotos. Reproduced by permission; *Figures 1.1b, 1.2b, 1.3a, b and d, 4.2 and 4.7b* Copyright © Andy Sutton Photography; *Figure 1.1c* http://photo.agiweb.org. Reproduced by courtesy of the American Geological Institute; *Figures 1.1d, 1.3c, 2.7d, 2.9a, 2.13 and 3.12* Peter Webb, The Open University; *Figure 1.2a* Copyright © Beagle2. www.beagle2.com; *Figures 1.2c and d* Copyright © the Trustees of The British Museum; *Figures 1.2e, 2.9b, 3.9c, 4.1a, 4.1b and 4.14* Copyright © National Museums and Galleries of Wales; *Figure 2.6* Copyright © Professor David L. Reid, Dept. of Geological Sciences, University of Cape Town, South Africa; *Figure 2.10* Cerny, P. (1991) 'Rare-element granite pegmatites, Part 1: Anatomy and internal evolution of pegmatite deposits', *Geoscience Canada*, **18**(2), p. 54; *Figure 2.12* Copyright © Michael Collier; *Figures 2.17c and 4.7a* Courtesy of Dr Richard Bevins, of the National Museum of Wales; *Figure 3.3b* Photograph courtesy of Richards Bay Minerals; *Figure 3.4* Dixon, C. J. (1979) *Atlas of Economic Mineral Deposits*, Chapman & Hall; *Figure 3.5 left* de Chetelat, E. (1967) *Bulletin Soc. Geol. France*, **17**, reproduced by permission of the Société Géologique de France; *Figure 3.6* Copyright © Alcoa Inc; *Figure 3.7* Mason, B. (1966) *Principles of Geochemistry*, reprinted by permission of John Wiley & Sons; *Figures 3.8a and b* Dixon, C. J. (1979) *Atlas of Economic Mineral Deposits*, Chapman & Hall; *Figure 3.9b* Copyright © Ian Cuthbertson, Anglesey Mining plc; *Figure 3.10* Park, C. F. and MacDiarmid, R. A. (1970) *Ore Deposits*, Freeman, Copyright © 1970 by W. H. Freeman and Company, used with permission; *Figure 3.11* Dewey, J. F. and Horsfield, B. (1970) 'Plate tectonics, orogeny and continental growth', *Nature*, **225**, reprinted with permission from Nature. Copyright © 1970 Macmillan Magazines Limited; *Figures 3.13b and c* Images courtesy of Rio Tinto; *Figure 3.14a* Copyright © 2002 State University of New York College at Geneseo; *Figure 3.14b* Cross-section of ferromanganese nodule from the Blake Plateau with phosphate pebbles as nuclei, from the collection of Dr Frank T. Manheim, U.S. Geological Survey, Woods Hole, MA (photo credit: Dann Blackwood). Photo obtained from the NOAA National Geophysical Data Center (http://www.ngdc.noaa.gov/); *Figure 4.3b and 4.9b* Evans, A. M. (1993) *Ore Geology and Industrial Minerals: An Introduction*, Blackwell Scientific Publications; *Figure 4.6* E. Roedder, US Department of the Interior Geological Survey; *Figure 4.10* OAR/National Undersea Research Program (NURP), NOAA; *Figure 4.12* Barnes, J. W. (1981 and 1993) *Basic Geological Mapping*,

GLOSSARY

Items in this Glossary are printed in **bold** in the main text, usually where they are first mentioned. Terms printed in *italics* below are defined elsewhere in the Glossary.

acid mine drainage (AMD)   Pumped minewater or surface run-off from mine wastes made highly acidic (pH 1–3) through oxidation reactions breaking down exposed sulphide minerals to form hydrogen ions and sulphate ions; AMD also contains toxic metals.

adsorption   The process by which a substance adheres to the surface of a solid, such as ions onto clay minerals. Unlike absorption, whereby a substance (like a sponge) takes a liquid or gas within itself.

alloy   A metallic material consisting of a mixture of metals (e.g. copper and zinc in brass), or a mixture of a metal with a non-metal in which the metal is the major component (e.g. iron and carbon in steel).

anhydrous mineral   A mineral that contains no water in its structure. Contrast with *hydrous mineral*.

argillic alteration   Formation of clay minerals by reaction of acidic and oxidizing hydrothermal solutions with feldspars and micas at low temperatures.

average minimum exploitable grade   The average of *breakeven cut-off grades* for all mines, taking into account their individual contribution to world production.

background concentration   In the context of a geochemical survey, the concentration of a chemical component that is within the normal range for a particular sampling method and environment of sampling. Backgrounds differ according to the underlying rock type.

banded iron formation (BIF)   Bedded iron ores comprising finely banded layers several millimetres thick, rich in the iron oxide minerals, haematite, magnetite and goethite, alternating with layers of chert (precipitated silica). BIFs form extensive deposits of Precambrian age.

barren   Applies to unmineralized rocks or mineral veins lacking ore minerals.

base metals   Metals of low value (originally lead, copper, zinc and tin) by comparison with precious metals such as gold and silver.

baseline   Initial conditions, especially relating to chemical composition, pertaining prior to any activities taking place.

bauxite   A form of *laterite* rich in hydrated aluminium oxides, occurring as an earthy, often nodular deposit, reddish-brown to pale orange–white in colour.

benches   Terraces at the sides of an open pit that allow access to deeper levels, improve the stability of pit sides, and trap dislodged material.

bioavailability   A measure of the extent to which metals can be absorbed by organisms; dependent especially on the chemical form in which the metal occurs.

bioremediation   Biological methods of addressing environmental problems, such as wetland systems used to remove toxic metals from acidic minewaters.

black smokers   Smoky clouds emerging from the ocean floor due to hot fluids at temperatures in excess of 300 °C, which precipitate metal oxides and sulphides when they come into contact with cold seawater.

breakeven cut-off grade   The lowest *grade* of a particular deposit for which economic exploitation is possible. Often referred to as just 'cut-off grade'.

brine   A saline (salty) solution, such as seawater, or *hydrothermal fluid* containing high concentrations of salts in solution.

by-product   A secondary product obtained at the same time as the main product, especially when extracting metals from ores.

chemical sediment   A sediment composed of material precipitated from dissolved ions, by whatever process (inorganic or biochemical).

chemical weathering   The breakdown of rocks at the Earth's surface by chemical action, especially by water and aqueous solutions, e.g. the decomposition of feldspars to clay minerals and soluble ions. Contrast with *physical weathering*.

colloid   A suspension of very small (1–10 µm) particles in water, too small in size to settle as a sediment, and held in suspension partly by repulsion between negative surface charges.

compatible elements   Trace elements that readily enter the structures of common rock-forming minerals crystallizing from a magma, and, if *fractional crystallization* processes are operating, become depleted in the melt remaining. Contrast with *incompatible elements*.

complex ion   A group of atoms carrying the combined charge of their components; they often comprise a metal ion surrounded by anions: the gold bisulphide complex ion, $[Au(HS)_2]^-$, is an example.

confined deposits   Occurrences of ore minerals concentrated in relatively small volumes of rock, often where space was restricted, as in fractures where hydrothermal veins may form. Contrast with *dispersed deposits*.

continuous subsidence   Ground subsidence that proceeds over an extended period of time, caused by roof collapse in underground workings especially when overlain by weak strata. It is an expected consequence of longwall coal mining and underground mining of weak rocks such as evaporites. The effects at the surface are often extensive, but generally predictable. Contrast with *discontinuous subsidence*.

cumulate   Applies to products of the accumulation of minerals in a magma chamber by gravity settling to form a layered igneous intrusion.

detrital grains   Sedimentary grains of weathering-resistant minerals, such as quartz and zircon, derived from pre-existing rocks.

discontinuous subsidence   Sporadic, often rapid, and generally unpredictable subsidence frequently involving large, but localized displacements. Sometimes it is the eventual result of block caving, a mining method which employs roof collapse as a means to extract ore. Old mine workings can collapse unexpectedly when the supports decay, especially when decayed wooden platforms support a loose capping. Contrast with *continuous subsidence*.

dispersed deposits   Occurrences of ore minerals distributed at low grades throughout large volumes of rock. Contrast with *confined deposits*.

dredging (mining operation)   Extraction of material by conveyor or suction from underwater locations.

electromagnetic (EM) surveys   Exploration surveys that exploit the emission of EM radiation by a conductive orebody through which alternating electrical currents flow. In most EM surveys, such currents are induced in natural conductors by electromagnetic radiation produced by a transmitter that traverses the ground in the field or in an aircraft. The induced signals are detected by a receiver carried with the transmitter.

electronegativity   A measure of the ease by which atoms attract electrons. Metals generally give up electrons more easily than non-metals, and therefore have lower electronegativity values.

environmental impact assessment (EIA)   A document outlining the expected environmental impact of a mining operation and the *remediation* and *rehabilitation* procedures to be implemented to minimize long- and short-term impacts. In most countries the statement requires approval by governmental agencies before mining can start.

exhalative   Applies to the effusive nature of fluids emerging from geothermally active parts of the Earth's crust onto the land surface or onto the sea floor.

fertile   Refers to rocks such as black shales, which contain metals in a form allowing them to be leached by hydrothermal solutions. Contrast with *infertile*.

fines (ore processing)   Micron-sized particles produced by crushing and *milling* that are difficult to separate into mineral fractions.

flash   The rapid transformation of fluid to gas, as by decompression. Applicable to geothermal fluids being transformed to steam.

fluid inclusions   Pockets of fluid trapped in hydrothermal minerals during their crystallization.

formation water   Water, usually saline, trapped during burial within the pores of sedimentary rocks.

fractional crystallization   The process by which crystals of a mineral or minerals are removed from a magma to produce a magma with a different composition from the original melt, i.e. the initial magma has been separated into different fractions — the early-formed crystals and the remaining liquid.

fractionation   The concentration of minerals and/or elements by separation of physically and/or chemically distinct fractions.

froth flotation (ore processing)   A separation process involving the coating of ore mineral grains with a greasy organic layer to produce non-wetting surfaces that stick to bubbles in a frothing liquid. Suitable combinations of chemicals to enhance or impede wetting facilitate selective flotation of specific minerals. The efficiency of flotation also depends on the density and size of grains.

gangue   The worthless part of an ore that has to be mined in order to extract an ore mineral; it comprises waste rock and minerals.

geochemical anomaly   An elevated concentration of a chemical component that is distinct from *background concentrations*. It may be developed in rock, soil, water, sediment or vegetation, and may indicate the presence of a mineral deposit.

geochemical dispersion   Geological processes spread anomalous concentrations of elements away from a source of mineralization to create a broader but less-extreme *geochemical anomaly*. An anomaly resulting from dispersion is thus easier to detect than a localized occurrence of mineralization. Primary dispersion occurs at the time of formation of an ore deposit. Secondary dispersion results from weathering processes and groundwater movement.

gossan   The weathered surface layer, reddish-brown to bright orange in colour, rather like rust, of a sulphide-rich mineral deposit. It is composed largely of goethite ($FeO(OH)$), and is sometimes called 'iron cap'. The rich colour of gossan is distinctive and has helped to reveal many sulphide mineral deposits.

grade   The concentration of an element, especially a metal, present within a rock. For most elements, grade is expressed as a percentage by weight.

gravity survey   A form of geophysical survey that measures variations in the Earth's gravitational field. The results are usually displayed in the form of a gravity contour map. A positive gravity value indicates the presence of rocks with high density relative to their surroundings beneath the surface; a negative gravity value indicates relatively low-density rocks.

heap leaching (ore processing)   The extraction in solution of metals from *ore minerals* in piles of crushed ore. Oxidizing solutions that encourage the bacterium *Acidithiobacillus ferrooxidans* to thrive are used to break down iron-bearing sulphide minerals including the copper ore mineral, chalcopyrite. Solutions of sodium cyanide are used to extract gold from low-grade gold deposits.

heavy minerals   Dense minerals, often oxides and native metals, resistant to weathering and capable of concentration to form placer deposits.

hydrothermal alteration   A change in the chemistry and mineralogy of a rock due to interaction with *hydrothermal fluids*. It is a two-way process of chemical exchange, which also alters the composition of the fluid from which ore minerals may be precipitated.

hydrothermal fluids   Hot groundwaters that are often highly saline and capable of altering and dissolving rocks, and precipitating minerals.

hydrous mineral   A mineral, such as mica and amphibole, that contains combined water, often in the form of the hydroxyl group (OH), in its crystal structure. Contrast with *anhydrous mineral*.

hyperaccumulator plants   Plants that take up unusually large amounts of metals, especially toxic metals, during growth. They are adapted to grow in soils containing levels of metals that would be toxic to most plants. Some species have the potential for cleaning up polluted soils and to be a means of 'green' mining — by harvesting the foliage.

incompatible elements   Trace elements for which there are no suitable sites to enter in the common rock-forming minerals as a magma crystallizes. They become increasingly concentrated in the remaining liquid, and eventually reside within accessory minerals. Contrast with *compatible elements*.

induced polarization (IP)   An exploration method in which an electrical current is applied to the ground. Conductive minerals in the rocks below ground store charge (rather like a battery). When the current is switched off, a small current flows in the reverse direction due to dissipation of the stored charge. The time it takes for the measured, induced current to subside is a measure of the chargeability of the minerals. The method depends only on the presence of conductive grains; the grains do not have to be connected.

infertile   Applies to rocks that cannot easily supply metals to a hydrothermal fluid; quartzite is a good example. Contrast with *fertile*.

inheritance   The origin of geographically related ore deposits due to reworking of a major metal anomaly in the continental crust or underlying mantle by igneous, hydrothermal and sedimentary processes, so that new deposits of the metal continue to form in the same region, but at different times.

ionic substitution   The replacement of ions of one element by those of another element in a crystal structure. Ions most likely to substitute for each other have similar sizes and electrical charges.

laterites   Thick soils formed as residues of tropical weathering, composed mainly of kaolinite and the insoluble hydrated oxides of aluminium and iron(III), which gives them a deep brick-red colour.

liberation (ore processing)   The release of ore minerals from gangue and from each other by crushing and milling.

liquid immiscibility   A process whereby two liquids separate from one, when one can no longer be held in 'solution' in the other. For example, on cooling from a high temperature, a sulphide liquid may separate from silicate magma, so forming two immiscible liquids.

magmatic segregation deposits   Mineral deposits formed by the settling of minerals or immiscible liquids within a magma body (usually of basaltic composition).

magnetic surveys   Surveys that measure variations in the Earth's magnetic field (usually from the air). Only three minerals are sufficiently magnetized by the Earth's magnetic field to produce a measurable magnetic response, and only then when present in sufficient abundance. In order of decreasing magnetic strength they are magnetite (Fe_3O_4), ilmenite ($FeTiO_3$), and pyrrhotite (FeS).

manganese nodules   Objects with the appearance of 'burnt baked potatoes' scattered often in abundance over the surface of the deep ocean floor. They are composed of hydrated iron and manganese oxides built up in layers around a nucleus.

massive sulphide deposits   Mineral deposits formed from *hydrothermal fluids* escaping from the ocean floor. Comprising mainly iron, copper and zinc sulphides, they often contain collapsed *black smoker* chimneys, precipitated sulphide sediment and mineralized *stockwork*.

metal   An opaque, shiny, often silvery or grey-coloured material, which can be shaped by hammering, bending, or by melting and casting, and is generally a good transmitter of electricity and heat. Metals form positive ions.

metallogenic provinces   The occurrence of ore deposits of a similar kind within particular geographic regions. See also *inheritance*.

meteoric water   Fresh water derived from the atmosphere.

milling (ore processing)   The grinding of rock fragments to a fine grain size.

open pit (mining operation)   A large hole in the ground with a series of *benches* that provide access and pit wall stability, often having the form of an inverted cone.

opencast (mining operation)   A form of mining applicable to horizontally extensive shallow ore deposits, whereby *ore* is mined after *overburden* is removed. Subsequently, overburden is used to rehabilitate mined areas as mining proceeds progressively. Often called strip mining.

ore   A rock that can be worked economically for its metals, either at present or, with reasonable likelihood, in the near future.

ore mineral concentrate   Processed *ore*, enriched in ore minerals following *liberation* and separation, that is ready for smelting. It is ore from which most of the *gangue* has been removed.

ore minerals   Minerals from which metals may be obtained by economic methods, irrespective of whether or not their abundance in a particular rock is sufficient for that rock to be an *ore*.

overburden   Material that has to be stripped from the top of a workable deposit but has no economic value.

oxidation   A chemical process that may involve the addition of oxygen to an element or compound. Rusting is an example of oxidation. More strictly, oxidation is defined as the removal of electrons. Contrast with *reduction*.

pathfinder elements   Elements that typically accompany certain types of ore deposit and are easier to detect and analyse geochemically than the metal sought. Arsenic, bismuth and antimony are commonly used as pathfinders for gold.

pegmatites   Very coarse-grained igneous rocks, made up principally of quartz, feldspar and mica, sometimes accompanied by ore minerals of *incompatible elements*. Formed by crystallization of extremely hydrous granitic magma left after anhydrous minerals have crystallized.

permitting   The process during which governmental authorities decide whether a proposal for mining is in the interests of all stakeholders and whether the operation is sufficiently well planned and financed and contains sufficient assurances and safeguards in social, economic and environmental areas before allowing it to go ahead.

persistence   The spatial extent to which a *geochemical anomaly* can be detected; often used to describe anomalies in stream sediments.

pH   A numeric scale which expresses how acidic or alkaline a solution is. It is an inverse measure of the hydrogen ion (H^+) concentration in solution; thus, low pH values reflect high H^+ concentrations. Pure water with a pH of 7 is a neutral solution that contains equal concentrations of H^+ and OH^- ions.

physical weathering   Mechanical breakdown of rocks at the Earth's surface into smaller fragments, including individual mineral grains. Contrast with *chemical weathering*.

placer deposits   Concentrations of dense and chemically resistant *ore minerals* in sediments; they are often found in rivers (alluvial placers) and along coasts (beach placers).

podiform chromite deposits   Chromite mineral deposits forming high-grade, discontinuous, lens-shaped (hence podiform) bodies in rocks of oceanic crust. Individually their reserves of chromite ore rarely exceed a few millions of tonnes. Contrast with *stratiform chromite deposits*.

porphyry ore deposits   Extensive low-grade ore deposits formed following the emplacement of hydrous magmas at a high level in the crust. The separation of metal-rich fluids causes expansion, over-pressuring surrounding rocks, and creates fractures that provide pathways for mineralizing fluids.

radiometric survey   A form of geophysical survey measuring the radioactivity (gamma-ray emissions) of rocks. The detection of specific gamma-ray energies can be interpreted in terms of concentrations of U, Th and K.

reactivity   The ease by which substances take part in chemical reactions.

recovery (ore processing)   The proportion of ore minerals or metals in an ore that can be extracted. No procedure for separating and concentrating ore minerals can be 100% efficient.

reduction   A chemical process that may involve the removal of oxygen from an element or compound. During smelting, reduction frees a metal from its compounds. More strictly, reduction is defined as the addition of electrons. Contrast with *oxidation*.

refining   Chemical processing that removes impurities to form a purer product. Often applied to metals.

rehabilitation   The action of returning a site (as used in mining) either to its former state (restoration) or to an alternative, but environmentally acceptable state.

remediation   Measures put in place in both routine and emergency situations to alleviate environmental problems.

remote sensing   Gathering characterizing information or data at a distance from its source. Methods include aerial photography, airborne *magnetic*, *radiometric* and *gravity surveys* and satellite imaging of the electromagnetic spectrum emanating from the Earth's surface. It can be used in geological mapping and reconnaissance exploration for mineral deposits.

reserves   Quantities of resources that can be extracted profitably and legally under existing conditions, taking into account all mining factors.

residual deposit   The insoluble products of chemical weathering that remain in place at the Earth's surface: including *laterite* and *bauxite* deposits.

resistivity surveys   Geophysical surveys that measure electrical resistance between two points on the ground. They are used to map out underground layers of rock with varying conductivity, especially wet, porous rocks, which are better conductors than dry rocks. Most rock-forming minerals are poor conductors, but sulphide minerals are generally good conductors.

scavenging   A process in which constituents such as trace metals are extracted from a liquid such as magma, by an immiscible liquid, such as a sulphide melt or watery fluid.

secondary enrichment deposit   A mineral deposit in which the metal content has been increased by interaction of existing ore minerals with percolating groundwater containing metals that are soluble in oxidizing (near surface) solutions but are insoluble under reducing conditions (below the water table).

solid solution The ability for a particular mineral to have, as a result of *ionic substitution*, a range of possible chemical compositions between certain limits.

sorting The process by which minerals of different grain sizes are separated from one another during transport.

stockwork A complex network of tiny veinlets (sometimes mineralized) occupying highly fractured rock, often produced by the explosive release of gases. Associated with the formation of *porphyry ore deposits* and some *massive sulphide deposits*.

stoping (mining) The extraction of ore from above or below a tunnel driven horizontally into a vertically extensive orebody.

stratiform chromite deposits Chromite deposits in laterally extensive basaltic igneous intrusions in which chromite layers rarely exceed a few metres in thickness, although single layers can sometimes be traced for a kilometre or more. Although not high-grade deposits, their reserves of chromite ore can amount to billions of tonnes. Contrast with *podiform chromite deposits*.

stripping ratio (mining) The ratio of the total mass of waste material (including *overburden*) that has to be removed, to the mass of *ore* that can then be extracted.

substitution (resources) The use of an alternative resource for a particular purpose. A substitute is a material that, at least in part, replaces (or can replace) another material.

tailings The waste products, usually fine-grained, of ore processing; sometimes used to backfill worked-out mines. Such wastes are often produced in slurry form and *fines* are allowed to settle out in tailings ponds.

tailings dam A structure designed to contain and impound tailings, i.e. the slurry from ore processing. An embankment borders the structure and is built up in stages as the level of accumulated tailings rises. The fines from ore processing settle out and the water is either recycled or evaporates.

threshold value In a geochemical survey, the concentration level that separates background values from anomalous values.

unit cost The total cost of transforming one tonne of an ore in the ground into a saleable commodity (metal). Includes all variable costs in mining and processing, as well as a contribution of fixed costs.

unit value The value of metal obtained from one tonne of ore. It derives from ore grade, % recovery, and metal price per tonne.

winnowing The process which involves sediment being stirred up, such as by waves on beaches or by rapids in rivers. The lighter minerals such as clay and quartz are removed in the water flow, to be deposited elsewhere, leaving the larger and heavier mineral grains behind. Also applies to wind transport.

INDEX

Note that **bold** page numbers refer to where terms defined in the Glossary are printed in **bold** in the text.

The Periodic Table of elements

Legend:
- metals
- metalloids
- non-metals
- rare earth elements

1 H hydrogen																	2 He helium
3 Li lithium	4 Be beryllium											5 B boron	6 C carbon	7 N nitrogen	8 O oxygen	9 F fluorine	10 Ne neon
11 Na sodium	12 Mg magnesium											13 Al aluminium	14 Si silicon	15 P phosphorus	16 S sulphur	17 Cl chlorine	18 Ar argon
19 K potassium	20 Ca calcium	21 Sc scandium	22 Ti titanium	23 V vanadium	24 Cr chromium	25 Mn manganese	26 Fe iron	27 Co cobalt	28 Ni nickel	29 Cu copper	30 Zn zinc	31 Ga gallium	32 Ge germanium	33 As arsenic	34 Se selenium	35 Br bromine	36 Kr krypton
37 Rb rubidium	38 Sr strontium	39 Y yttrium	40 Zr zirconium	41 Nb niobium	42 Mo molybdenum	43 Tc technetium	44 Ru ruthenium	45 Rh rhodium	46 Pd palladium	47 Ag silver	48 Cd cadmium	49 In indium	50 Sn tin	51 Sb antimony	52 Te tellurium	53 I iodine	54 Xe xenon
55 Cs caesium	56 Ba barium	57 La lanthanum	72 Hf hafnium	73 Ta tantalum	74 W tungsten	75 Re rhenium	76 Os osmium	77 Ir iridium	78 Pt platinum	79 Au gold	80 Hg mercury	81 Tl thallium	82 Pb lead	83 Bi bismuth	84 Po polonium	85 At astatine	86 Rn radon
87 Fr francium	88 Ra radium	89 Ac actinium	104 Rf rutherfordium	105 Db dubnium	106 Sg seaborgium	107 Bh bohrium	108 Hs hassium	109 Mt meitnerium									

58 Ce cerium	59 Pr praseodymium	60 Nd neodymium	61 Pm promethium	62 Sm samarium	63 Eu europium	64 Gd gadolinium	65 Tb terbium	66 Dy dysprosium	67 Ho holmium	68 Er erbium	69 Tm thulium	70 Yb ytterbium	71 Lu lutetium
90 Th thorium	91 Pa protactinium	92 U uranium	93 Np neptunium	94 Pu plutonium	95 Am americium	96 Cm curium	97 Bk berkelium	98 Cf californium	99 Es einsteinium	100 Fm fermium	101 Md mendelevium	102 No nobelium	103 Lr lawrencium